W9-BNY-254

Determinants
of Infant Behaviour IV

Contributing Authors

THÉRÈSE GOUIN DÉCARIE

HAVA B. GEWIRTZ

JACOB L. GEWIRTZ

DAVID A. HAMBURG

HARRY F. HARLOW

MARGARET K. HARLOW

R. A. HINDE

I. CHARLES KAUFMAN

DALE F. LOTT

GEORGE A. MORGAN

HENRY N. RICCIUTI

M. P. M. RICHARDS

HARRIET L. RHEINGOLD

JAY S. ROSENBLATT

LEONARD A. ROSENBLUM

LOUIS W. SANDER

MARY D. SALTER AINSWORTH

BARBARA A. WITTIG

PETER H. WOLFF

Determinants
of Infant Behaviour IV

BASED ON THE PROCEEDINGS
OF THE FOURTH TAVISTOCK STUDY GROUP
ON MOTHER-INFANT INTERACTION
HELD AT THE HOUSE OF THE CIBA FOUNDATION, LONDON
SEPTEMBER 1965

Edited by B. M. FOSS

with a foreword by John Bowlby

LONDON: METHUEN & CO LTD

Contents

List of Plates   *page* vii

Contributors   ix

Editor's Note   xi

Foreword by John Bowlby   xiii

PART I: ANIMAL STUDIES

David A. Hamburg: Observations of Mother-Infant Interactions in Primate Field Studies   3

Harry F. Harlow and Margaret K. Harlow: Effects of Various
Mother-Infant Relationships on Rhesus Monkey Behaviors   15

R. A. Hinde: Influence of Social Companions and of Temporary Separation on Mother-Infant Relations in Rhesus
Monkeys   37

I. Charles Kaufman and Leonard A. Rosenblum: The Waning of
the Mother-Infant Bond in Two Species of Macaque   41

Dale F. Lott and Jay S. Rosenblatt: Development of Maternal
Responsiveness During Pregnancy in the Laboratory Rat   61

M. P. M. Richards: Some Effects of Experience on Maternal
Behaviour in Rodents   69

PART II: HUMAN STUDIES

Peter H. Wolff: The Natural History of Crying and Other
Vocalizations in Early Infancy   81

Contents

Mary D. Salter Ainsworth and Barbara A. Wittig: Attachment and Exploratory Behavior of One-year-olds in a Strange Situation *page* 111

Harriet L. Rheingold: The Effect of a Strange Environment on the Behavior of Infants 137

Thérèse Gouin Décarie: A Study of the Mental and Emotional Development of the Thalidomide Child 167

Louis W. Sander: The Longitudinal Course of Early Mother-Child Interaction: cross-case comparison in a sample of mother-child pairs 189

Hava B. Gewirtz and Jacob L. Gewirtz: Caretaking Settings, Background Events and Behavior Differences in Four Israeli Child-rearing Environments: some preliminary trends 229

George A. Morgan and Henry N. Ricciuti: Infants' Responses to Strangers During the First Year 253

DISCUSSION ON CAUSES OF DISTRESS IN INFANTS 273

References 283

Index 299

Plates

Between pages 130 and 131

1 Self-clutching by monkeys raised in social isolation

2 Ventral-ventral clinging by pair of 'together-together' infants

3 Unmothered infants arranged in 'choo-choo' pattern

4 A group of bonnet mothers in characteristic *passive-contact* huddle

5 A young bonnet in an early stage of departure from its mother

6 A bonnet infant taking a cabbage leaf from the hands of its mother

7 A pigtail mother prevents access to the nipple

8 A pigtail mother punishing her infant to induce it to break contact with her

9 Bonnet infant initiating *social play*

10 Sequence of 'basic ' human cries

11 Further 'basic' cries

12 Sequence of 'mad' cries

13 Initial vocal response to pain

14 Initial vocal response to frustration

15 Cries of babies with various pathologies

16 'Fake' cry or vocal signal not obviously related to distress

17 Transition from vocalization to fussing

18 Second example of vocalization to fussing

19 Laughter in response to tickling

20 Vocal 'imitation'.

Plates

Plates 21 to 30 behaviour of a male infant:

21 Exploration

22 Comes to mother briefly

23 Responds to stranger

24 Hugs mother when she returns

25 Throws himself on the floor when his mother puts him down

26 Maintains contact with his mother

27 Turns to her with a cry and clings

28 Cries and rocks when left alone

29 Comforted by the stranger

30 Clings when his mother returns again

Plates 31 to 36 Thalidomide babies:

31 Dystactylia and syndactylia of the right hand

32 Bilateral paraxal hemimelia by absence of radius

33 Dysgenesis of four extremities. Hypoplasis of mandible and aplasia of the tongue

34 Quadruple phocomelia

35 Bilateral phocomelia of upper extremities

36 Bilateral phocomelia of upper extremities. Dysgenesis of the right ear.

Authors and Members of the Fourth Tavistock Study Group

*MARY D. SALTER AINSWORTH, Professor of Psychology, Johns Hopkins University

*J. A. AMBROSE, Director, Behaviour Development Research Unit, St Mary's Hospital Medical School, London

*GENEVIEVE APPELL, Psychologist, Institut de Service Social Pouponnière Amyot, Montrouge, Paris

*JOHN BOWLBY, Consultant Psychiatrist, Member of External Scientific Staff of Medical Research Council, Tavistock Clinic, London

*BETTYE CALDWELL, Director, Children's Center, Upstate Medical Center, Syracuse, N.Y.

*BRIAN M. FOSS, Professor of Psychology, Bedford College, London University

*DAN FREEDMAN, Associate Professor, Committee on Human Development, University of Chicago

HAVA B. GEWIRTZ, Research Associate, Institute for Behavioral Research, Silver Spring, Maryland

*JACOB L. GEWIRTZ, Chief, Section on Early Learning and Development, National Institute of Mental Health, Bethesda

*THÉRÈSE GOUIN DÉCARIE, Professor, Institute of Psychology, University of Montreal, and Consultant Psychologist, Institute of Rehabilitation

*MAVIS GUNTHER, Paediatric Research Worker, University College Hospital, London

*DAVID A. HAMBURG, Professor and Executive Head, Department of Psychiatry, Stanford University School of Medicine

*HARRY F. HARLOW, Professor, University of Wisconsin

MARGARET K. HARLOW, University of Wisconsin

*R. A. HINDE, Professor, Sub-Department of Animal Behaviour, Department of Zoology, University of Cambridge

Authors and Members of the Fourth Tavistock Study Group

I. CHARLES KAUFMAN, Professor of Psychiatry, University of Colorado Medical Center, Denver

*SOL KRAMER, Chief, Division of Behavioral Sciences, University of Florida

DALE F. LOTT, Psychology Department, University of California, Davis

*R. MAC KEITH, Physician in Children's Department, Guy's Hospital, London

GEORGE MORGAN, Department of Psychology, Hiram College, Ohio

*HARRIET L. RHEINGOLD, Professor, Department of Psychology, University of North Carolina

*HENRY RICCIUTI, Professor of Psychology, Cornell University

*M. P. M. RICHARDS, Biologist, Unit for Research on Medical Applications of Psychology, University of Cambridge

*JAY S. ROSENBLATT, Institute of Animal Behavior, Rutgers.

LEONARD A. ROSENBLUM, Primate Behavior Laboratory, Department of Psychiatry, Downstate Medical Center, Brooklyn

*LOUIS W. SANDER, Associate Research Professor of Psychiatry, Boston University Medical Center

BARBARA A. WITTIG, Department of Psychology, Johns Hopkins University

*PETER H. WOLFF, Assistant Professor of Psychiatry, Harvard Medical School, and Director of Psychiatric Research, Children's Hospital Medical Center and Judge Baker Guidance Center, Boston

* Member of the Fourth Study Group

Editor's Note

This last volume in the series comes three years after the Tavistock study group on which it is based. Two of the papers appearing here, those by Kaufman and Rosenblum, and Morgan and Ricciuti were not presented at the study group, and the remaining authors have had opportunities to bring their papers up to date. In previous volumes, selections from all the discussions were printed. This time I decided that only one extended passage justified inclusion. It is an edited version of discussions which arose largely from the paper presented by Peter Wolff.

Once more it is a pleasure to thank members of the Ciba Foundation and the Tavistock Clinic for unstinted help, and especially John Bowlby who chaired the group and who inspired much of what appears in the following pages.

B. M. F.

Foreword

JOHN BOWLBY

The fourth and final meeting of the Tavistock Seminar on Mother-Infant Interaction took place in September 1965 and bore all the hallmarks of the previous ones: all but a few of the original members were present; our guests added fuel to the fires of our discussions; we viewed the development of mother-child interaction in the light of empirical evidence and an evolutionary perspective; and we enjoyed the unrivalled facilities and hospitality of the Ciba Foundation.

These four meetings followed a design for interdisciplinary discussion pioneered by Dr Frank Fremont-Smith at the Josiah Macy Jr. Foundation. A small group of research workers, drawn from a number of disciplines and countries, and all concerned with a single problem, are invited to meet for three or four days at a stretch on a number of successive occasions. At each meeting only a few formal presentations are planned, the remaining time given to discussion and impromptu reports. As the series of meetings proceeds, it is hoped, reserves and misconceptions, inevitable when strangers from strange disciplines first meet, will recede and give place to an increasing grasp of what the other is attempting and why; to cross-fertilization of related fields; to mutual understanding and personal friendship.

Having experienced these beneficent effects during a series of seminars on the Psychobiological Development of the Child, convened by the World Health Organization in the early nineteen-fifties under the chairmanship of Frank Fremont-Smith himself, it was natural to adopt the design again. By setting the intervals between meetings of the new series at two years, however, double time was given for members to digest the lessons of previous meetings and to apply them to their work.

The design proved its worth. By the fourth meeting many areas of agreement had been discovered that had previously gone unrecognized, ideas and methods current in one field had been applied in another, real differences of opinion had been distinguished from false, new problems had been identified and new approaches mooted. To the conveners nothing was more heartening at our final meeting than to hear, again and again, how work now reported had been influenced or even initiated as a result of discussions that had occurred at our previous meetings or as a result of visits or correspondence that had been started at them.

To convey on printed page the sense of increased understanding that has taken place is not easy. Should the four volumes prepared by Brian Foss from the heterogeneous material available prove half as useful to the reader as they already have been to the writer of this Foreword they will, however, serve a purpose.

It is a great pleasure to express my personal gratitude to all those who contributed to the success of the meetings, especially to those who prepared papers for presentation, to Anthony Ambrose for his part in organising the series, to Brian Foss for his services as editor, to the Ciba Foundation for its hospitality, and to the staff of the Foundation for their unfailing kindness and help. We are grateful also to the National Health Service and the Medical Research Council for their support of the work of members of the Tavistock Child Development Research Unit.

PART I

Animal Studies

Observations of Mother-Infant Interactions in Primate Field Studies

DAVID A. HAMBURG[1]

The behavior of animals is a major contributing factor for their survival and, consequently, through the mechanisms of heredity, for the course of evolution. Maintaining favorable relations with the environment is largely a function of behavior. Possessing efficient skeletal, circulatory, digestive, sense organ, and effector systems is not enough. All these must be used effectively in activities such as food getting, reproduction and defense. Behavioral incompetence leads to extinction as surely as does morphological disproportion or deficiency in any vital organ. (Nissen, 1958).

Animal behavior may be investigated in the laboratory, or in artificial colonies, or under natural conditions. The kinds of information gained from these different approaches are largely complementary, and all are necessary if the complex roots of behavior are to be understood.

The field studies are extremely helpful in understanding the way that structure and behavior are adapted to environmental conditions; it is really the adaptive aspect that makes the field studies so interesting. For example, the complex relations with other species must initially be studied in the field. The full description of the natural behavior will raise many problems of interpretation that can be settled only by experiments. The richness of primate field studies makes possible a useful interaction between field observations and laboratory experimental data; so far there are very few research settings in which that has actually been pursued, i.e. an intimate, continuous, long-term interplay between laboratory and field studies

[1] During the past decade, I have had the opportunity to collaborate with Sherwood Washburn in studying the evolution of human behavior, one result being a series of papers in which we have tried to approach some of the principal behavioral categories in evolutionary terms: motivation, emotion, stress, fear, learning, and aggression. I am deeply grateful for his stimulation and guidance.

B

3

of primate behavior development. Washburn at Berkeley and we at Stanford are trying to develop situations of this kind.

I have selected a few aspects of mother-infant relations in species that are of special interest to me; especially chimpanzee, gorilla, baboon, and rhesus macaque. First, a few general remarks about primate field studies, since they are really very recent. The amount of dependable information in primate field studies ten years ago was very small; and indeed a remarkable acceleration in this field has occurred in the past five years. The workers who have pursued primate field studies have, in the main, come from zoology, anthropology and psychology.

Let me just draw your attention to the fact that there are about fifty genera and several hundred species of living primates; there are reliable field studies of behavior of only about twenty. The laboratory studies have not used very many species either. The scientific community has been quite limited in study of primates; this is one important caution about the present early stage of development of the field studies. Of the usually recognized families of primates, that of the great apes (gibbon, orang-utan, chimpanzee and gorilla) is the only family in which most of the genera have been the subject of systematic, long-term observation under natural conditions.

There has been a radical shift in what field workers consider necessary to make fruitful observations; at the present time the minimal conditions for an effective study are considered to be about a thousand hours in the field, distributed over a year. Jane Goodall, who has done exceedingly important work with chimpanzees, has so far spent about four thousand hours distributed over four years, and indeed much of the critical information has come during the past year. In the first year, she saw only little black blobs in the distance at about five hundred yards. Habituation of the animals to the observer is an important consideration; the ability of the observer to recognize individual animals; observational units that are long enough to observe rare but adaptively critical events – these are some of the methodological problems of the field studies.

Now, with such a variety of species to choose from, what primates are most interesting? This, of course, depends on the question one is asking, and for different purposes different primates will prove to be most suitable. In terms of a general interest in human evolution, it is possible to provide criteria for choice of species upon which to focus. That is to say, certain species are more likely than others to provide interesting leads that stimulate research in the contemporary human species from an evolutionary perspective. The criteria I would accordingly cite are the following: in regard to behavioral criteria, (1) species that spend a substantial portion of their time on the ground; (2) species that show a tendency toward bipedalism; (3) species that show a relatively great complexity of learning; and (4) species that show a great complexity of social interaction. Non-behavioral criteria would include: (1) maximal similarity of central nervous system circuitry; (2) greatest similarity of locomotor anatomy, especially in the brachiating complex of the upper limbs and trunk; (3) maximum similarity in the number and form of chromosomes; (4) maximum similarity of blood proteins and immunological responses.

Now let us turn to a few general findings emerging from the recent field studies. Several original reports and major reviews have recently been published (DeVore, 1965; Jay, 1967; Schrier *et al.*, 1965). They provide a basic resource for the reader who wishes to pursue this area in detail.

In brief, the newer studies strongly support the concept that, in primate evolution, social organization has functioned as biological adaptation. Both the recent field observations of non-human primates and also some interesting studies of hunting-and-gathering societies suggest that group-living has conferred a powerful selective advantage upon the more highly developed primates. This selective advantage derived from social organization has probably included: (1) protection against predation; (2) meeting nutritional requirements; (3) protection against climatic variation; (4) coping with injuries; (5) facilitating reproduction and perhaps above all; (6) preparing the young to meet the requirements and exploit the opportunities of a given environment, whatever its characteristics may be. I shall return to this point shortly.

One of the most consistent and striking observations has been the extraordinary richness and diversity of inter-animal contact during the years of growth and development; perhaps only films or first-hand observation can convey this point adequately. The stark, barren poverty of most laboratory situations in comparison to field environments is very difficult to convey in words. When we put the social isolation experiments in juxtaposition to field observations of social behavior, it makes a very sharp and vivid contrast. Take one example: in some of the experiments in Harlow's laboratory, a remarkable degree of compensation for maternal deprivation has been attained by permitting a modest amount of peer play – on a time scale of minutes per day. In the field, the same species plays hours per day, rather than minutes; it varies with ecological conditions in interesting ways, but has been observed to be as much as five hours per day in some groups of rhesus macaque. This contrast adds interest to the experimental finding. The developmental potentialities of peer relations deserve much further investigation.

All species of monkeys and apes so far studied live in social groups; there is, however, immense variation in the size and pattern of the groups. The usual group varies between about ten and fifty, but in gibbons the group is a pair of adults and their offspring, whereas it may be composed of some hundreds in baboons and macaques. Their cohesion, dominance, patterns of sexuality are very different in the great variety of primate groups, but all monkeys and apes spend the greater part of their lives in close association with other members of the same species.

There appears to be a general tendency toward differences between (1) species that live entirely in the trees and (2) species that divide their time between the trees and the ground. In my view, this is important from the standpoint of evolution and helps us to sort out certain major behavioral characteristics. Life on the ground exposes a species to far more predators than does life in the trees; not only are there fewer potential predators in the trees, but escape is relatively easy. By going beneath the canopy to escape predatorial birds or, moving across small branches to an adjacent tree to escape from felines, arboreal species can easily escape most predators except man. The ultimate safety of all non-human primates is in the trees, and even the ground-living baboons and macaques will take refuge in trees or on cliffs when a predator approaches (except man, from whom they often wisely escape by running). Much of the day, however, baboons may be as far as a mile from safe refuge, and on the open plains a troop's only protection is the fighting ability of its adult males.

The social organization of the baboon troop, particularly when the animals are moving across an open area, surrounds the females and infants with adult males. At the approach of a predator, the adult males are quickly interposed between the troop and the source of danger. Dominant adult males are the focal point for the other troop members in baboons, macaques, and gorillas – all heavily ground-living species. In most circumstances, when the males eat, the troop eats; when the males move, the others follow.

The adult male's relation to the mother and infant in such species is highlighted by a behavior sequence observed in one of Washburn's studies. A mother baboon was seen with a newborn infant, probably only a few hours old. The infant still could not cling adequately, and its mother repeatedly helped it with one hand. The three-legged walking was difficult for the mother and she lagged behind the main body of the troop of baboons and sat down every few yards. Right beside her walked an adult male. When she sat, he sat; when she started up, he started up. His actions were timed to hers, and she was never left without protection during this awkward period. This type of observation occurs repeatedly in the substantially ground-living forms.

In general, the shift from exclusively tree-living behavior to substantial ground-living activity is associated with the following: (1) larger home range; (2) larger group size; (3) greater social cohesion; (4) larger body size; (5) lower population density; (6) more aggression – at least in display; (7) more exploratory behavior; (8) more dominance in behavior; (9) more sexual dimorphism; (10) increased fighting ability of males; (11) wider geographical distribution of the species; (12) closer relationship of adult male and infant. That is, all of these characteristics tend to increase in proportion to the amount of time spent on the ground. There are exceptions; I am talking about general trends covering many species. The adaptive situation can be summarized as follows: the basic opportunity in the shift toward ground-living is the finding of more food sources and exploitation of a greater variety of ecological features; the concomitant risk is much greater predator pressure. One sees a variety of responses to this adaptive problem; it is a stimulating area for future field studies.

In general, in both the tree and ground-living forms, the infant non-human primate is afforded much special attention and care to ensure its survival. Depending on the species, there are differences in the relationship of the infant to its mother and to other adults in the group. In ground-living species, the mother and infant stay in the most protected portion of the group and enjoy the constant protection of adult males; whereas in the tree-living monkeys, such as langurs, the mother and infant may be seen on the edge of the group as often as in its center. It also appears, although this is going to need much more research, that the social status of the mother is of less importance to the young in arboreal species than in terrestrial species, where the associations and development of an infant may be substantially affected by the mother's status. This was first reported from the Japan Monkey Center, essentially that in Japanese Macaques the mothers support their infants in interactions not only with other infants but with juveniles and some adults. Jane Goodall recently reported similar behavior in chimps; the infant of a dominant female may act quite aggressively in respect to an older and much larger animal if the mother supports it. This is an instance of a larger category: the formation of coalitions. Dominance is not only a matter of linear herarchy; there are a variety of coalitions that affect the prerogatives of a particular animal at a given time. In many social interactions, there is a lot of looking around and apparently checking to see whether a particular animal is present.

In all species of monkeys for which data are available it is apparent that the mother-infant relationship is an important part of the group-wide matrix of social relationships, and cannot be understood fully apart from the group. Infant survival depends on the adaptation of the whole group. It is quite clear that the mother with a newborn is the focus of attention and they are very attractive to other group members; the sociometric star is the infant. The infant in most of these species is a different colour in the early part of life, typically black; whether this perceptual feature is important in the responses that are elicited can certainly lend itself to experimental analysis.

The mother-infant relationship is the most intense (in terms of time, energy and affect) in the primate group; it outlasts any other social bond. In some of Jane Goodall's recent work, it is quite clear that a chimpanzee mother's offspring keep coming back to her from time to time up to about twelve years; that is, until they are fully adults, there is important association. Even though the young have a widening world as they pass beyond infancy, it is by no means a contact of short duration between the mother and offspring. In the chimp situation, which is a very interesting and unusual one, the only invariant group, the only highly stable social unit over a long time interval within the chimp community is the mother and her offspring, usually several of her offspring. This is a kind of stable core, a set of stable sub-groups within a chimp community.

Now, I would like briefly to touch on the problem of prolongation of immaturity. Many of the Old World monkeys take several years until they become fully adult. The time required for the great apes is longer, being longest in the chimp, about twelve years. This period is, of course, greatest in humans. Thus, there is a broad trend toward prolongation of immaturity which carries with it certain short-term adaptive disadvantages. I have already referred to motor limitations imposed upon the baboon mother by virture of having to look after her infant; this is quite clear also in the chimpanzee material. The mother cannot move as freely as she otherwise would. Other members of the group must similarly restrict their activities and make adjustments to take account of the infant's motor limitations. In addition, there are reproductive limitations: not only that the mother could move farther and faster if she did not have to carry or walk beside her infant, she could also produce more infants if the period of dependency were shorter. Typically, the adult female primate does not become sexually receptive again until after lactation is over.

Thus, at first glance it would appear that the trend toward prolonged immaturity in the primates has occurred in the face of some selective disadvantages. What kind of adaptive gain could possibly override the disadvantages of this sort? The principal gain probably is that this very long protected time can be utilized for learning purposes. It is long enough so that simple elements of learning can be combined in very complex sequences. The learning which is accomplished during this very long protected time can be adapted to the specific conditions of a given environment, whatever those conditions may be: hot, cold; wet, dry; predators here, predators there. A very diverse array of environments may be adapted to through the shaping of behavior in the long protected interval of immaturity. This, it seems to me, is the principal adaptive gain that can offset the short-term disadvantages.

If one looks at mother-infant relations and developmental patterns in these primate field studies from the standpoint I have just mentioned, it is interesting to ask whether there are indications of an implicit preparation for the environment of adult life. I am not talking about what the animals intend – I do not know what they intend. What I am assuming is that, over a very long time period, natural selection favors behavior patterns that are in fact capable of dealing with highly variable environments. Let us look at a few aspects of mother-infant relations in this context as a sort of implicit preparation of the young for adult life. Perhaps the most striking observation is the female's interest in and experience with young that will

9

presumably ultimately be useful in the care of her own young. This interest begins very early and goes all the way through the life span in the higher primate species for which relevant data are so far available. It looks as though there is a sex difference, quite possible a major sex difference, in the attractiveness of the infant to males and females. However, there is also much evidence of male interest in the young, but male interest appears more variable than female interest in young; this variability appears from species to species, and from one time to another in the individual male's life span. There is much evidence of experience in the handling of infants by older female infants, as well as by juvenile and adolescent females; the occurrance of a pre-adult female who is naïve in respect to parent-young behavior appears very rare indeed in the wild.

There is another kind of early behavioral sex difference in which males show much more interest and experience than females. There is abundant evidence of the young male's interest in and experience with rapid, coordinated, complex movements and patterns of aggressive behavior; this behavior is such that it would appear to be ultimately useful in defence of the group. This type of sex difference has been documented in both laboratory and field studies, especially in regard to early peer play.

In baboon studies, DeVore (1965) emphasizes that the older juvenile and sub-adult females appear to be very highly motivated toward contact with the newborn infant, whereas the juvenile and young adult male merely show a perfunctory interest. There are many observations of female practice in handling infants – in langur, baboon chimp, and gorilla material, including both the major chimp studies. There is a rich variety of ways in which immature females may participate in care of infant chimps. In this context, one thinks of Harlow's experiments and the difficulties that his surrogate-reared animals had in maternal care, in contrast with this field situation of years of experience in caring functions. One thinks in a different way of Robert Hinde's 'auntie' experiments in this context: i.e. experimental analysis of contact of monkey infants with females other than their own mothers.

Now a word about the transition from maximal dependence toward more independent functioning, although independent functioning always has to be kept in mind as being within a group; it is rather less independence than we have in mind for the human child today. The field observations suggest a complex regulation of the outward movement of the infant from its mother which involves integrating the needs for (*a*) an increase in independent skills, (*b*) safety from environmental risks, such as falling out of trees, becoming separated from the group, or exposure to predators. This regulation involves the infant and its mother, and also involves other animals, both the males and the females. There does seem to be a kind of limit-setting which can be observed, in which many animals participate. The motivation to move outward, to explore the environment, seems to be present and persistent in the infants, though there is much variation in the rate of its development and in patterns of its expression. There may be a difference between some of the Old World monkeys and the chimps: the Old World monkey mothers seem to have a tendency to push the young out, like the rejection behavior that Harlow has described. In contrast, Goodall has so far observed remarkably little of such behavior among chimps; at any rate the transition is more gradual. In the case of the chimp, the infant's initiative is very strongly persistent in respect to weaning, exploration, peer relations, and relation to adolescents. Overall, there is evidence in the primate field studies of much infant initiative in outward movement from the mother-infant dependence, although there are notable differences in how that movement is regulated.

The newer field studies suggest the adaptive significance of observational learning in a social context. Time and again, one encounters the following sequence: (1) close observation of one animal by another; (2) imitation by the observing animal of the behavior of the observed animal; and (3) the later practice of the observed behavior, particularly in the play group, in the case of young animals. For illustrative purposes, a food-getting adaptation observed by Goodall will be useful here. It is shown very well in the excellent films made by her husband, Hugo van Lawick.

At the beginning of the rainy season, for a period of about nine weeks, these chimpanzees feed for one or two hours daily on a species of termite common in the area. At this time the fertile termites grow wings, ready to leave the nest and found new colonies. Their passages are extended to the surface of the termite hill and then sealed over lightly while the insects await their flying conditions. Chimpanzees were observed examining termite hills after a heavy rainstorm several weeks before the termite season actually started.

When a chimpanzee in this area sees a sealed up hole, it scrapes

11

away the thin layer of soil with index finger or thumb, picks a grass stalk, thin twig or piece of vine, and pokes this carefully down the hole. It waits for a moment and then withdraws the tool. The end is coated with termites, and these are picked off with the chimp's lips. The length of grass or other material selected is rarely longer than about 12 inches. When one end becomes bent, the chimpanzee either turns it around and uses the other end, or breaks off the bent part. When the tool becomes too short to be of use, a new one is selected. If this is too long, the chimpanzee usually breaks a piece off; if it is a leafy twig or vine the leaves are stripped off with the lips or fingers.

The chimpanzees also show discrimination in choice of materials: a tangle of vines may be briefly examined and rejected; when working in an exceptionally deep hole they will select a longer stick, and so on. There are definite preferences of different animals for particular types of material.

On several occasions when the nearest termite hill was 100 feet away and out of sight, the chimpanzee picked up a grass stalk, carried it to the termite hill and used it as a tool. Young animals closely observe adults in this behavior and imitate both immediately and later, and they practice. They have particularly been observed to practice two operations. (1) They are rather clumsy initially, a number of termites fall off, and the chimps do a mopping operation with the forearm, which the adults are very skillful at; the young can be seen sometimes for an hour or so practicing mopping. (2) They also practice picking grass and preparing grass or a twig. This may occur several hours after they have observed the adults in this behavior.

This is interesting also in the fact that we are dealing here not only with tool use but to a limited extent with tool making according to an established tradition. In the Reynold's study of chimpanzees in a different area, no such behavior was observed, which may only mean the observers did not see it, or it may suggest the variability of local adaptations presumably based on social learning. There is abundant evidence in the recent field studies on local variations in behavior within a species.

Goodall has some other striking instances of this sequence: observation-imitation-practice. For example, chimp mothers sometimes hang their infants in the air for ten minutes or so; some hang them upside down by the leg. Immature females are often observed imitating and practising this behavior. Similarly, there was much

12

observation-imitation-practice with respect to sexual behavior. Goodall has one young male who directly investigated the genitalia and observed copulation 27 times. The infants mount their peers early and also practice on estrous females, who are markedly co-operative in this practice. The same kind of sequence in observa-tion-imitation-practice is quite striking in both the Goodall and Reynolds material in respect to nest building. Bernstein has reported an experiment on chimps indicating the importance of learning in the nest-building art.

Are there any leads as to the conditions under which this sequence of observation-imitation-practice is likely to be initiated? Hall has called attention to a friendly relationship with the operating animal as an important factor; another may be strong affect on the part of any animal in the group. It is an interesting question whether there is anything like identification in non-human primates. Hall has some observations on Patas monkeys, both in the field and in the laboratory – the experiments growing out of the field observations – that suggest a kind of special, fearful attraction of the young male to the adult male; it suggests a kind of rudimentary identification. In this context, Hall calls attention to strong arousal and conflicting tendencies as facilitating factors in social learning.

There are many observations indicating that fear draws mother and infant together with maximal effectiveness. The infant often clings to the mother's hair or to her nipple in a frightening situation. The infant's scream is terribly effective in bringing the mother to him; it appears to elicit intense distress in the mother. It is useful to think of these adaptive responses to noxious stimuli in terms of a mother-infant unit. Thus, in a frightening situation the infant may go to the mother, or the mother may go to the infant; it appears that the mother's fear is at least as significant as the infant's fear in bring-ing them together – on the basis of observations of baboons, langurs, chimps, and gorillas. The early learning of what to fear, what is dangerous in a particular environment, seems to be quite flexible; such fear may attach to different objects and different circumstances in different environments; but these fear commitments tend to be long-lasting. This is similar to the experimental literature on the difficulty in extinction of avoidance responses; here too, the responses learned in fear can be attached to a variety of objects early, but tend to be quite enduring through the life span. This raises very interest-ing questions. What happens when there are rapid environmental

13

changes within the life span of the individual? Under these conditions, are persistent fear responses likely to become maladaptive?

I would like to add something about loss and adaptation to loss. In several species, primates carry dead infants for days – even a week. It is striking to see a baboon mother carry the dead infant until it is almost shreaded; DeVore has recorded such a sequence on film. Goodall has observed it in chimps, noting that for a few days the mother stares a lot at other infants after she has finally given up her own. There is a heavy infant mortality in primate groups; Goodall estimates 50 per cent in the chimpanzees. It is worth noting that probably most of human history has been similar in this respect. Thus, there is an adaptive premium on adequate preparation of those who survive infancy.

Quite recently, Goodall has observed two exceedingly interesting cases in which an infant chimp has been adopted by an older (though still immature) sibling after loss of its mother. There are preliminary indications that, even with persistent effort, the immature siblings cannot provide adequate care. The variety and effectiveness of adaptation to mother loss will be a point of much interest in future field studies and a stimulating point of contact with the growing experimental literature on this subject.

Effects of Various Mother-Infant Relationships on Rhesus Monkey Behaviors[1]

HARRY F. HARLOW and MARGARET K. HARLOW

During the last eight years we have studied the effects of a wide variety of mother-infant rearing relationships on the social development of rhesus monkeys. At one extreme we have raised monkeys from birth onward without mothers or playmates, and at the other extreme we have raised monkeys with normal mothers and easily available playmates. The intermediate rearing conditions include normal mothering without playmates and a variety of situations in which playmates were available but mothering ranged from total denial of any mother, to inanimate, nonresponsive surrogate mothers, indifferent or brutal mothers, and a rotating series of individual mothers.

Effects of Denial of Both Mother and Age-Mate Relationships

Our extreme condition of affectionless upbringing was rearing monkeys in social isolation from birth until various predetermined ages. In isolation there was no opportunity to experience maternal or peer affection or to develop affection for other monkeys. We have employed two conditions of social isolation: Monkeys in *subtotal isolation*[2] were raised in individual wire cages which permitted visual and auditory access to other infants but denied any opportunity for physical interaction. Monkeys in *total isolation* were raised in individual enclosed sheet-metal chambers which prevented viewing of other monkeys or of humans (see Harlow & Harlow, 1962).

[1] This research was supported by USPHS grants MH-11894 and FR-0167 from the National Institutes of Health to the University of Wisconsin Primate Laboratory and Regional Primate Research Center, respectively.

[2] In previous papers we have used the term partial social isolation to describe this condition. Subtotal is a more appropriate name since both maternal and age-mate affection is completely denied, and the long-term effects of this raising condition are severely socially debilitating.

15

Individual Behaviors Developing During Social Isolation

Rhesus monkeys raised under either of these isolation conditions for long periods of time develop many aberrant individual and social behavior patterns (see Cross and Harlow, 1965). Typical individual behavior patterns associated with isolation include: (1) Increased non-nutritional orality directed toward the physical environment or the animal's own body, with almost any body part fixated – thumb, fingers, toes, nipple, or penis. The frequency of this pattern is high during the first two years and then gradually drops to a normal level by the fifth year of life. (2) A second pattern is that of self-clutching in which monkeys, particularly infants, tightly clasp their bodies

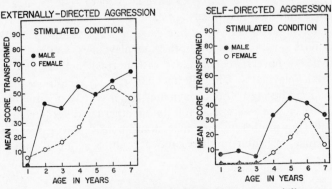

FIG. 1 Development of aggressive patterns by socially
isolated monkeys.

and/or heads with their hands and feet as shown in Plate 1. The frequency of this pattern decreases after the first year and reaches a baseline for males by Year 2 and for females by Year 4. (3) A third pattern is that of social indifference with vacant staring; the animal is unresponsive to ordinary stimulation in the environment such as calls or movement of other animals in the room or the activity of caretakers. This pattern of social apathy may take an extremely bizarre form, to which we have given the name 'catatonic contracture'. While a monkey sits in a quiescent state, an arm floats upward with con-current flexion of the wrist and fingers – a movement made as if the limb were not an integral part of the monkey's own body. (4) A fourth abnormal behavior is that of fixed, stereotyped repetitive movements, such as pacing back and forth or circling over and over from the top to the bottom of the cage. This pattern in one form or

Harry F. Harlow and *Margaret K. Harlow*

another has been observed in many laboratories and for many mammalian species. (5) A fifth pattern is that of aggression. Aggression was measured by having one observer run his hand, covered by a large black laboratory glove (used by handlers when making direct contact with the animals), over the monkey's living cage. The development of two patterns of aggression was traced (see Figure 1): aggression directed against the observer, and aggression directed against the animal's own body – biting its own hand, arm, foot, or leg. Both aggressive patterns appeared earlier in the males than in the females, but even for the males externally directed aggression was infrequent until the second year of life and self-directed aggression low until the fourth year. It is the self-directed aggression which differentiates the isolated subjects from normal animals.

Effects of Isolation on Social Behavior

The effects of raising monkeys in total social isolation during the first 3, 6, and 12 months of life on their later capability of adjusting to age-mates in our playroom situation are well established. Two independent studies (Boelkins, 1963; Griffin & Harlow, 1966) showed that monkeys socially deprived for the first 3 months were terrified upon release but rapidly adjusted to age-mates. No differences in social threat and no significant differences in play behavior were disclosed, even in the first month of playroom testing (see Figure 2).

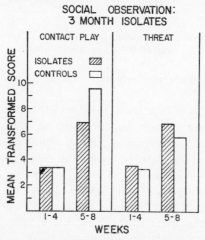

FIG. 2 Social threat and play responses by three-month isolated monkeys and controls.

17

Subsequently an independent, unpublished study by Sackett[1] suggested some depression of exploratory-curiosity behaviors, probably not of a permanent nature.

These data relating to play and sex behavior in 3-month isolates are in strong contrast with the effects of 6 months of total social isolation (Rowland, 1964; Harlow, Dodsworth & Harlow, 1965) tested by placing pairs of 6-month isolates in the playroom with pairs of control subjects. Play and social threat during the first two test months were essentially nonexistent for the isolates, as shown in Figure 3. Even after 32 test weeks, frequency of play by the isolates

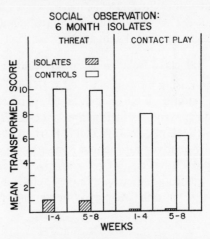

FIG. 3 Social threat and play responses by six-month isolated monkeys and controls.

was low and limited to contacts with each other, never with the controls.

Twelve months of total social isolation left even more devastating effects. Social behavior on the part of the isolates was almost completely absent. Even individual play, a preliminary to social play, was negligible, as illustrated in Figure 4, and a similar pattern existed for each of the wide variety of social behaviors measured in the playroom situation. Social testing in the 12-month isolate groups had to be discontinued after 10 weeks because the control animals were mauling and abusing the helpless isolates to the point that they could not have survived continuing interaction.

[1] G. P. Sackett, personal communication, 1966.

Long-term deprivation effects have been assessed (Mitchell, Raymond, Ruppenthal & Harlow, 1966) by testing these isolate animals 2 or 3 years later, after they had been housed in individual wire-mesh cages in a colony room without physical contacts with peers. In social pairings with adults, age-mates, and 1-year-old juveniles, the 6-month isolates, then 2½ to 3½ years of age, showed no normal sexual behavior, and such attempts as they made toward play were inept. Aggression, however, was frequent in these animals, though totally abnormal in objects. They often engaged in near-

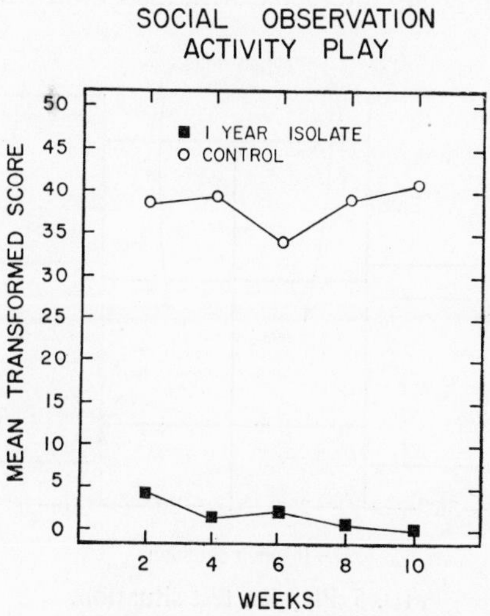

SOCIAL   OBSERVATION
ACTIVITY   PLAY

FIG. 4 Individual play by 12-month isolated monkeys and controls.

suicidal acts of threat or assault against the huge adult males. Even though fearful of juveniles, they attacked and bit them, a response we rarely see in socially raised animals, male or female. The 12-month isolates at the same ages exhibited fear of all social contacts, showed essentially no play or sex behavior, and engaged in no acts of physical aggression. However, one year later (at 3½ to 4½ years of age) two 12-month isolates (one male and one female) displayed abnormal aggression toward both adults and age-mates.

It is clear that denial of both maternal and age-mate affection during the first 6 months to 1 year of life produces a syndrome of persisting social and sexual ineptitude and abnormal aggression in monkeys even though in some animals the appearance of aggression is much delayed. A wealth of additional data presented by Harlow & Harlow (1962), Mason (1963), and Mason & Sponholz (1963) corroborates this conclusion.

Effects of Peer Deprivation During Normal Mothering

The consequences of deprivation of peer experience on infants provided normal mothering from birth have been studied by Alexander (1966) in the playpen situation (Figure 5; also, see Harlow & Harlow, 1962). A control group interacted with their mothers from birth and

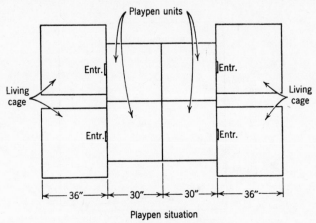

Playpen situation

FIG. 5 Playpen test situation.

with each other from the third week onward. Two experimental groups were also raised by normal mothers but were denied sight of, and all association with, other infants and other mothers for the first 4 and the first 8 months of life, respectively, by placement of opaque panels between adjacent cages and playpens. We refer to the infants in the experimental groups as the playmate-deprived or peer-deprived infants. The experimental mothers developed ambiguous relationships toward these offspring; they tended to be oversolicitous and eventually, also, overpunishing as compared with control mothers, the 8-month group being more punitive than the 4-month group, although negative behaviors never became a dominant feature in treatment of offspring.

The infants that were peer-deprived for 4 months and then allowed to interact with other infants rapidly developed adequate, typical play patterns and appeared to be socially and sexually normal except for their wariness of bodily contact, lessened frequency of affectionate interchanges with peers, and a tendency toward increased agonistic responses as compared with the control group. The infants in the 8-month playmate-deprived group also made rapid and effective social and heterosexual adjustments when allowed to interact with peers. Compared with the 4-month group, however, the 8-month group showed even less bodily contact, still fewer affectional interchanges, and even more agonistic responses. After separation of the young monkeys from their mothers at 13 months of age, additional tests were made of peer interactions and of treatment of stranger 6-month-old infants. The 8-month group was consistently hyper-aggressive, the 4-month group intermediate, and the control group low in aggression within groups. In affectionate behavior within groups, the three groups ranked in reverse order, the control group scoring high, the 4-month group intermediate, and the 8-month group low. In behavior toward stranger infants, the 8-month group again was most hostile, the 4-month group next, and the control group least hostile. No group showed a tendency to make positive responses toward the infants; rather, absence of aggressive behavior was accompanied by ignoring the intruders.

We have previously pointed out that six months of combined mother and peer deprivation produces serious, long-term social maladjustment in monkeys. In contrast, eight months of peer deprivation alters social behavior but much less severely although the implications of the social characteristics of the peer-deprived monkeys are not entirely clear. Such animals placed in a heterogeneous social group including animals of all ages might well become loners or outcasts by virtue of their lower affiliative tendencies and higher aggressive tendencies. In a group restricted to age-mates, however, they could conceivably establish themselves as dominant members because of their readiness to aggress. Nevertheless, in a group similarly reared they do show adequate play and normal sex behavior, suggesting that to a large extent mothers may substitute fairly effectively for age-mates in at least the first eight months of the rhesus monkey's life. This occurs in spite of the fact that rhesus mothers engage in little interactive play with their infants, unlike chimpanzee mothers (Yerkes & Tomilin, 1935) and certainly unlike human mothers. The human mother not only plays with her child but continuously debases her play level to that appropriate to the maturational age of the infant.

Recently, Joslyn[1] observed the behavior of two young monkeys, a male and a female, normally mothered but peer-deprived for the first 20 months. Both mothers were solicitous and protective but also punished their offspring occasionally. When these long-term, peer-deprived juveniles were given the opportunity to associate with each other, they were fearful and neither interacted nor displayed physical contact. Subsequently both juveniles were given daily opportunity to interact or not interact with a normal, unfamiliar peer. The peer-deprived female made no attempt at social interaction throughout 2 months of testing. The male rapidly adjusted to his playmate with no detectable signs of social abnormality except that his sexual behavior was poorly developed. The extreme individual differences were striking, since these two peer-deprived animals, raised under identical conditions, would have been at diverse poles of any social adjustment scale. Similar differences developed with sex reversed in an earlier pair of monkeys raised by their mothers and given the opportunity to interact in the playpen at 7 months of age. In this instance the female repeatedly attempted to establish contact but the male never left the living cage in two months of daily exposures to the female; moreover, the male's mother prevented the female from entering the male's living cage. Subsequently in the playroom, after separation from their mothers, this pair developed no interactive play in two months of exposure.

Effects of Peer Deprivation During Surrogate Mothering

Although we have conducted no experiments specifically on the social consequences of raising monkeys from birth on cloth surrogate mothers while denying them any peer interactions during the first half-year or year of life, we do have a considerable body of relevant data. The early mother-surrogate studies (Harlow, 1958; Harlow & Zimmermann, 1959) showed that infants so raised formed strong attachments to their inanimate mothers and that in a strange situation the cloth surrogates (but not wire surrogates) imparted strong security feelings to the infants, then 3 to 6 months of age. The social contribution of surrogate mothers probably ends with the infant's development of security and trust.

[1] W. D. Joslyn, personal communication, 1966.

Only one research suggests any long-term effect favoring surrogate-reared animals over those raised in bare wire cages (Harlow, Harlow, Dodsworth, and Arling, 1966). In this study of mothers raised without real mothers and without peer experience in the first 7 to 12 months, it was found that of the 7 females raised with cloth surrogates, 2 were abusive, 3 were indifferent, and 2 were adequate as compared with 6 abusive, 4 indifferent, and 3 adequate mothers among the 13 wire-cage-raised females. The numbers are too small for conclusiveness but hold out the possibility that surrogate mothering has some long-term effect which reduces the extreme aggression which these 'motherless-mothers' would otherwise exhibit towards their own infants. Nonetheless, the maternal performance of the cloth-surrogate group considered alone is far from exemplary, as is their record of sexual behavior – 2 were impregnated involuntarily and none of the remaining 5 fell within normal limits in copulatory behavior. No surrogate-raised male has even achieved a normal mount, and none has achieved intromission. Even in social interactions in the second year of life surrogate-raised monkeys, male and female, were as inadequate as wire-cage-raised animals. These shortcomings contrast with those of the mother-reared, peer-deprived infants of the Alexander study (1966), which show social behaviors that are within normal limits or approach normal limits even though they are affectively different from those of animals also provided with early peer experience.

Effects of Total Maternal Deprivation

We have also raised macaque monkeys in situations in which they have had no mothering whatsoever, real or surrogate, but have been given opportunity to interact with other infants, either in pairs, groups of four, or groups of six. We have called these monkeys our 'together-together' infants. These monkeys placed together in the first weeks of life have strong propensities to seek contact comfort, as seen in their quickly developed physical attachments to each other. These attachments resemble those that neonatal and infant monkeys form to real or surrogate mothers, and they largely replace the self-cling patterns typical of infants raised in total or partial social isolation.

Unmothered infants raised in pairs typically enter into the tight ventral-ventral clinging pattern shown in Plate 2. This pattern may persist for many weeks and retard the development of normal play responses. Eventually, however, this pattern is broken and play is established. Unmothered infants raised in unchanging groups of four or six form a dorsoventral clinging pattern, illustrated in Plate 3, which we have called the 'choo-choo' effect. Such simulated mother-infant attachment patterns in larger groups are more easily broken than are the infant pair patterns, and interactive play is exhibited earlier, although it is delayed by comparison with that obtained under more normal rearing conditions.

Our predictions concerning the eventual social capabilities of these unmothered, 'together-together' infants were gloomy, but the infants' long-term social adjustments have been far better than expected. Interactive play patterns did develop, aggression within groups was low, and normal heterosexual adjustments were the rule, not the exception. One female has thus far become a mother, and her behavior toward her infant has been normal in every respect. Thus, in the special, highly protected environment of the laboratory, infant interactions appear to have compensated reasonably well for lack of mothering. We do not believe, however, that normal mothering is in any sense dispensable under feral conditions, nor could it be put to test, for abandoned or orphaned infants would certainly be adopted very soon or perish.

Recently a major 'together-together' study has been completed by Chamove (1966), who compared the social behavior of five different groups of six monkeys each which were raised in individual cages for the first 11 weeks of life and then subjected to one of a variety of living conditions for a period of 12 weeks. These situations were: (1) living together as a group of six; (2) living continuously with one partner; (3) living with the same partner during alternate weeks and alone between weeks of social living; (4) living with each of five partners in successive weeks and then recycling with the individual partners throughout the experimental treatment period; (5) living in individual cages as during the first 11 weeks of life (control condition). At the conclusion of the 12-week period, when the monkeys were approximately 6 months old, the three groups living under paired conditions were placed together in groups of six for a period of 7 weeks. The other two groups were continued in their living conditions. All animals were then raised for 10 weeks in individual cages, after which they resumed the original experimental treatment for 10 weeks. Following this, all groups, including the control animals, were placed in group-living conditions (groups of six) for 5 weeks. During this last situation they attained their first birthday. Animals were observed in their cages throughout the experiment, and starting with the tenth experimental week, all groups, including the controls, were observed in the playroom on seven occasions as a group of six.

Through the first 40 experimental weeks there were no differences among the social groups in home-cage behavior, but starting with the first group test in the playroom, differences between groups were apparent and tended to increase through the course of the testing. In general the animals raised with changing partners closely resembled the animals raised as a group of six, and the animals raised with a continuous single partner in the experimental rearing periods closely resembled the animals raised with a single partner but only during alternate weeks. The control animals differed from the four social groups in most respects.

Aggression showed striking differences through the course of playroom testing. The control subjects, which were, in fact, subtotal social isolates, showed almost no aggression on the first six tests, which preceded their initial experience in social living. On the seventh test, at the conclusion of five weeks of social living, these same control subjects showed two and one-half times as much aggression as the next most aggressive groups and more than fifteen times as much aggression as the low groups. In their home cage, in the last week of group living, one animal was severely injured and separated for three days and three others had to be separated for periods of 24 hours to insure their survival. Of the social groups, the monkeys raised as a group of six were the least aggressive over all, showing very small frequencies, and the monkeys raised with changing partners were also low in aggression. Neither group showed difficulties in group living during the final 5-week period. The two groups with single partners during the experimental treatment were similar to each other and intermediate in aggression in the playroom. During the final week of the 5-week group-living period, both these groups showed serious aggression in the home cage.

Social play and individual play in the playroom tests also differed by rearing condition. The two groups reared with multiple partners were similar in displaying high levels of both kinds of play. The single-partner groups tended to be slightly lower in individual play and considerably lower in social play. The control animals rarely showed social play and tended to be low on self-play as well (see Figure 6 for group social and nonsocial play scores). Play measures, of course, are not independent of aggression measures, for animals involved in fighting are not able, simultaneously, to be engaged in play. Nonetheless, the control animals on the first six tests were low both in play – social and individual – and in aggression.

Clinging followed no regular course for the various social groups. Social clinging tended to be high in the group raised as six together and in the group raised with the continuous single partner. Social

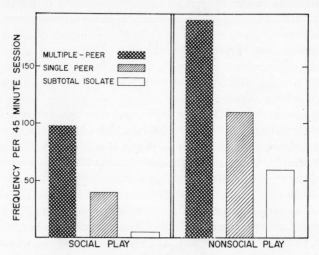

FIG. 6 Social and nonsocial play scores by unmothered
infants and controls.

clinging rarely occurred with control subjects, and the groups with changing partners or a discontinuous single partner generally showed low social clinging in the test situation. Self-clinging, on the other hand, showed almost an inverse relationship to social clinging, being exceedingly high in the control animals, low in the two groups with multiple partners, and intermediate in the two single-partner groups. This behavior, of course, is incompatible with either fighting or play.

More than a year later the animals were retested. In the intervening time they lived successively for 2 weeks in individual cages, 10 weeks as groups of six, 40 weeks in individual cages, and, finally, for 5 weeks under their original experimental treatment condition. They were tested on successive days in a strange playroom alone with an infant less than a month old, a female 9 to 12 months old, and a 4-year-old male. On subsequent days they were exposed with an age-mate from their group to new stimulus animals in the same sex and age classifications.

For all groups aggression was almost nonexistent towards the infant in both test conditions. Aggression towards the age-mate occurred only for the control animals, other groups aggressing, if at all, only towards stranger animals. Whether alone or with the peer, the constant, single-partner animals aggressed most against the young female. Other groups showed low levels of aggression. Against the large male, however, the controls aggressed most of all the groups when alone and at about the same level when with a peer. The multiple-peer-raised groups rarely aggressed against the male. The animals raised with a single peer in alternate weeks displayed the most striking pattern in behavior towards, the large male, showing fairly low aggression when alone but extremely high aggression when with their partner. The other constant-partner group showed low aggression towards the male when alone but moderate aggression when with the partner. Thus, as with other studies of isolates, the controls were indiscriminate in aggression, attacking peers and large males. In contrast, the constant-partner group tended to inhibit aggression towards the male when alone but to display it when in the presence of the partner, the two acting as a team. Alone or apart, however, they showed high aggression towards the young female. The multiple-peer groups, like earlier group-raised animals, showed low aggression generally.

Play behavior paralleled the findings of the group tests a year earlier. Multiple-peer-raised animals showed high self-play and high social play with a peer; controls showed little play of either kind; single-partner-raised animals were intermediate. No group played with the stimulus animals, nor did any cling to these strangers. Controls showed high self-clinging and no social clinging to peers. Multiple-peer groups showed the least amount of self-cling and the single-peer groups, an intermediate amount. Socially directed clinging was greatest in the groups in which partners were constant and consistent and intermediate in the two inconsistent partner groups.

These data strongly suggest that early experience with multiple peers, whether as a group or consecutively, produces ties among group members which maximize play and affiliative behavior and minimize aggression within the group or towards outsiders. Early experience with constant single partners, on the other hand, produces strong partner-ties but little carry-over to peers encountered subsequently, resulting in moderate levels of play and in affiliation within pairs but high aggression between partner-pairs and, sometimes, towards outsiders. Animals raised alone for one year and then placed in a group-living situation show high aggression among themselves and little play or affiliative behaviors. Their aggression carries over to a threatening larger animal although they tend to ignore smaller animals. A second factor is the constancy of association, for there was a tendency for constant-group animals, whether the group of six or the pairs, to show stronger affiliative tendencies to their constant peers than the animals with changing partners or alternate-week partners.

The monkeys raised as a constant group of six in some ways resemble the group of six refugee children studied by Freud & Dann (1951). These children who lost their parents at birth or in the early months of life were shifted about as a group for several years with inconstant caretaking and showed social characteristics in common with our unmothered monkey group of six. Most strikingly, the children showed very low hostility and extremely high affiliative tendencies within their group, as did our monkeys. Their adjustment to other children is not known, nor has this been tested adequately with our monkeys. The child situation demanded an adjustment to adults which the monkey situation did not, and in this respect the comparison of groups cannot be made. Both situations, limited as they are in scope, do certainly point to the important role age-mates may play in the development of affection and socialization, but they both leave untested the potential adjustment of the members to the larger, more heterogeneous social group.

Effects of Surrogate Mother Raising Without Peer Deprivation

As we have already stated, cloth-surrogate mothers are obviously substandard monkey mothers since they are devoid of facial, vocal, and gestural language; cannot protect their infants; cannot punish their infants; and cannot respond reciprocally to their infants' behavior. Even so, macaque monkeys raised on cloth-surrogate mothers but given ample opportunity to interact with other infants show remarkably effective social and sexual development.

Two studies at the Primate Laboratory have given peer experience to surrogate-raised infants. Rosenblum (1961) observed two groups of four monkeys each separated from their mothers at birth and raised in individual cages with a cloth surrogate or both a cloth and a wire surrogate. Each group was placed in the playroom with a cloth surrogate present 18 minutes a day, 7 days a week initially, then 5 days a week until the groups completed 140 sessions in the playroom. The animals averaged 12 days of age at the start. Although the dissertation data were limited to these sessions, systematic observations were continued on a less rigorous schedule for almost 15 months.

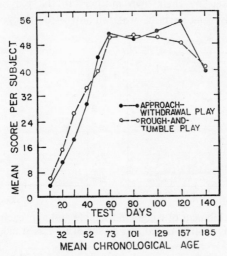

FIG. 7 Development of rough-and-tumble and approach-withdrawal play by normal monkeys.

Both groups developed exploratory behavior, then social play, coming to exhibit highly complex interactions and appropriate sexual behavior. The development of rough-and-tumble and approach-withdrawal play is graphed in Figure 7 and shows effective play patterns appearing early in life. Although the development of these two patterns always shows extensive overlap, greater lag in the appearance of approach-withdrawal play has been found generally in our studies. Before the end of the first test year Rosenblum reported the appearance of aggressive play during which there was vigorous and painful clasp-pulling and biting but no blood-letting.

In spite of their limited time periods for play, Rosenblum's animals

29

compared favorably in their social behavior with animals subsequently raised in the playpen situation (Hansen, 1966) with or without real mothers. Direct comparisons are difficult because the playroom probably offers more stimulation to play owing to its greater floor space, depth, and variety of equipment than does the playpen. To what extent longer play sessions in the playpen compensate for the less rich physical environment is a matter for conjecture in the absence of controlled comparison studies. Hansen compared the social development of a group of four monkeys raised from birth to 21 months with cloth surrogates in the playpen with that of four monkeys raised by their own mothers in the playpen apparatus. Unfortunately, one variable was uncontrolled; the four animals in

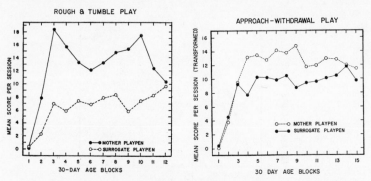

FIG. 8 Development of rough-and-tumble and approach-withdrawal play by mother-raised and by surrogate-raised monkeys.

the surrogate group were balanced for sex but the mother-raised group was all male. Inasmuch as sex differences in activity and play appear by the second and third months and increase subsequently, it is likely that Hansen's differences between groups are enhanced by the sex composition of the groups.

On all social measures the Hansen results showed the mother-raised babies were in advance of the surrogate-raised babies, typified by measures of rough-and-tumble and approach-withdrawal play illustrated in Figure 8, but the group differences lessened with time and by the end of the first year the groups were similar. A third group of two males and two females raised by their mothers from birth in two-unit playpens and transferred at 9 months to four-unit playpens was closely similar to the surrogate group in the second year. When the 12 animals were separated from their mothers at 18 to 21 months and tested together, the surrogate-raised group was indistinguishable in social behavior, but the sexual behavior of the two surrogate-raised males was not normal in that when testing ended the double foot-clasp pattern had not appeared. One mother-raised male did not display adult-type mounting behavior as of this time.

The results suggest that live mothers impart a social advantage to their offspring in the first half-year, but this is in part negated in the second half-year when the mother-raised infants are subjected to considerable ambivalence from their mothers. It is during this period that disturbance scores rise for the mother-raised group. Surrogate mothers, on the other hand, are constant in their stimulus values. It is likely that the surrogate babies would be disadvantaged if they interacted in the early months with mother-raised infants and that the social consequences could become fixed, but under the experimental condition of interaction with others in the same rearing condition until late in the second year, this problem is avoided.

Effects of Indifferent and Brutal Mothering

Female monkeys raised in subtotal social isolation from birth through adolescence are frequently inadequate mothers to their first infants regardless of the way their impregnation is achieved (see Harlow, Harlow, Dodsworth & Arling, 1966). These so-called 'motherless mothers', denied both maternal and age-mate affection early in life, are typically indifferent or brutal to their offspring.

Seay, Alexander & Harlow (1964) traced the course of infant-infant or peer affection in four infants, three males and one female, of near equal ages raised by motherless mothers in the playpen situation. Peer affection, measured by contact play responses, was initially delayed in the motherless-mother infants as compared with infants of normal mothers (see Figure 9), but essentially no differences were found from the third month onward. The developmental course of the more complex play pattern of noncontact play was depressed for infants of motherless mothers compared with normal mothers. Although differences persisted throughout the 6-month test period, they were not statistically significant. Early in life these motherless-mother infants exhibited normal, if not precocious, sexual development. There was also a trend of heightened agonistic responses in the group, with the female and one male tending to dominate the other two males. Retested at 3 years of age, these motherless-mother animals

31

showed less adequate play and more aggression than normal-mother-raised monkeys, leaving open the question concerning long-term effects of the early rearing. The social adjustment of the motherless-mother monkeys was, at least, much closer to that of monkeys raised by normal mothers than that of equal-aged monkeys subjected to early subtotal social isolation.

This motherless-mother study has recently been replicated by Arling (1966), who compared the behavior of four sex-matched infants raised by motherless mothers with a control group of four sex-matched infants raised by normal mothers, and he extended the

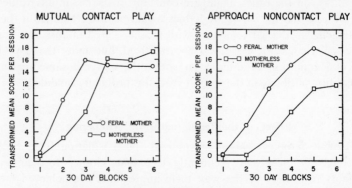

FIG. 9 Development of contact play and noncontact play by infants of motherless mothers and normal mothers.

period of study until the infants were 8 months old. The motherless-mother infants were significantly inferior in this experiment to the controlls in the development of play and in overall sex behavior, and they displayed significantly more aggressive behavior. These findings tend to support the trends in the earlier study suggesting that poor mothering retards early peer adjustment and encourages aggressive behavior.

Effects of Multiple-Mother-Raising on Infant Social Adjustment

Griffin (1966) has recently completed an investigation comparing the social behavior of two groups of four infants raised in playpens by their own mothers with a group of four infants rotated on a bi-weekly schedule within a group of four mothers. The most notable effect of the multiple-mothering treatment was an abnormally high level of disturbance behavior in these infants as compared with the

Harry F. Harlow and *Margaret K. Harlow*

controls (see Figure 10), and the overall groups effect was significant. However, the mothers in the multiple-mother group did not exhibit maternal behaviors significantly different from those of the mothers in the control groups although it is possible that maternal variance was enhanced. When the multiple-mothered infants were allowed to interact with peers, they did not show any deficiencies in play or sexual behavior nor did they show aberrant aggressive responses.

Data collected by Griffin and Sackett[1] on these infants at 8 months of age in a situation where they could choose either a stranger adult or a stranger infant do show differences. The infants from the single-

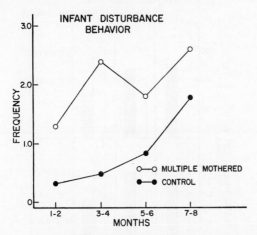

FIG. 10 Disturbance behavior of multiple-mothered infants and controls.

mother groups showed a preference for the infant over the adult, but the multiple-mothered infants showed no preference.

In a series of experiments (Sackett, Griffin, Pratt, Joslyn & Ruppenthal, 1966) multiple mothers, normal mothers, motherless mothers, and their infants were given preference tests to see if mothers preferred their own infants and infants their own mothers. The test apparatus, described by Sackett, Porter & Holmes (1965), allows test monkeys to choose among four compartments to each of which is attached a cage containing a stimulus monkey. The test monkey can be near, see, and hear the stimulus animal by entering the choice compartment but has no physical access to the animal. When the

[1] G. A. Griffin and G. P. Sackett, personal communication, 1966.

stimuli were mothers, the test animals were infants. When infants were stimuli, test animals were mothers. In all tests one stimulus animal was the test monkey's natural mother or infant. Preference is indicated by the amount of time spent in each choice compartment during the 10-minute trial. The results (see Figure 11) show that normal mothers and their offspring preferred each other to familiar but unrelated animals. The multiple-mothered infants and mothers did not prefer their own relative. This was expected because these

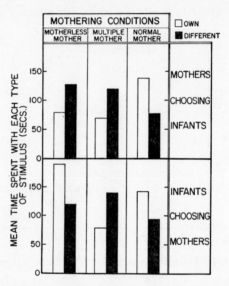

FIG. 11 Preferences of mothers and infants from normal-mothered, multiple-mothered, and motherless-mothered groups.

infants spent equal time during rearing with all mothers in the group. Among all the infants, the infants of inadequate motherless mothers had the greatest preference for their own mothers. The motherless mothers, however, did not prefer their own infants. These tests were conducted when the infants were one year old, within one month of final separation from their mothers. Thus, infants reared by indifferent or hostile mothers seem to have developed greater attachment to their mothers than did infants of normal mothers, but motherless mothers appear to lack the attachment to their infants demonstrated by normal mothers.

Harry F. Harlow and *Margaret K. Harlow*

Summary

This paper has been concerned with assessing the effects of diverse mothering situations for rhesus infants while varying simultaneously the opportunities for peer association. The rearing conditions considered range from total deprivation of mothering and peers to normal mothering and regular peer experience from the first weeks of life.

The isolation conditions have effects that are directly related to duration of the imposed deprivation and degree of isolation. Three months of subtotal or total social isolation followed by extensive opportunity to interact with peers results in rapid adjustment and leaves no obvious deficits. Doubling or quadrupling this period of isolation produces dramatic social debilitation which is far more severe for the total as compared with the subtotal condition. These crippling or devastating effects are not alleviated when social isolates attain adolescence or early adulthood. Prolonged maternal and age-mate deprivation produces affectionless monkeys which exhibit: (*a*) inadequate social and even nonsocial play, (*b*) avoidance of physical contact, (*c*) absence of normal heterosexual behavior, and (*d*) inability to inhibit antisocial aggression when the animal is not too terrified to aggress.

If the deprivation condition is confined to mothering and the monkeys are given regular opportunity to interact socially with multiple age-mates from at least three months of age, they make an adequate social adjustment to their age-mates by all available criteria. Thus far, no negative long-term effects have been uncovered for these animals. Social adjustment is less adequate for monkeys deprived of mothering and provided social experience with only a single peer. They show strong attachments to partners, but otherwise display adjustment inferior to that of multiple-peer groups but in no sense comparable to that of long-term isolates. Similarly, monkeys raised from birth onward with inanimate cloth mothers or with indifferent or brutal natural mothers or passed from one mother to another adjust effectively to age-mates when they are available. Such data as exist indicate either no serious long-term adverse social effects or, at worst, that the infants' social adjustments are within or approach normal limits.

Earlier data led Harlow & Harlow (1962) to postulate that the age-mate or peer affectional system, developed through intimate contact play, was the primary socialization mechanism – the basic mechanism through which macaque monkeys developed deep and enduring affection for members of their own species. Whether or not this is the most effective and efficient manner of interpreting the development of intraspecies affection and socialization may be open to question, but the crucial importance of peer affection as a socialization variable is obvious.

Although peer affection is a remarkably efficient substitute for normal mothering, experiments reported in this paper also show that maternal affection may partially substitute for early peer interaction. Infant monkeys raised by normal monkey mothers but denied age-mate contacts for periods of time that would be socially destructive under conditions of subtotal or total social isolation adjust variably to age-mates, some appearing to be essentially normal and others showing extreme difficulties. When they grow to adolescence and early adulthood they may or may not adjust socially to age-mates, older adults, juveniles, and infants – prolonged peer denial, at least in some cases, can be socially destructive. Just as age-mate affection partially compensates for inadequate mothering, so does maternal affection partially compensate for inadequate and delayed peer socialization.

In a broad sense it is inappropriate to pit the importance of one of these affectional systems against the other. The fact that either may compensate in whole or in part for deficiencies in the other provides an enormous social safeguard, since mothers may be deficient or age-mates unavailable in the critical early period of social development. In primates – monkeys, apes, and men – socialization is essential to survival, and the hazards of normal socialization are multiple and diverse. The biological utility of compensatory social mechanisms is obvious, and that effective social safeguards should have developed over the course of evolutionary development is in no way surprising.

Influence of Social Companions and of Temporary Separation on Mother-Infant Relations in Rhesus Monkeys

R. A. HINDE

Some Effects of Social Companions on Mother-Infant Relations

When rhesus monkeys are kept in groups, each infant is exposed to interactions with a number of females in addition to its own mother. Such females (or 'aunts' as we have come to call them, though without implication of blood relationship) may attempt to behave maternally towards the infants, to play with them, groom them, mate with them, behave sexually towards them, and so on.

A previous contribution to this series (Hinde, 1965) described how, in two cases, mother-infant relations were influenced by the presence of an aunt in the group. The aunt in this case was an adolescent female, who received the support of an adult male in any disputes with the mothers. She could therefore take the infants with some impunity, and used not infrequently to hold one of them for several hours at a stretch. As a result of this the mothers of these infants became very restrictive, seldom letting their infants go to any distance from them at ages at which, from observations on other mother-infant pairs, we had come to expect infants to range widely.

This was a dramatic example of the extent to which an aunt could influence the nature of mother-infant interaction. We wished to see whether similar principles operated even when the effects were less conspicuous. Accordingly we compared the behavior of nine mother-infant pairs living in small groups with that of four pairs ('isolates') living alone in cages of similar size. The observations extended over the first year of each infant's life, the method of observation being described elsewhere (Hinde, Rowell & Spencer-Booth, 1964). The differences fell into three main groups:

(1) During the first twelve weeks of life the isolate infants spent more time with their eyes closed than did the group-living infants. We

37

ascribe this to the smaller disturbance suffered by the isolate mothers. The difference was not present during the rest of the first year.

(2) Compared with the group-living infants, the isolates spent less time with their eyes open on the nipple, less time on their mothers but off the nipple, more time off their mothers, and went to a distance of two feet from their mothers more often. We ascribe all these differences to the greater restrictiveness of the group-living mothers. This interpretation was supported by data showing that the proportion of occasions on which the distance between infant and mother increased from less than two feet to more than two feet which were due to movement by the mother, was greater in the isolates.

(3) The proportion of half-minutes which the infants spent wholly more than two feet from the mother was greater in the isolates during the first ten weeks, but smaller subsequently. Thus during the latter period, although the isolates were more often more than two feet from their mothers, they went to that distance for shorter periods. This difference probably arose because the isolates had fewer distractions to keep them at a distance from their mothers: after the first ten weeks of life the group-living infants spent much time playing with each other. This probably accounts also for our findings that the isolates were groomed more frequently by their mothers, and that a higher proportion of their attempts to gain the nipple met with rejection. It was also noteworthy that the only male infant born into our colony which has been seen to masturbate was one of these isolates, and that three of them were often seen running along the wire netting, watching and keeping as close as possible to infants in other pens.

Thus there were clear differences in the nature of the mother-infant interactions between the isolates and the group-living animals. Since the mothers of the isolate group were selected at random from the monkeys coming to the laboratory, the differences are unlikely to be genetic and we ascribe them to the difference in social conditions. Further details are given in Hinde & Spencer-Booth (1967).

The Influence of Six Days Maternal Deprivation on Mother-Infant Relations

Bowlby's view (1962) that deprivation of maternal care for a period may have far-reaching effects on an infant's future development is on the whole well-supported (Ainsworth, 1962), though it has given rise to some controversy. Some of the issues involved are difficult to resolve with human subjects, since experimental studies are out of the question. It seems possible, however, that monkeys can be used to attack some of them. Rhesus monkey infants are known to be adversely affected by a period of maternal deprivation though, of the three previous studies, one was concerned with only very brief periods of separation (Jensen & Tolman, 1962), and in the other two the effects of the separation were studied only for 2-3 weeks after reunion (Seay, Hansen & Harlow, 1962; Seay & Harlow, 1965; see also chapter 2 in this volume).

The present study concerned four mother-infant pairs, each living in a small social group. In each case the mother was removed from the group for a period of six days when the infant was 30-32 weeks old. Before separation the behavior of all of the infants was similar to that of the eight control infants who had no separation experience.

When the mother was removed, there was an immediate increase in 'whoo' calls. During the separation period the infants directed some of the behavior previously directed towards their mothers towards other adults in the group, but received much less care from them than they had had previously from their mothers. Their behavior was 'depressed': they became much less active, sitting about in a characteristic hunched posture. As the separation period progressed they became active for more of the time, but their activity was less vigorous.

On the first day of the mother's return, all four infants spent a higher proportion of their time clinging to her than they had before separation. When they did leave her, they went to a distance from her less often. The more they had been off their mother before the separation, the less clinging were they on her return.

Even four weeks after the mother's return the rate of 'whoo' calling for all four infants was higher than before separation, though all but one of the infants had returned to the pre-separation level of activity by this time. The amount of time spent off the mother recovered in the first few days after the mother's return, but then regressed for a while, the permanent recovery occurring more slowly. This was clearly a period of great instability in mother-infant relations, with the mother at first yielding to the infant's excessive demands but later rejecting them. It seems probable that this period immediately after reunion may be one of crucial importance for the re-establishment of mother-infant relations, and would repay future study.

In two animals the effects of the separation experience on the time spent off the mother were still apparent a month later, and in one of these they persisted at least to the end of the first year.

These results show that some rhesus infants of 30-32 weeks are adversely affected by a six-day period of maternal deprivation. The severity of the effects vary with the nature of the preseparation relationship, but they may persist for at least some weeks. The symptoms shown by the monkey infants parallel in many ways those shown by human infants in similar circumstances. Further details are given by Spencer-Booth & Hinde (in press).

The Waning of the Mother-Infant Bond in Two Species of Macaque[1]

I. CHARLES KAUFMAN
and LEONARD A. ROSENBLUM[2]

The rapid growth of interest in the behavior of nonhuman primates has been accompanied by an increasing attention to the vital role of the mother-infant relationship as it influences individual and social behavior and its development. The fine early researches of both laboratory and field workers on a variety of primate forms (e.g., Lashley & Watson, 1913; Tinklepaugh & Hartman, 1932; Hines, 1942) lay the basis for much of the detailed investigation recently completed or underway. (See e.g., Rheingold, 1963; DeVore, 1965; Hinde et al., 1964; Jensen & Bobbitt, 1965; Rosenblum & Kaufman, 1966). These early workers, often with great precision, outlined the gradual transition of the dyadic relationship in monkeys and apes from an initial period of virtually continuous physical attachment and codirected attention, through several transitional stages, to an ultimate state of independent and separate functioning of the offspring and mother. Such independence is obviously necessary for the infants to enter into the adult activities of their species, and for the mother to turn her attention to her next offspring when it appears.

In light of the relatively prolonged periods of infantile dependence in the primates, compared with most phyletically lower forms, it is clearly of considerable importance to examine not only the behavioral mechanisms involved in the *establishment* of the mother-infant bond, but also those which are involved in the *attenuation*, and to some degree at least, the ultimate *termination* of this rather enduring relationship.

[1] The research upon which this study was based was supported by United States Public Health Service Grant #MH-04670. The authors wish to thank A. J. Stynes for his considerable assistance in carrying out the work reported in this paper.

[2] Research Career Development Awardee (level 2; Grant #MH-23,685-03). National Institute of Mental Health, U.S.P.H.S.

It is upon this latter phase in the course of the dyadic relationship, i.e., those behaviors involved in the waning of the bond, that we should like to focus this paper.

A number of investigators have considered the question of the diminishing mother-infant relationship in various species under both laboratory and field conditions (DeVore, 1965; Harlow, Harlow & Hansen, 1963; Jay, 1963; Jensen & Bobbitt, 1965; Hansen, 1966; Kaufmann, 1966). Studies of most species suggest little variation in the theme that the infant itself initiates and enlarges its repertoire and length of engagement in non-maternally directed behaviors (depending of course upon the scope of activities possible in the given situation), while initially maintaining intense dependence upon the mother. The mother meanwhile shows a gradual re-emergence of non-infant-directed adult female social behaviors during the early life of her infant, while still focusing most of her attention upon, and while still remaining continuously solicitous towards, her infant.

The picture of the later stages of the relationship, however, becomes more inconsistent when one views different species of primates and even the same species in different settings. Although it is exceedingly difficult to judge the relative contributions of each participant in a continuously changing interactional relationship, various authors have attempted to assess the relative role (1) of the expanding interests and involvement of the growing infant in group activities and (2) the negative responses of the mother towards the infant (for example, weaning or physical punishment), as they contribute to the diminution of the mother-infant relationship. Hansen (1966) for example, working with rhesus monkeys in a laboratory setting in which the interactions between mothers and their young were quite circumscribed, tends to stress the 'Maternal contributions to infant emancipation . . . via the development of punishment and rejection responses' (p. 143). J. H. Kaufmann (1966, p. 25) on the other hand, in discussing the growing independence of rhesus infants from their mothers in the free-ranging bands on Cayo, Santiago, in which access to other animals was unrestricted, indicates that 'rejection of the infants seemed insignificant compared to the infants' interest in other monkeys, especially other infants'.

In light of the difficulties inherent in determining the factors contributing to changes in the mother-infant relationship, considerably more basic data on the course of the decline in the bond and on the behaviors implicated in it are necessary before any valid

Charles Kaufman and *Leonard A. Rosenblum*

conclusions may be drawn. The current paper is an attempt to describe a part of this ebbing relationship in two species of macaque, observed in laboratory groups under identical controlled conditions.[1] Normative, quantiative observations detailed in this report were made on two groups of *Macaca nemestrina* (pigtails) and two of *M. radiata* (bonnets). A total of 9 pigtail and 8 bonnet mother-infant dyads were observed for this purpose. Additional groups of both species, including numerous mother-infant pairs, have also been observed for special experimental purposes. The data to be presented cover the first fifteen months of infant life before siblings were born.

Each group was housed in a pen 8 feet wide, 7 feet high and 13 feet deep containing shelves and bars at differing heights (for further details, see Rosenblum *et al.*, 1964). All observations were made through one-way vision screens set into the front walls of the group pens. This was done, since it was felt that even after long periods of observation from exposed positions, subtle distortions of the emotion-sensitive mother-infant relationship might be induced by the presence of the observer. To make our quantitative observations, the observer focused his attention successively, in random order, upon each animal in the group for a fixed period which was varied from time to time between 180 and 900 seconds. *E* dictated the observed behaviors into a continuously-running tape dictation machine, recording the beginning of each behavior in which the focus *S* engaged, including those that it initiated and those of which it was the recipient, along with the partner or partners involved. The continuously running dictation tape provided an accurate time record of the occurrence of each behavior observed; a clock was connected in parallel with the playback of the recorder such that a typed record could be provided in which the time occurrence of each behavior was indicated. These records were then key-punched and fed by cards into an I.B.M. 1620 computer, which had had placed within its memory the contingent relationships between all the behaviors in our observational system, i.e. which behaviors terminated which others, which were independent, etc. This enabled the computer to determine the cessation of each behavior and thereby calculate its duration. Summary tabulation programs produced week-by-week records for each animal for all behaviors, including both the relative frequency and

[1] Preliminary analyses of data concerned with the early stages of the mother-infant relationship in these two species is presented in Rosenblum & Kaufman (1966).

duration of occurrence, in terms of the total amount of observations made during that period.

Of the large number of diverse behavior categories included in the observational system in an attempt to canvass the entire spectrum of behavior in each species,[1] the following categories were considered pertinent to the consideration of the declining course of the mother-infant relationship:

Maternal Behaviors

Carriage

(a) *Cradle Carriage:* Locomotion of the mother with manual holding and support of the infant at her ventral surface.

(b) *Passive-Support Carriage:* Locomotion with the infant supporting himself at her ventral surface, without her holding or bracing him.

Cradle

While seated, grasping and pressing of the infant to the ventral surface of her body through the active use of her hands.

Enclosure

While seated, more or less tight surrounding of the clasping infant with the flexed forearms and/or flexed hind limbs.

Guard

Maintenance of *Passive Contact* of one or both hands with the free infant, or moving along next to (within one foot) or above the loco-moting infant.

Passive Contact

Remaining in physical contact with another without engaging the other in any additional categorized social behavior.

Passive Support

Sitting with the infant resting or supporting himself at her ventral surface without a *Cradle* or *Enclosure* by her.

Punitive Deterrence

Constrained biting of the limbs, shoulders, and head of the infant, or violent shaking of the infant's body.

[1] The entire taxonomy of behavior used in carrying out this research program is described in detail in Kaufman & Rosenblum (1966).

Retrieval

(a) *Physical-Danger Retrieval:* Grasping and rapid cradling of the free infant who is in a precarious position, or who has just fallen or suffered some other mishap.

(b) *Social-Danger Retrieval:* Grasping and rapid cradling of the free infant in reaction to an activity directed towards the infant by another member of the group.

Weaning

(a) *Mouth-Nipple-Contact* Deterrence: Prevention of the infant from reaching the nipple with its mouth, e.g., by holding the infant's head between her arm and the side of her body.

(b) *Nipple Withdrawal:* Removal of the nipple from the infant's mouth, e.g, by the lifting of her arms and jerking up and away of her breast, or the manual pushing away of the infant from the breast.

Infant Behaviors

Exercise Play

Vigorous jumping, climbing or running without either social or inanimate object referents.

Social Play

(a) *Chasing Play:* The playful chasing of one animal by another, frequently with intermittent reversal of roles.

(b) *Rough-and-Tumble Play:* Playful mauling, biting and wrestling which rarely results in even mild injury to either partner.

Ventral Contact

(a) *Ventral-Ventral Cling:* Tight clinging to the mother with all four limbs and with the head and chest pressed closely to her thorax.

(b) *Ventral-Ventral Hold:* Clasping of the mother with two to four limbs, but with head and chest not in contact with her thorax.

Other Behaviors

Horizontal Departure

Separation of the dyad beyond *Proximity* in the horizontal plane.

Proximity

Passive standing or sitting within twelve inches of another animal without making contact or engaging in any additional categorized social behavior.

Vertical Departure

Vertical movement which separates the dyad by more than 12 inches.

Data and Discussion

The most obvious indication of the growing independence of mother and infant is the decreasing amount of time which the infant spends at the mother's ventrum. As we see in Figure 12, this inter-

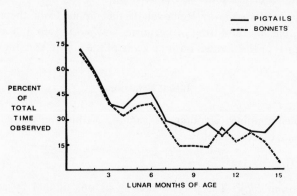

FIG. 12 Mean duration of ventral contact in pigtail and bonnet dyads during the first 15 months of life.

active pattern, which in the first days of life is maintained almost continuously, gradually decreases, reaching a low plateau in both species in the seventh or eighth month. By the second to third month of life, when the infant is in ventral contact, the mother's behavior is that of *enclosure* (Plate 4) and this remains characteristic from then on. *Cradle*, in which the infant is actively grasped, though prevalent in the first month of life, virtually disappears by the third or fourth month. Finally, towards the end of the first half year, the mother will, on occasion, offer the infant only *passive support* at her ventrum. Similarly, *carriage* of the infant, which is almost always at the mother's ventrum becomes extremely infrequent by the seventh month of life in both species.

46

In considering these maternal patterns, however, it is important to point out that under conditions of group stress or danger, even at the end of the first year of life, mothers will cradle and carry their infants for extended periods. Of course the infant and mother also make contact in a variety of ways other than that at the ventrum, including the infant's climbing on the mother and resting at her side, but these relate more to the early stages of the relationship and will be described in detail elsewhere.

In virtually all dyads of both species that we have observed, it is the infant that initiates most of the breaks in contact from very early in life onward. The initial breaks in contact are quite brief, and the

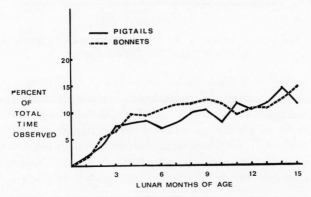

FIG. 13 Mean duration of medium-distance separations (horizontal departures) in pigtail and bonnet dyads during the first 15 months of life.

infant, guarded closely by the mother, does not venture far from her. (Plate 5) There is then a gradual increase in the amount of time spent more than a foot away from the mother, but still on the same level of the pen (Figure 13). These medium-distance separations follow basically similar developmental courses in the two species, leveling off in the fourth or fifth month. Once the infant has initated the break in contact, mothers show a considerably greater willingness, particularly during *the second half year* of life, to move away from their separated infants. (Figure 14) During the first several months, however, although the infant is able to move further and further from the mother and for longer periods, and even though she may be backing or walking somewhat away from her infant, rarely does more than a moment go by in which the mother ceases to watch intently her

47

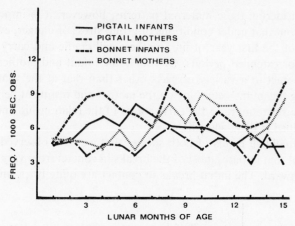

FIG. 14 The relative frequency of horizontal departures by mothers and infants in pigtail and bonnet dyads.

separated infant. Indeed, the separated infant, two, three, or four feet from the mother, is often *retrieved* in an instant in response to stimuli perceived by the mother but often undetected by the observer.

Beginning in the second month of life, although initially quite rarely, the infants, when separated from their mothers begin to move to other levels of the pen, leaving their mothers behind. As we see in Figures 15 and 16, the frequency and duration of these *vertical*

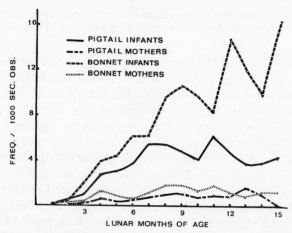

FIG. 15 The relative frequency of vertical departures by mothers and infants in pigtails and bonnet dyads.

departures increases dramatically after the first month and reach a high asymptotic level at about the eighth month. It is clear from Figure 15 that it is the infants who are primarily responsible for these separations. Consideration of the frequency and total duration of these maximum separations between mother and infant provides the first evidence of a distinction between the bonnet and pigtail infants developing in our laboratory. From about the third month of life onward, bonnet infants consistently spend more time than pigtails at different levels of the pen than their mothers. It is likely, particularly early in life, that these maximum separations reflect what may be considered the relative security of the infant in his physical and social

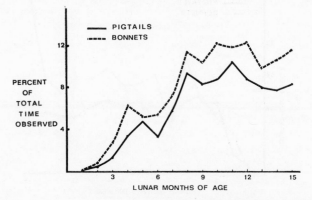

FIG. 16 Mean duration of maximum-distance separations (vertical departures) in pigtail and bonnet dyads.

environment. This greater relative security from early on in the bonnet infants we consider to be a significant index of what we believe is a real difference between them and pigtail infants in their relative dependence upon the mother as they mature. Other indications of this distinction as well as data on factors which contribute to it will be presented below.

Although the total length of time infants spend maximally separated from their mothers in our pens continues to increase until about the eighth month, the duration of each *vertical departure* levels off by about month four. As we see in Figure 17, initial excursions in the second month generally last but 10 to 15 seconds. From the fourth month of life onward, the infants usually remain maximally separated in our laboratory situation for only some 35 to 55 seconds.

The somewhat restricted size of our pens makes very distant excursions by the infant impossible and may in some way limit the time spent away from mother. Nevertheless, it is apparent that even at the end of the first year the infants of these two species seem content to return with relative frequency to the close vicinity of the mother, spending between 10 and 15 per cent of their daylight hours on the same level of the pen as she is (Figure 13) and approximately seventy per cent of the day in *proximity* or in actual contact with her.

After the end of the first half year of life, those behaviors which served to enhance or maintain the cohesiveness of the dyad have all

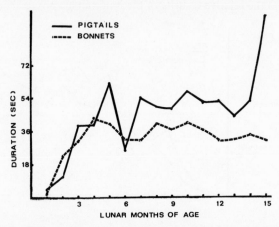

FIG. 17 Mean bout lengths of maximum separations between the members of pigtail and bonnet dyads during the first 15 months of life.

but disappeared. Ventral-ventral contact has waned sharply; the mother no longer restrains the infant in his attempts to break contact with her; she no longer *guards* it when contact has been broken, and indeed, no longer watches it continuously even when it has moved to another level of the pen. As we see in Figure 18, even the most enduring maternal protective behavior, *retrieval* of the separated infant when the latter is in some danger, which peaks in months three and four in pigtails and in the second month in bonnets, drops to very low levels (by month seven in the pigtails, even earlier in the bonnets). It is of interest to note that retrieval, reflecting as it does maternal apprehension over the welfare of the separated infant, appears considerably less often, peaks earlier and wanes more rapidly, in bonnet as compared to pigtail mothers. The lesser degree of retrieval

50

Charles Kaufman and Leonard A. Rosenblum

by bonnet mothers is undoubtedly related to the greater degree of maximum separation shown by bonnet infants; as such it appears to be an important contributing factor to the previously noted distinction between the species in the developmental course of the infants, and perhaps reflects a mutual casualness of mother and infant during these separations.

In both species as maternal solicitude wanes, maternal behaviors appear which actively encourage increasing separation of the mother-infant dyad. The two most prevalent and dramatic forms of this abdyadic maternal behavior are *nipple-withdrawal* (and the related *mouth-nipple – contact deterrence*) and *punitive deterrence*.

Although some mothers undoubtedly suffer some sensitivity of the nipples and intermittently interrupt nursing during the early days of life, weaning behavior (i.e., nipple withdrawal) which seems to indicate reduced maternal interest in nursing occurs most frequently in the fourth month in both species and declines thereafter[1] (Figure 19). Since at this age the infant is still dependent on the breast for part of its nutriment, and perhaps more importantly, obviously still consistently seeks the nipple when disturbed, it does not immediately adapt to these maternal rejections. Violent whole-body muscle spasms, vocalizations and often forcefully repeated attempts to re-establish nipple contact are generally observed.

The weaning technics vary. When the infant is on the nipple she may jerk her arm up, pulling the nipple out of its mouth. Initially with

[1] It would be important to distinguish between nutritive and non-nutritive nipple behavior by the infants, but our laboratory situation used for this study was not ideally suited to this task, since the animals were living in groups and were observed by us at some distance and at varying angles of orientation. We know that by the fourth month the infants had been eating solid foods for some time (Plate 6). We know also that both before and long after this time an appreciable amount of nipple behavior was clearly non-nutritive, i.e., it was not accompanied by sucking. It is difficult to know whether this peak in weaning behavior was related to changes in the mother (e.g., decreased lactation) or in the infant (e.g., teething, biting). In any case the peak in weaning behavior at this time did not bring nipple behavior by the infant to an abrupt end. Some form of nipple contact continued into the second year of life and we have even seen efforts of sucking by the older infant *after* the birth of a sibling, unlike Simonds (1965) who reported that for bonnets in the field, 'No female was observed allowing last year's infant to nurse after the birth of a new one.' What direct effect direct nipple deterrence behavior may have had on the amount of actual sucking and nipple contact generally may be answered by further computer analysis of our data on a day-to-day basis. These extended analyses and further studies under more desirable conditions for acquiring these data will be carried out to clarify this matter.

E   51

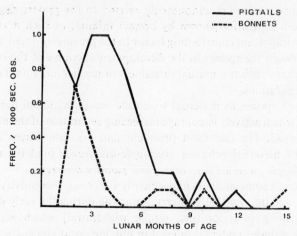

FIG. 18 The relative frequency of *retrieval* by pigtail and bonnet mothers during the first 15 months of their infant's life.

the younger infant, the mother may then simply clamp the infant's head between her arms and her body, thus preventing for a time further access to the nipple (Plate 7). Perhaps the most efficient pattern yet observed in this regard occurred in an old pigtail mother who removed the nipple from her young infant's mouth by sliding her middle finger down along the nipple and allowing her infant to suck on this interposed finger.

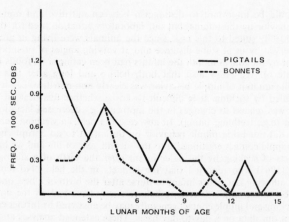

FIG. 19 The relative frequency of nipple withdrawal by pigtail and bonnet mothers.

At about the same time as *nipple withdrawal* increases, the mother will often attempt to prevent contact altogether. The persistence of the infant during these rejection periods appears to be the stimulus to the mother for *punitive deterrence* (Plate 8). As seen in Figure 20, this behavior in bonnets peaks in the fourth month as did *nipple withdrawal*, but in pigtails it continues to increase in frequency for several months thereafter. In both species, punitive deterrence continues to appear at low frequencies well into the second year of life. It is obvious from Figures 19 and 20 that from the fifth to the tenth month abdyadic behavior is considerably greater in pigtail

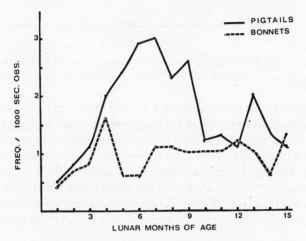

FIG. 20 The relative frequency of *punitive deterrence* by pigtail and bonnet mothers.

mothers than bonnets. To recapitulate, the bonnet mother retrieves less, weans less and punishes less. She appears to allow, but not necessarily to coerce the developing freedom and independence of her offspring during the first year, which it seems to us in large measure contributes to the developmental distinction between the species.

Overlapping greatly with the changing pattern of mother-infant relations is the continuously increasing interest of the growing infant in his peers and in the environment about him. The infant's growing dexterity and co-ordination is coupled with his increasing freedom of departure from the mother, as her restraining and protective behaviors diminish. Rather rapidly, the initially tentative and hesitant movements away from her merge into energetic play activities. As we see

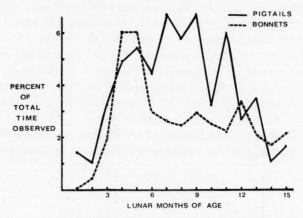

FIG. 21 Mean duration of *exercise play* in pigtail and bonnet infants during the first 15 months of life.

in Figure 21 the infant displays a rapidly developing involvement in nonsocially directed play in the environment, which we term *exercise play*. These playful behaviors become increasingly focused on peers, and *social play* behaviors soon become the most prominent nonfilial infant activity. Indeed, as Figure 21 illustrates, there is actually a decrease in *exercise play* during the second half year of life. *Social play* of various sorts (Figure 22) continues to develop during the first nine or ten months and then levels off. It is striking that almost con-

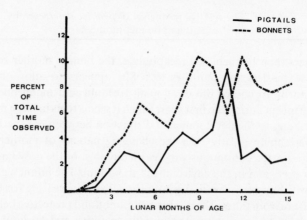

FIG. 22 Mean duration of *social play* in pigtail and bonnet infants during the first 15 months of life.

tinuously for the first 15 months of life, bonnet infants engage in more social play than do pigtails (Plate 9). The nonsocial *exercise play* levels on the other hand, though greater in pigtails than in bonnets in months seven through eleven, are quite comparable in the two species at the beginning and by the end of the first year. During the seventh through eleventh month, when total play is very high in both species, an analysis of social and exercise play combined indicates a mean total play involvement of 10·9 per cent in pigtail and 10·4 per cent of total time observed in bonnet infants. Thus, involvement in play during this latter half of the first year is comparable in

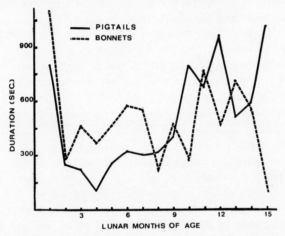

FIG. 23 Mean bout lengths of ventral contact between the members of pigtail and bonnet dyads during the first 15 months of life.

the two species, being primarily autonomous in pigtails and socially directed in bonnets. From the twelfth month onward, and even beyond the limits of the data presented here, total play, primarily social in focus, is several times greater in bonnet than pigtail infants.

Finally it is appropriate to consider the state of the relationship between the mother and infant after the rejection period of the mother has peaked and declined and after the peer relations just discussed have developed. It is clear that at the end of the first year and on into the second, the mother-infant bond continues to display considerable strength; indeed, although infants are much less often observed on or near their mothers, it is apparent from Figure 23 that towards the end of the first year, whenever infants do re-establish contact with the mother, the length of each of these ventral contacts is increasingly prolonged. Night time observations indicate that infants of this age still sleep at the mothers' ventrum. Furthermore, observations made when the mothers included in this study gave birth to second infants, 15 to 18 months after the first, indicate that despite an initial period of rejection, older infants were still allowed to sleep pressed tightly to the mother's side and were occasionally groomed by her. In several instances we observed mothers even reaccepting an older infant to the ventrum when the second infant had begun to move away from her. The birth of a sibling alters the relationship to mother, but clearly it does not terminate the relationship.

These data have been presented with a view towards considering some of the detailed changes which occur in the mother-infant relationship in monkeys as the infants pass through the first 15 months of life. It is apparent that a distinction exists between bonnet and pigtail dyads during this period, which is evident in various aspects of the developing behavior patterns, The general cohesiveness of bonnet groups as compared with comparatively treated pigtail groups, so strongly manifest in the bonnets' long periods of *passive contact* between adult group members has been considered in earlier reports (e.g., Rosenblum *et al.*, 1964). This tendency towards minimal individual distances between bonnet adults seems to be reflected in a relatively relaxed maternal disposition. Bonnet mothers relatively at ease in the presence of their peers, are less likely to suddenly retrieve their separated infants than are pigtail mothers. Similarly, bonnet mothers seem more tolerant of the continued closeness of their growing infants, manifesting less *nipple withdrawal* and *punitive deterrence*. The bonnet infants, paralleling this relative maternal relaxation, leave and maximally separate from their mothers more frequently in the early days of life and continuously spend more total time maximally separated from their mothers than do pigtail infants; they consistently engage in more social play than do pigtail infants. We may see here the mechanism by which the species-characteristic gregariousness may be perpetuated. Although all these differences in the infants' developmental patterns may be due to direct genetic differences in the pigtail and bonnet infants, it is our feeling at this time that the species-characteristic social milieu in which the dyad develops exerts a prominent behavioral force in producing the distinctions observed. We hope in future studies of cross-rearing in the two species to further clarify the relative contributions of both the genetic and early environmental factors.

Finally, what do these data contribute to a consideration of the relative contribution of maternal rejection behavior to the ultimate independence of the infant? Two facets of the present material seem of direct relevance in this regard. Firstly, it will be noted in Figure 12 that in months five and six, there is a change in the slope of the decreasing ventral contact time in both species, and perhaps even an inversion in the curve at that point. It is perhaps significant that these are the months of life which follow upon or are convergent with the heightened period of maternal rejection in the form of *nipple withdrawal* and *punitive deterrence* (Figure 19 and 20). This sort of positive relation between increased rejection and increased contact time has also been reported (Rosenblum & Harlow, 1963) in the case of rhesus monkeys raised on an artificial mother surrogate which periodically directed a strongly aversive air blast at the clinging infant but which terminated the rejection if the infant broke contact. It was proposed, at that time, that the aversive stimulation of the infant, even though 'coming from the mother', producing as it did violent disturbance behavior, served to enhance the infant's attempts to seek the mothers' ventrum, the latter being the most characteristic response to disturbance in infants of this age. Although the two sets of data are not directly parallel, it is likely that particularly during the time when the infant is still rather young, intermittent rejection by the natural mother does serve to increase rather than decrease the infant's dependent behavior and his desire for what Harlow has called 'contact comfort'.

We may appreciate the problem better by a consideration of levels of psychological development especially those of cognitive structure and object relationship. For the very young organism of any species objects such as 'mother' do not exist in their own right but only as functional elements in the infant's economy which are assimilated in terms of the present only. When out of sight the object is out of mind except perhaps as a fleeting image which may be recognized but which has no continuity, permanence or substance. In Piaget's terms there is no conservation of the object; in psychoanalytic terms there is no object constancy. Distressing stimuli activate species characteristic behaviors, such as clinging, which will ordinarily be to the mother, who is there. For the infant this may represent 'contact comfort', but its adaptive value in terms of survival is obvious since the mother does in fact deal with all the dangers that in any way threaten the infant's existence. The infant responds with clinging even if the distressing stimuli emanate from the object to which it clings since the infant's cognitive structure doesn't allow recognition of the sameness of the object. We believe that this may explain the findings of Rosenblum and Harlow, i.e., their infants didn't recognize that the aversive stimuli were 'coming from mother'. Our findings may have a similar explanation, or they may reflect more complex developmental processes. We don't yet know if, or when, macaque infants growing up with their natural mothers achieve the cognitive structure necessary for object constancy and true object relationship to develop, as happens in the human infant from about seven months on, when objects become detached from action, take on an independent and separate existence and are endowed as such with emotional value. (We believe that something like this does take place in the monkey. Our other developmental studies and our studies of the reactions of infants to separation from mother at various ages should shed light on this matter.) We know from the human that after object relationship has been established in the infant, intermittent maternal rejection, moderate and specific, plays a powerful role in further development, helping to establish modes of behavior and systems of value. This it does by threatening the relationship, which the growing child must preserve, a task made more difficult by the fact that her rejection also provokes his aggressiveness to her. He responds by being good, by suppressing his aggressiveness, by behaving as she wants and by seeking reassurance from her, as in clinging to her to prove that she still exists, and that she loves and accepts him. This is very different from the automatic clinging of the neonate. The whole episode is a reminder of his dependency and evokes behavior directed to her. It is only massive rejections that destroy the relationship and bring about withdrawal by the infant or child. We don't mean to impute to our monkey infants a complexity of development and motivation as described for the human. We do believe that by the fifth month of life in a normal monkey the increased clinging that follows rejection is more than just the automatic attachment behavior of the neonate.

Secondly, comparison of the developmental trends in the two species does not support the idea that maternal rejection behavior is an important determinant of the growing independence of the young. Bonnet mothers, in terms of the data presented here, reject their infants far less often than do pigtail mothers. Yet, in terms of the amount of time spent maximally separated from the mother, and in terms of play involvement with peers, both important measures of relative independence, bonnet infants by the end of the first year seem less dependent on their mothers than do pigtails.

It would appear then, that factors other than maternal rejection *per se* must be taken into account in considering the waning of the mother-infant bond in macaques. As the processes of physical growth and maturation proceed, and the sensorimotor apparatus[1] elaborates and differentiates, the infant progressively engages his environment. His emerging interest in his social environment is subject to various influences. Some which act in the field are not readily evident in the laboratory. Among those which act in the laboratory to effect his growing independence are the increasing freedom of movement over space and time and in social interaction, allowed by the mother, a social preference for peers and the unrestricted availability of peers in a varied environment. The powerful influence of maternal behavior is seen in the differential rate of development of independence between the bonnets and pigtails, the bonnet mothers fostering independence not through rejection but through freedom and security.

---

[1] In other developmental studies we are attempting to assess sensorimotor development by special technics, to allow for more precise correlations with other developmental processes and the varieties of life experience. One such technic appears to isolate the capacity for perceptual disembedding. (Rosenblum, *et al.*, 1965).

Development of Maternal Responsiveness During Pregnancy in the Laboratory Rat[1]

DALE F. LOTT and JAY S. ROSENBLATT

The female rat, unlike the female of a number of other mammalian species (e.g., mouse, goat, infrahuman primates and humans) who exhibit maternal behavior as virgins and outside of lactation, generally does not show maternal behavior except during a specific period. Maternal behavior begins at parturition and ends some three or four weeks later. For this reason it is generally believed that maternal behavior is under the control of hormonal secretions in the rat. Recent attempts to *induce* maternal behavior with the hormones, estrogen, progesterone, and prolactin, singly and in combinations (Lott, 1962; Lott & Fuchs, 1962; Beach & Wilson, 1963) were unsuccessful. This raises doubt about earlier studies (e.g., Riddle, Lahr & Bates, 1942) which identified the maternal hormone as prolactin. We can add our own inability to *maintain* maternal behavior with prolactin and oxytocin in 'practising mothers', whose pups were removed shortly after birth (Rosenblatt, unpublished). Nevertheless the feeling persists that maternal behavior in the rat is a hormone-dependent behavior pattern.

We decided to adopt a different approach to this problem. Could we determine the earliest time during pregnancy when maternal responsiveness could be detected? We felt that if somewhere between mating and the beginning of parturition, some 22 days later, at which time the female displays full-blow maternal behavior, we could find

[1] This research was supported by United States Public Health Service Grant MH-08604 to JSR and Postdoctoral Fellowship from the National Institutes Mental Health (MH-17, 462) to DFL. We wish to extend our appreciation to Dr D. S. Lehrman for suggestions made during the course of the study and together with Dr E. Hansen, for critical reading of the manuscript. We are grateful to Miss Alice Trattner for conducting a considerable portion of the study.

a period when maternal responsiveness began to emerge then this period could be intensively studied for concurrent changes in hormonal secretion. Virgins and non-pregnant nor lactating females have been shown, by Wiesner & Sheard (1933), to be unresponsive to newborn even after four days of continuous contact with them, in 60 to 70 per cent of the animals studied. The problem therefore was to see whether there was a period during pregnancy, earlier than parturition, when females would respond to pups that were placed with them, by displaying maternal behavior.

Ordinarily the pregnant female is shy of pups, making little or no contact with them during one hour daily tests. This fact prompted us to use the procedure of terminating pregnancy by performing Caesarean-section deliveries on our females. It has already been shown that this operation performed on females as early as the 19th day of pregnancy, some three days prior to normal parturition (Wiesner & Sheard, 1933), is followed shortly afterward (i.e., within 24 hours) by the appearance of retrieving, nestbuilding and 'nursing' maternal responses. If pregnancies were to be terminated at progressively earlier times, relative to normal parturition on the 22nd day, a time would be found, we reasoned, when maternal behavior would no longer appear following the operation. Between that time and one several days later in pregnancy when the operation was still followed by the appearance of maternal behavior would lie the period we were searching for, the period when maternal responsiveness emerged.

Since all of the different groups of females whose pregnancies were terminated at progressively earlier points were subjected to the same operation to end the pregnancy, the Caesarean-section delivery, though a factor in the appearance of maternal behavior at the various times, would not account for *differences* among the groups in the appearance of maternal behavior. These differences might consist of different rates for the appearance of maternal behavior or whether or not it was exhibited. The difference between two groups, one operated on late in pregnancy and another early, could be attributed to the pregnancy period intervening between the operations.

We included in our study a group of virgins. Since our procedure for testing the maternal responsiveness of the pregnant females delivered by Caesarean-section was different from that used by Wiesner and Sheard (1933) to test their virgins we felt it necessary to re-evaluate the maternal responsiveness of virgins with this new procedure. Sham operations were not done on these animals, however, since it was not our object to analyse features of the Caesarean-operation, separating the effects of *an* operation from those specific to the Caesarean operation. Parenthetically we may say that the maternal performance of operated virgins (i.e., ovariectomy) does not differ from that of the virgins on whom we shall report.

Procedure

Five groups of pregnant rats bearing their first litters, and one group of virgins were used; they totaled 66 females. Caesarean deliveries were performed under diambutal anesthesia, using ventral incisions, on the 8th day of pregnancy (n=8), the 10th day (n=11), the 13th day (n=9), the 16th day (n=16), and the 19th day (n=8). In the first three groups bilateral hysterectomies were performed to remove the fetuses: 4 of the 19-day pregnant animals and 6 of the 16-day pregnant females were bilaterally hysterectomized, but the remainder were left with uterus in place. Since the hysterectomized and nonhysterectomized females in each of the latter two groups did not differ in their performances during maternal behavior tests no further mention will be made of the two different procedures used to deliver the fetuses and placentas in these groups.

Twenty-four hours postoperatively the operated females and virgins were given 5 pups, aged 5- to 10-days and were tested for retrieving and other items of maternal behavior (crouching over young, nest-building, and licking pups). To test for retrieving, a group of pups was placed at the front of the cage and a female's reactions were observed for 30 minutes. Each female was then observed for 1 minute every 20 minutes for an additional four hours. The five pups were left with the females until the next morning, when they were replaced by five new pups in the same age range. Daily replacement of litters was made necessary because lactation did not occur in any of the females operated on before the 16th day of pregnancy and the lactation induced in one animal each from the 16th and 19th day C-section groups was insufficient to maintain the pups. Immediately following this replacement the female was observed for 15 minutes to test for retrieving and again observed one minute every 20 minutes for four hours. This procedure was followed for 10 more days giving a total of 12 such tests in 12 days. However, if retrieving was shown in three tests before the 10th day testing was stopped on the 10th day. The purpose of the four-hour observation period was to note the appearance of retrieving and other items of maternal behavior over a longer period than the retrieving test and under conditions when the female had become accustomed to the presence of pups in the cage.

Animals were maintained on a 12-hour reversed daylight/night cycle, each animal being housed in a 20 in × 20 in × 14 in high cage with three walls of clear plexiglass. Subjects were placed in these cages at least 48 hours before testing began. Food and water were always present and a large amount of nesting material (hay and coarse wood shavings or paper toweling) was spread on the floor of the cage shortly after the animals were returned postoperatively to the home cage.

Results

The results of our study, presented in Figure 24, show that during no period from the 19th to the 8th day of pregnancy could retrieving not be elicited from all of the females following the delivery by Caesarean-section. Further, nearly all of the virgins could also be

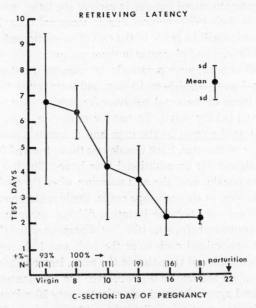

FIG. 24 Latency of retrieving (in days) in virgins and five groups of females delivered by Caesarean-section at progressively later times during pregnancy.

induced to retrieve the test pups provided the period of continuous contact with them was long enough; in some cases a period of eleven days of contact was necessary. Wiesner & Sheard (1933) provided only four days of continuous contact during which 30 to 40 per cent of their virgins began to retrieve. At the end of a similar period (i.e., 5th day testing) 33 per cent of our virgins had retrieved also, confirming their results, but the percentage rose to 80 per cent after 7 days and to 93 per cent after 11 days of continuous contact with pups. Since such a high percentage of virgins show retrieving under appropriate stimulation, it is not surprising therefore that, under the same stimulation, females that have been pregnant for varying durations should also show retrieving.

There were differences in the rate of onset of retrieving in the different groups of operated pregnant females. The latencies for the onset of retrieving were longest for the virgin and 8-day pregnant females, of medium duration in the 10- and 13-day pregnant animals, and shortest for the 16- and 19-day pregnant animals ($F = 14.23$, $df = 5/60$, $p < .01$). Among the groups of pregnant animals (excluding the virgins) the decline in the latency was significant also ($F = 14.85$, $df = 4/47$, $p < .01$). There are therefore changes in maternal responsiveness (i.e., retrieving responsiveness) during pregnancy, but not, as we formerly believed, from a zero level in the virgin. The overall change is from a virgin level to one which, as pregnancy advances, more and more approaches the high level of responsiveness of the parturient female.

We can trace the course of these changes in maternal responsiveness during pregnancy by comparing the mean latencies for the onset of retrieving in successive groups, starting with the virgins [Duncan's New Multiple Range test at the ·05 level of confidence, extended for unequal-sized groups (Kramer, 1956)]. The latency for retrieving remained unchanged, from the virgin level, in the 8-day operated animals but underwent a significant shortening between the 8th and 10th day during which interval the average latency decreased by more than two days (6·37 days to 4·18 days). Between the 10th day operates and the 16th day delivered females there was a further significant shortening of the latency for retrieving (4·18 days to 2·31 days). The position of the females terminated in pregnancy on the 13-day exemplifies the transitional nature of the period from the 10th to the 16th day of pregnancy; their average latency was shorter than that of the 10-day group, and longer than that of the 16-day group, but was not significantly different from either of them. Between the 16th day and the 19th day of pregnancy there was no further change in the latency for retrieving.

During the course of pregnancy there were, therefore, two periods during which maternal responsiveness (i.e., with respect to retrieving) increased and there is probably a third which follows the 19th day and leads to the high level of responsiveness exhibited by the 22-day parturient female.

A pertinent question is whether there were differences in the ages of the pups to which females of the different groups were exposed which might account for the differences in latency for the onset of retrieving. Two groups will be compared with respect to the average age of the test pups: these groups were chosen for comparison because they were large-sized groups and there was a significant difference between their average latencies for the onset of retrieving. The females delivered by Caesarean-section on the 16th day of pregnancy were given pups ranging in average age from 6·7 days to 8·4 days over the first eight days of testing; all of the females showed retrieving by the 4th day. The virgins were given pups ranging in average age from 7·0 days to 8·4 days over the same period and more than 40 per cent of the females did not initiate retrieving until the 7th and 8th days.

Our findings, with respect to retrieving, are paralleled, with some differences, by our findings, with respect to the other items of maternal behavior which we studied, namely, nestbuilding, licking and crouching over the young.

Discussion

Our study has brought to light two new facts which a theory of the development of maternal behavior in the rat must incorporate. The first is that the virgin is capable of exhibiting retrieving and other items of maternal behavior (i.e., nestbuilding, licking and crouching over young) when stimulated by pups for periods beyond four days. The second is that the latency for the appearance of retrieving, (and other items of maternal behavior) undergoes a general shortening – maternal responsiveness increases – as pregnancies are terminated by Caesarean-section delivery at progressively later times. The first increase in maternal responsiveness, above the virgin level, is discernible after the 8th day of pregnancy (in operates) and the second increase is evident at the 16th day of pregnancy (in operates).

As is evident, our findings were unexpected, since there was no basis for expecting that the virgins would be as maternally responsive as they were, and the technique of Caesarean-section delivery had not been used to study maternal responsiveness earlier than the 19th day of pregnancy. We have therefore opened up a number of problems which require further study before our findings can receive any explanation. What is the basis for the maternal responsiveness of the virgin? Is it hormonal in nature? What produces the changes in maternal responsiveness during pregnancy as revealed by Caesarean-section delivery? Is this an hormonal effect? What does the operation contribute to maternal responsiveness? Are the relevant processes only those which precede the operation or does something happen after the operation which is critical for maternal behavior to appear? These and a number of other problems are now engaging our attention. Perhaps at a reunion of the study group, which I assume there are plans for, some five years hence, we shall have the answers to these questions.

Some Effects of Experience on Maternal Behaviour in Rodents

M. P. M. RICHARDS[1]

Introduction

It has been known for some time that previous experience of young may have a profound influence on later maternal behavior. Except for Noirot's (1964 a, b, 1965) work on mice, there has been almost no systematic investigation of these phenomena. I should like to present the results of some experiments with Golden Hamsters and try and fit these in with the data for other species.

The factors involved in rodent maternal behaviour may be divided into three categories: the stimuli from the young, the endocrine condition of the female and her previous experience of young. Though these categories form a very convenient way of organising the material they are, of course, arbitrary in the sense that they are not independent from one another. So, though I am mainly concerned with the influence of the female's previous experience of young, some of the discussion involves the other two factors. In particular, it is necessary to show that different ages of young evoke different kinds and amounts of maternal responses as these differences are later exploited in the analysis of the experience effects. Discussion of endocrine factors is included because these interact in a very specific way with the experience effects. This is illustrated by an experiment in which maternal responsiveness of virgin, pregnant and lactating females is compared.

Methods and Procedures

A Standard testing situation was used for all the hamster experiments to which I shall refer. Animals were individually housed in

[1] The experiments described in this paper were carried out while the author held a Research Studentship from the Science Research Council. The author is grateful to Professor R. A. Hinde for much helpful discussion.

large observation cages for at least a week before testing. Three pups were placed in the female's nest and a fifteen minute recording session began when the female first sniffed a pup. The occurrence and duration of the following behavior patterns were recorded with a moving paper event marker: sniffing and licking, carrying, nursing, attacking and eating the young; nest-building and territorial marking. The animals were maintained on a 12 hr/12 hr reversed light schedule and all tests were carried out under red lights during the first three hours of darkness. This time coincides with the most active phase of the hamsters' diurnal activity cycle.

All these experiments used naïve virgin females. That is to say, females that have been reared from the time of weaning (at about 25 days) until testing (at 2 to 3 months) in complete isolation from young. This precaution was taken as preliminary observations with both hamsters and mice (Noirot, pers. comm.) have suggested that females reared in the same room as breeding females and their litters are more responsive to young than females without such experience. Details of these methods are described more fully elsewhere (Richards, 1965).

The Age of the Young as a Variable

In the Golden Hamster, as in other rodents, maternal responses may be elicited from non-lactating females by the presence of young. The nature of these responses varies with the age of the foster young.

This experiment was designed to quantify these changes with the age of the young (Richards, 1966a). One hundred and forty-four naïve virgin females were each given a single standard test with three pups of a particular age. Pups aged from day 1 (i.e. <24 hr old) to day 18 were used; eight females being tested with each age of young.

The responses of the females fell into three phases, dependent on the ages of the test pups. Pups aged from day 1 to day 6 were attacked after a very brief latency, killed and eaten. The behaviour closely resembles that seen with living prey (e.g. cockroaches). Very few maternal responses were elicited by pups of this age. Young of an intermediate age (day 6 to day 11) were also attacked but after rather longer latencies. These attacks were usually followed by maternal responses and little or no eating of the young was seen. The most commonly evoked maternal responses were licking and nest-building. More rarely the females adopted the nursing position.

The responses elicited by pups older than day 11 suggest that they were being treated as strange adults. Pups were attacked after very long latencies. These attacks were not followed by eating and consisted of the sideways kicking and biting usually seen in adult – adult fights (c.f. Rowell, 1959). Prey killing attacks were not seen. Territorial marking, another response seen in adult – adult encounters, was also evoked. Very few maternal responses occurred. These results confirm earlier work with lactating hamsters (Rowell, 1960) but are very different from the results which have been obtained with rats or mice (Wiesner & Sheard, 1933; Noirot, 1964a). In both these species the youngest pups are the most effective for eliciting maternal responses. This is what one might expect on functional grounds as the youngest pups require the most maternal care. It is possible that this rather striking difference between the Golden Hamster and rats and mice may be explained in terms of the hamster's evolutionary history. The evidence (c.f. Richards, 1965) suggests that the Golden Hamster is a relatively recent species. Gestation length is one of the characteristics which marks off the Golden Hamster from most other species of the group; this is 16 days as opposed to 20 to 21 days in the other species. A reduction in the gestation length would need to be accompanied by a change in the stimulus characteristics of young of each age and/or a modification of the females' responses to those stimuli, if the youngest pups were to remain the most effective for eliciting maternal responses. These changes may not yet be complete in the Golden Hamster so that newborn young still provide less effective stimuli than young of the ancestral newborn age.

Effects of Previous Exposure to Young

We have evidence for both rats and mice that indicates that exposure to young increases responsiveness to young encountered at a later date, (c.f. Richards, 1967). For example, a dead newborn mouse elicits very little maternal behaviour from a naïve female. However, if dead young are presented to females which have had a previous five minute period of exposure to living newborns, they now evoke many maternal responses (Noirot, 1964b). In this, and other experiments, the increase in the females' responsiveness was seen after exposure to young of an age which evoked much maternal behaviour. The following experiment with hamsters (Noirot & Richards, 1966) was designed to investigate the effects of exposure to various ages of young, which elicit varying amounts of maternal behaviour, on later maternal responsiveness.

Naïve virgin female hamsters were given a standard test with either day 1 (group 1–6), day 6 (group 6–6), or day 10 pups (group 10–6) and then a second test two days later with day 6 pups. The design of the experiment is set out in Table 1. The behavior of each

TABLE 1

Ages of Pups used in First and Second Tests

Group	N	1st test	2nd test
0–6	16	day 6 pups	—
6–6	8	day 6 pups	day 6 pups
1–6	8	day 1 pups	day 6 pups
10–6	8	day 10 pups	day 6 pups

group with day 6 pups was compared with a control group (group 0–6) which received a single test with day 6 pups.

The results of this experiment are given in Tables 2 and 3. Group 1–6 and 10–6 both spent more time nest-building and carrying the pups and less time eating them than the group 0–6 females.

TABLE 2

Behaviour with day 6 Pups – Mean Duration of Responses in Seconds

Group	0–6	6–6	1–6	10–6
Nest-building	1·6	8·1	28·3	15·5
		p < ·01	p < ·002	p < ·002
Nursing	32·4	48·9	12·1	22·0
position		ns	ns	ns
Carrying pups	4·5	5·1	20·0	32·3
		ns	p < ·02	p > ·05 < ·1
Eating pups	276·3	238·0	155·5	no eating
		ns	p < ·05	

Probabilities comparing groups to group 0–6 (2-tailed Mann-Whitney U test) ns=not significant.

Mean durations were calculated for all the animals in each group whether or not they showed the behaviour pattern in question. N=8 for all the groups except 0–6 where N=16.

TABLE 3

Attacking Behaviour with Day 6 Pups

Group	0–6	6–6	1–6	10–6	test used
No. of females attacking	15-16	7-8 ns	7-8 ns	1-8 p ·01	Fisher's exact test
Median no. of attacks	6·0	5·5 ns	7·0 ns	0 p ·002	Mann-Whitney U test
Median latency to first attack (sec.)	55	44 ns	2·5 p > ·05 < ·1	—	Mann-Whitney U test

Probabilities comparing groups to group 0–6. All tests are two-tailed.

Group 6–6 showed the same trends, but only the increased time spent nest-building was significantly different from group 0–6. Attacking behaviour gave a rather different pattern; in each case the behaviour in the second test resembled that which would have been expected had the age of the pups been the same as in the initial test. Thus, only one female in group 10–6 attacked day 6 pups while seven did so in group 1–6. Latencies to the first attack were very brief in group 1–6 as they had been in the initial test with day 1 pups. The results for group 6–6 and 0–6 were similar for all measures of attacking.

These results demonstrate that in hamsters, like mice and rats, previous exposure to young increases maternal responsiveness in a subsequent test. The increase was much less marked in the group (6–6) receiving the same aged pups in both tests suggesting that a difference in the stimuli provided by the young in the two tests may be an important factor. With this proviso, the increase in maternal responsiveness seems independent of the amount of maternal behaviour evoked by the pups used in the first exposure. An initial exposure to day 1 pups (which were killed and eaten) produced a similar increase in responsiveness as a first test with day 10 pups (the most effective age for evoking maternal responses). These results confirm a suggestion of Noirot's (1964b). Her mice data indicate that the increase in responsiveness is independent of previous performance of the maternal response and is thus caused solely by exposure to certain stimuli coming from the young. In the present experiment, an increase in responsiveness occurred after initial contact with day 1 pups which did not elicit maternal responses.

It is tempting to ascribe these increases in responsiveness to an induced hormonal change. However, as similar effects have been described in intact, castrate and hypophysectomised male and female mice and rats (Leblond & Nelson, 1937, Rosenblatt, 1967), involvement of the hormones of the pituitary–gonadal axis seems most unlikely. Furthermore, in the present experiment all the hamsters continued to show normal oestrous cycles during the period of testing. This rules out any major change in ovarian hormone production.

Any hypothesis about the physiological basis of these changes in responsiveness must take into account the time course of the changes. In mice (Noirot, 1964c) the increase in responsiveness appeared very quickly and was relatively long lasting; it was seen equally when the second test was given about a minute or two to eight days after the first exposure. The hamster results seem similar. In some of the tests in the first experiment reported here, initial attacking behaviour was replaced by maternal responses after a few minutes while in the second experiment the interval between tests was two days. Thus, whatever physiological changes underly the increase in responsiveness, they must occur within a matter of minutes and persist for several days.

Effects of Pregnancy

The literature suggests that there are few differences in responsiveness to young between virgin and pregnant females (Wiesner and Sheard, 1933; Rosenblatt & Lehrman, 1963; Beniest-Noirot, 1958; Rowell, 1961). So it is generally assumed that there is a sudden increase in responsiveness at the time of parturition (c.f. Richards, 1967).

I decided to re-examine the question of the timing of the increase in responsiveness in the hamster in the hope that a precise knowledge of the timing might give some clues to its physiological basis (Richards, 1966b).

Using the standard procedure, groups of virgin, pregnant and lactating females were tested with day 1 pups. The pregnant and lactating groups, breeding for the first time, were tested within 24 hrs of parturition. The lactating females' own litters were removed immediately before the beginning of the test.

The results are shown in Tables 4 and 5. As in the previous experiments, all the virgin females attacked, killed and ate the newborn pups given to them. Most of the pregnant females also attacked and six of them ate at least one pup. But in most cases there was then a

TABLE 4

Responses of females to newborn pups. N = 8 for each group. Group V are virgin females, group P pregnant females and group L lactating females.

Number of females responding and mean duration of response (secs)				Statistical comparison*		
Group	V	P	L	V–P	P–L	V–L
Sniffing &	8	8	8	ns	ns	ns
licking	10·3	161·0	168·4	p=·006	ns	p<·001
Nest-building	5	8	8	ns	ns	ns
	5·0	105·8	99·9	p<·001	ns	p<·001
Nursing	0	5	7	p=·05	ns	p=·05
	0	207·5	453·5	p<·001	ns	p<·001
Eating pups	8	6	1	ns	p=·05	p=·01
	360·8	141·5	15·6	p=·006	p=·002	p<·001

* Fisher exact test was used for the number of females responding and the Mann-Whitney U test for the mean times. All tests are two-tailed. ns=Not significant.

TABLE 5

Responses of females to newborn pups. N = 8 for each group. Group V are virgin females, group P pregnant females and group L lactating females

Responses				Statistical Comparison*		
	V	P	L	V–P	P–L	V–L
Mean No. of Attacks	5·1	3·8	0·1	p=·064	p<·001	p<·001
Mean No. of pups killed	3·000	1·375	0·004	p<·001	p<·001	p<·001
Median time to 1st Attack (secs)	3·5	3·0	00	ns	—	—
No. of females Attacking	8	8	1	ns	p=·01	p=·01

* Mann-Whitney U test was used except for the number of females attacking. These scores were compared with the Fisher exact test. All tests are two-tailed.

sudden change in behaviour and maternal responses were elicited by the remaining pups in the later part of the tests. With one exception, maternal responses but no attacking behaviour were shown by the lactating females.

These results clearly indicate that by the last day of pregnancy females are more responsive to young than virgin females. In the tests with pregnant females there was a change from attacking behaviour to maternal responses during the course of the test. This is further evidence that exposure to pups increases maternal responsiveness. In the experiment described earlier the increase in responsiveness was only apparent when virgin females were given a second test; in the initial test all the day 1 pups were killed and eaten. In the present experiment the increase in responsiveness as indicated by the change in the females' behaviour was apparent before the end of the fifteen minute test. So the physiological changes of pregnancy have increase responsiveness to young, or, to put it another way, they have reduced the duration of exposure to young necessary to effect a change from attacking to maternal responses.

After parturition, attacking behaviour had almost completely disappeared. This change could be the result of physiological events associated with parturition or factors dependent on the actual physical process of birth or a combination of these two. The lactating females also differ from the other two groups as these females have had experience of their own young. Further experiments are required to separate the roles of these factors.

The results of this last experiment illustrate very clearly the interaction between endocrine factors and those related to the females' previous experience of young. Exposure to young increases maternal responsiveness; an effect which is apparently not mediated through the endocrine system, or at least not through the pituitary–gonadal axis. However, the physiological changes interact with this effect in such a way that a briefer period of exposure to young is required to produce an increase in maternal responsiveness. What the relevant physiological changes are is not known, but it seems likely that ovarian and placental hormones are involved (c.f. Richards, 1967).

Conclusions

As we have seen there is good evidence that exposure to young increases latent maternal responsiveness in nonlactating hamsters, mice and rats. We can say rather little about the physiological basis of these changes except that it does not seem to involve the hormones of the pituitary – gonadal axis and the mechanism responds very quickly (within minutes) and persists at least for a matter of days. If asked to speculate about the mechanisms I think it would be reasonable to say that it should be looked for within and not outside the central nervous system. Clearly much further work is required.

These kinds of effects have only been looked for in these rodent species so we don't know how widespread they are within the mammals. However, the results of experiments with 'motherless mother' rhesus monkeys which Dr Harlow presents in this book at least suggest the possibility that exposure to young increases latent maternal responsiveness in that species too. But care should be taken with generalizations involving such widely separated species. Even if a similar process is described in the rhesus monkey one could not assume without further experiment that it has the same physiological basis.

Apart from the interest of these effects in their own right, knowledge of them has important implications for the design of experiments on maternal behaviour and for the interpretation of existing results. The evidence indicates that mere exposure to certain stimuli from the young is sufficient to increase responsiveness. It seems likely that the ultrasonic calls of the young are one of the stimuli involved and there is some direct evidence to support this in mice (Noirot, pers. comm.). Assuming this to be so, in experiments on maternal behaviour one must control for *all* previous experience of young and that must include sounds of a frequency well above the human threshold. Failure to do this in the past has led to some erroneous conclusions being drawn from experimental results. For example, Riddle (Riddle, Lahr & Bates, 1942) concluded from his experiments that prolactin and certain other hormones increased maternal responsiveness in rats. Several attempts to repeat this result have failed (Lott, 1962, Lott & Fuchs, 1962; Beach & Wilson, 1963). In Riddle's experiments rats receiving hormone injections were given a larger exposure to young that the control animals (c.f. Richards, 1967). So it seems likely that what was at first interpreted as an effect of the hormones was in fact a result of exposure to young.

PART II

Human Studies

The Natural History of Crying and Other Vocalizations in Early Infancy

PETER H. WOLFF[1]

Introduction

The broader context for this report is a longitudinal study on the development of human affect expressions, that was briefly described at an earlier Tavistock meeting (Wolff, 1963); it is a preliminary report rather than an exhaustive description of infant vocalizations; and some of its items pertain to isolated observations or anecdotal reports, while others were either demonstrated repeatedly in the whole group of infants, or confirmed by *ad hoc* experiments.

Most of the data were gathered in the home, where I have tried to fulfill the role of an unobtrusive participant observer, whose presence was obviously known to all members of the family. I was neither hidden behind a one-way vision mirror nor recording from long-distance electronic transmitting devices; and as the material indicates, I was very much a part of the *ad hoc* experiments, either by serving as a test-object, or by directing the mother to alter a procedure in her caretaking functions momentarily.

Eighteen infants were observed over a one month period for about 30 hours per week; this includes four Japanese babies on whom I have *not* included comparative data. Twelve of these babies were observed for the first three months; and five of these in turn were followed up to six months. For observations beyond the first month the total time in the home was reduced to 12–15 hours a week because behavior items that interested me changed more slowly than during the first month, and did not require the detailed attention of the first month.

The primary aim of this report is to render a functional analysis of

[1] Work for this report was undertaken while the author was supported by a Career Development grant of the U.S.P.H.S.—N.I.M.H. Grant No. MK-3461, and a research grant of the U.S.P.H.S.—N.I.M.H. Grant No. M6034.

crying. To this end I have described discrete and sufficient causes of crying in the young infant, distinguished the different patterns of crying in response to these causes, explored their specific effects on the mother, compared the effect of various interventions that will arrest crying to define the causal conditions more precisely, and traced the changing relation between the causes, pattern, and adequate means in the arrest of crying over the first six months. Because cry and non-cry vocalization seemed to have a functional relation, I also included preliminary data on the early development of non-cry vocalizations (lalling, gurgling, laughing).

So that the analysis of vocalizations would not depend exclusively on the subjective impressions of the adult listener, crying was recorded on magnetic tape, samples of which were then represented visually as sound spectrograms. The spectrograms to be shown were written at double the recording speed in order to bring out temporal sequences in crying which proved to be an important distinguishing feature among the different types. Each specimen of crying therefore represents a duration of about 5 seconds along the horizontal axis, and a frequency range of 0 to 4000 cycles per second along the vertical. Broad band (300 cycles per second) filters were found to be more useful than a narrow (50 cycles per second) band filter for the analysis of cries.[1]

The Morphology of Early Vocalizations

The pattern of crying illustrated in Plates 10 and 11, has sometimes been called the *hunger cry*, since it usually is heard while the baby is hungry (see, for example, Lynip, 1951; Karelitz *et al.*, 1963; Wasz-Hockert *et al.*, 1962). The term is misleading if it implies a causal relation between hunger and a particular pattern of crying, since this is simply a 'basic' pattern to which the infant sooner or later reverts from other crying, and it has no unique causal relation to hunger. This 'basic' pattern is characteristically rhythmical and varies in fundamental frequency from 250 to 450 cycles per second in both sexes, with a predominance in the range from 350 to 400 cycles per second. A typical sequence as shown in Plates 10 and 11, consists of the cry proper (mean duration 0·6 per second), followed by a brief silence (0·2 seconds), a short inspiratory whistle (0·1–0·2 seconds) of higher fundamental frequency than the cry proper, and another brief

[1] For the technical aspects of sound spectrography, see Potter *et al.*, 1947; Joos, 1948; Fant, 1960.

rest period before the next cry proper begins. Unless the infant is overly excited, the interval between the cry proper and the inspiration is shorter than the interval between inspiration and the next cry, so that one hears the natural unit as a cry followed by an inspiration rather than an inspiration followed by a cry.

In Table 6 the durations of separate events (cry, rest, inspirations, rest), for one sequence of rhythmical crying were tabulated to show the stability of the rhythm in the neonatal period. The measures were

TABLE 6

Rhythmical Cry – 4-day-old Infant

Cry Proper	Rest	Inspiration	Rest
·63 secs	·08 secs	·03 secs	·17 secs
·62	·05	·03	·15
·70	·06	·04	·26
·51	·08	·03	·15
·87	·10	—	—
·24	·05	—	—
·64	·02	·04	·17
—	—	·04	·28
·57	·04	·04	·17
·64	·03	·03	·27
·70	·09	·04	·09
·64	·16	·04	·14
·64	(?)	·05	·24
·61	·24	·04	·24
·79	·09	·04	·21
·59	·10	·04	·19
·56	·09	·05	·19
·06	—	—	—

taken from one continuous sequence represented in serial spectrograms. Such a temporal sequence is observed within a half hour after birth, and remains constant until the end of the second month when the pattern becomes generally more variable although the crying of infants at 6 months still shows long sequences of rhythmical crying which are of the same temporal order as the basic cry of the neonate.

On the spectrograph the shape of these cries (see Plates 10 and 11) is a gentle arc with a slight rise in frequency at the start and a tapering off at the end. The form is characteristic for rhythmical crying wherever it occurs; the first full cry of the neonate shows it, and six months later the gentle arc is still the predominant form of crying, even though the temporal sequences are much more variable than at the start.

A second type of cry observed in most neonates and identified by parents as the 'mad' or angry cry, is shown in Plate 12. Most mothers whose babies I have observed make an explicit distinction between the basic or hunger cry and the angry cry; and infer exasperation or rage from the latter.

TABLE 7

'Mad' Cry – 3-day-old Infant

Cry Proper	Rest	Inspiration	Rest
·78 secs	·18 secs	·04 secs	·17 secs
·69	·15	·04	·15
·69	·19	·04	·24
·77	·21	·06	·15
·74	·23	·04	·14
·68	·24	·04	·11
·65	·29	—	—
·60	·27	·04	·06
·70	·30	·06	·09
·62	·23	·06	·11
·62	·30	·07	·02
·62	·18	·10	·06
		·06	·09
		·08	·04
·09	·15	·03	·04
		·04	·12
·62	·09	·03	·15
·76	·21	·06	·12
·67	·06	·03	·15
·67	·04	·03	·12
·61	·24	·03	·09

The 'mad cry' is a variation of the basic pattern; the temporal sequences of the two types are the same (see Table 7), but the excess air forced through the vocal cords when the baby is 'mad' creates a turbulence or 'paraphonation' (Truby, 1962) that appears on the spectrogram as a dense black distortion of frequency bands.

Since it is general hospital practice to take a blood sample by heel prick from every infant during the lying-in period, we were able to record cries which were the first vocal response to physical pain, by recording only those instances when the infant had not been crying before the blood sample was taken.

The spectrogram shown in Plate 13 is typical of the vocalizations after a heel prick. The first pain cry in this case lasted 4·2 seconds, and was followed by 7 seconds of complete silence during which the infant lay totally inactive, holding his breath in expiration; then came the inspiratory gasp followed by expiratory cries of variable duration, and eventually the crying settled down to the basic pattern described above (See Table 8). Other infants gave at least two or three unusually long expiratory cries, each with its extended period of breath-holding before settling down to a rhythmical pattern.

TABLE 8

Crying in Response to Physical Pain. 3-day-old Infant

Cry Proper	Rest	Inspiration	Rest
4·10	7·20	·27	·10
3·56	·78	·09	·23
1·98	·48	—	—
1·02	·47	·04	·15
·78	·39	·10	·37
·70	·05	·12	·23
·64	·08	·06	—

The subjective features which distinguish the pain cry from other patterns are: (1) a sudden onset of loud crying without preliminary moaning, (2) the initial long cry, and (3) the extended period of breath holding in expiration after the long cry. The 'natural unit' which one hears when there is more than one long pain cry, consists of an inspiratory whistle immediately followed by a long expiratory cry rather than a cry followed by an inspiration.

Plate 14 illustrates a morphological variation of the pain cry that is provoked when the baby is experimentally 'frustrated'. If one gives an alert and contented infant a pacifier to suck for 30 seconds, removes it for 15-20 seconds, gives it back for another 30 seconds, and keeps up this sequence of giving and witholding, the infant sooner or later starts to cry. The first two or three cries after each withdrawal are long and drawn out (3-5 seconds), and like the pain cry they start from a condition of complete silence, since sucking inhibits any vocalizations. But since there is no prolonged breath-holding after the initial cries, and the inspiratory whistle follows shortly after the expiration, one hears the 'natural unit' as a cry followed by an inspiratory whistle rather than as an inspiration followed by a cry. This gives the listener a different subjective impression than does the pain or hunger cry.

Although I have selected ideal types of crying for these illustrations to emphasize structural differences, the different types were found to occur in all the babies whose cry patterns have been recorded

TABLE 9

Cry in Response to Removal of Pacifier
5-day-old Infant

Cry Proper	Rest	Inspiration	Rest
3·21	·06	·06	·29
1·46	·06	—	—
·93	·03	·09	·27
·87	·04	·07	·23
1·38	·04	·09	·12
·80	·04	·10	·18
·67	·05	·15	·10

systematically. On any one day there were of course many transitional forms and patterns which did not fit into the simple classification offered here; but individual variations of intermediate types were sufficiently great, and their causal significance sufficiently obscure so that an exhaustive typology of neonatal cry patterns would at this point have been premature.

The Functional Significance of Early Vocalizations

Neonatal Period

During the first week the range of physical and physiological conditions that can provoke crying is wider than has commonly been thought. Since hunger is probably the most common causal factor, its effects on the duration, quality and intensity of crying have been studied in greatest detail (Aldrich *et al.*, 1949; Irwin, 1932; Richards, 1936; Hellbrügge *et al.*, 1959).

By comparing the number of babies in a nursery who were crying during the half hour before and the half hour after a meal, it was possible to demonstrate indirectly that hungry babies cry more than satiated babies (see Wolff, 1966a) but such a comparison did not clarify the reasons for this relation. To rule out the possibility that crying on the third or fourth day is simply the conditioned response to being picked up repeatedly, and no longer related to hunger *per se*, I picked up a group of 12 crying 4-day-old babies shortly before a meal and held them for as long as it would take to feed them without giving a bottle, and subsequently asked nursery nurses to carry out the same procedure. As one might expect, many babies stopped crying as soon as they were picked up, and some remained quiet as long as they were held. But the majority of those who had not fallen asleep while being held started to cry (or continued to cry) as soon as they were returned to their cribs. Even those who fell asleep in my arms awoke either in the process of being replaced or shortly afterwards. When these same babies were later fed by 'propping', so that they had no more body contact than was necessary for burping, most of them fell asleep during, or within 20 minutes after, the completion of feeding and then remained asleep. Such findings led to the not surprising conclusion that being fed rather than being held was the adequate intervention which terminated crying.

But feeding is itself a complex function whose short-term sleep-inducing effects may be due to one or more factors, including sucking, swallowing, gastric distension, and the absorption of metabolites with their various central nervous system effects (Anand, 1963). In various experiments to isolate the behavioral elements which contribute to the sleepy disposition of a baby after eating, I studied the feeding behavior of infants with tracheo-esophageal fistulas during the time of their convalescence from surgery. Tracheo-esophageal fistula babies are ideal for these studies since they are at first fed exclusively by gastrostomy tube and subsequently, while they still retain the tube, by mouth. One can therefore isolate effects of gastric filling from those of sucking, the effects of sucking from those of swallowing (by feeding the infant through the gastrostomy tube while permitting him to suck on the pacifier); and once the baby tolerates oral feedings but still retains the gastrostomy tube, one can isolate the effects of sucking and swallowing from those of gastric filling, by sham feedings (removing the gastric contents as the baby sucks on the bottle).

Since the primary aim of the studies on infants with congenital tracheo-esophageal fistulas was to determine effect of hunger on the serial organization of rhythmical sucking (Wolff, 1966b), I will summarize here only the observations which are directly related to hunger as a cause of crying. The findings on seven otherwise healthy, full-term infants with tracheo-esophageal fistulas have shown with consistency that: (1) the hungry infants did not stop crying after being allowed to suck on the pacifier for periods of up to 15-25 minutes when they were not fed by gastrostomy; (2) the same infants stopped crying and went to sleep within 20 minutes after food was given by gastrostomy tube but they were not given a pacifier to suck, and made no concerted efforts to suck their hands; (3) sham feedings given by mouth and simultaneously removed by gastrostomy tube did not arrest crying or induce sleep within the first hour after the 'meal' (except on rare occasions when the infants appeared to be exhausted); and, (4) re-introducing the gastric contents (removed by gastric tube) through the gastrostomy tube an hour after the sham feeding, caused the baby to stop crying within 5-10 minutes after the start of feeding, and induced sleep or quiet alertness within 20 minutes after the end of the feeding. Until now we have not been successful in isolating the factor of gastric filling from that of gastric filling with an absorbable nutriment. The three infants in whom we tried to introduce a gastric balloon through the gastrostomy tube to simulate the gastric filling, did not tolerate the balloon and cried vigorously as soon as it was inflated with either air or water. The tentative conclusion from these studies is that the rhythmical crying of neonates usually observed shortly before a meal, when other known offending causes have been relieved, is probably related to a lack of gastric filling rather than an unsatisfied need for sucking or for oral stimulation. For technical reasons it was impossible to test empirically whether mechanical gastric filling without the absorption of nutriment has any quieting effect on a hungry crying infant.

Mothers and nurses sometimes believe that during the early weeks wet or dirty diapers are a sufficient cause of crying, and their belief is strengthened by the transient success one has when changing the baby's soiled diapers. I therefore asked nursery nurses to change the soiled diapers for each of nine neonates on six separate occasions when they were crying after a recent feeding; but in half of the trials I instructed the nurses to put the wet diaper back on after simulating the usual motions of a change, while in the other instances the diapers were actually changed. Infants who had been given a 'sham change' stopped crying as often after the procedure as those who had been given clean diapers, and then went to sleep readily once put to bed. There were no statistically significant differences in amount of crying in the two groups.

A confounding factor that might give spurious results under

natural conditions, but was controlled for in this case, is that wet diapers also cool the skin, so that the wet babies may get cold and then cry. I therefore compared the total amount of crying of ten infants when their Armstrong crib was kept at a temperature of 88-90 degrees F., and when it was kept at 78 degrees F., and found temperature to have a decisive influence on their behavior: the babies cried more and slept less when they were in the cool than the warm environment. A cooler temperature by itself may not be a sufficient cause of crying, but since babies sleep more and more deeply when kept warm, the fact that they are cold may raise their state of arousal and make them more responsive to noxious stimuli which would be sub-threshold during deep sleep (for example, when they are kept warm). (See also Irwin, 1933.)

Some neonates of the group began after the third day to cry when they were undressed, and showed this reaction until the end of the third or fourth week. When these babies had been awake and content before their clothes were changed, they started to cry as soon as they were undressed, in a significant number of instances, and also stopped crying when covered with a blanket or re-dressed in the usual clothes. Only seven of the eighteen consistently responded in this way in the first week, but they reacted in the same manner with increased vigor and greater consistency in the second and third weeks, while the response of the other eleven was variable. Temperature was not the critical factor since the response was observed in summer as well as winter, in a pre-heated Armstrong crib as well as in an open bassinette. Both the elimination of skin contact and the release from the confinement of clothing apparently contributed to the provocation of crying. When a baby from the group who were sensitive to nakedness, had failed to stop crying after he was covered with a blanket, his crying usually stopped as soon as he was swaddled or dressed in the appropriate clothes. In order to be effective, cloth contact had to be with the ventral surface of the chest and abdomen, and covering only the legs and arms did not have the desired effect. The texture of the clothing made a considerable difference: a bath towel, a diaper, or a blanket arrested crying far more effectively than plastic or a rubber sheet.

Physical pain as a sufficient cause of crying in the neonatal period is obvious to anyone who has taken blood by heel puncture, or assisted at a circumsicion. The causal relation between *visceral* pain and crying is less obvious and more difficult to demonstrate. The behavior of 'colicky' infants and the therapeutic effects of anti-spasmodic drugs on such behavior is clinical evidence in support of a causal relation between visceral pain and crying. Additional circumstantial evidence comes from the observation that in a significant number of instances crying will temporarily stop right after a healthy baby has passed gas, spit up or burped; but such observations cannot be tested experimentally. The cry of presumptive gastro-intestinal discomfort differs from other types in several respects. It has a higher pitch (a fundamental frequency from 450-550 cycles per second), is non-rhythmical, and is interspersed with shrill shrieks that have no constant configuration.

The causal relation between spontaneous jerks and crying is of only peripheral interest for a developmental account, since it is only apparent during the first one or $1\frac{1}{2}$ weeks. But for a 'causal' analysis, crying after a spontaneous jerk is of some interest because it is the first naturally concurring instance of crying due to the disruption of sleep. Almost all healthy infants will jerk spontaneously during regular sleep and drowsiness; during regular sleep the jerk usually does not disturb the baby, but during drowsiness infants who startle frequently and vigorously are apt to wake up every time they jerk just as they are dropping off to sleep, and may then cry (Wolff, 1966a). While it seems perfectly reasonable to the causal observer that a baby should cry when he is rudely awakened, it is not self-evident why the disruption of sleep should itself be a sufficient cause of crying, especially during early infancy.

Among the various *interventions* that arrest crying in the neonate, I have selected a few for more detailed explorations. Some of these were discussed in connection with the classification of causes, when the causes had to be inferred from the interventions that terminated crying (e.g., feeding, contact-comfort, passing gas, etc.). Other interventions have a general inhibiting effect on crying, and do not suggest any specific antecedent cause. *Pacifier sucking* is among the most effective of these interventions during the first week, and unless the baby is too greatly aroused, he usually accepts the pacifier and then stops crying. Even after a baby has gone for 3 or 4 hours without any food, he will sometimes pass from a highly aroused state to sleep after sucking for 10-15 minutes, although such sleep is usually unstable, and the slightest disturbance will reawaken him to full arousal and crying if the pacifier has been removed during sleep. But if the pacifier has been kept in place during sleep, even a hungry infant may remain in stable sleep for relatively long periods (20 minutes to a half hour). A pacifier in the mouth seems to 'protect' sleep against otherwise disturbing stimuli even when the baby does not suck on it. Mr Simmons and I have found that the pacifier in the mouth of a sleeping baby who is not sucking, will block the usual diffuse activity in response to a noxious stimulus (tickling), as if the activity were channeled into sucking. If the pacifier is removed during sleep, the same stimulus provokes prolonged diffuse activity which often awakens the baby and may make him cry. (Unpublished study). One has the impression that pacifier sucking 'protects' sleep because it inhibits diffuse activity, and therefore reduces the inflow of arousing peripheral self-stimulations of diffuse activity.

Thus one might assume that: (*a*) babies do not go to sleep as long as they are motorically active because the proprioceptive feedbacks maintain a high state of arousal, and because one of the preconditions for sleep is a relative absence of variable stimulation; (*b*) babies remain in a state of high arousal and crying long after the effect of the offending stimulus has worn off because diffuse thrashing, once it has been initiated by an adequate stimulus, maintains itself like a temper tantrum; (*c*) pacifier sucking is the dominant behavior in the hierarchy of motor patterns of the young infant, and will inhibit competing motor behaviors, including diffuse activity (see Wolff & White, 1965); (*d*) pacifier sucking quiets the baby not so much because it directly answers a baby's instinctive or instinctual needs but because it inhibits diffuse motility, thereby interrupts the self-arousing cycle of crying and thrashing, and promotes the necessary preconditions for sleep.

From such a speculation it would follow that anything which either reduces the total amount of proprioceptive feedback or renders the background of exteroceptive and proprioceptive stimulations constant or rhythmical, will lower the general arousal state, inhibit crying, and prepare the baby for sleep or quiet alertness. Some of the indirect evidence in support of this speculation may also help us to identify the common element among the various effective means which are used around the world to quiet babies. Studies on continuous and intermittent rhythmical stimulation, for example, bear directly on the complex of events that make rocking so successful. Continuous non-painful stimulation, whether in the form of *white noise* or *white light*, has a sustained hypnagogic effect. Not only does it arrest crying for the duration of stimulation, it also converts a state of high excitation and crying to regular sleep which is maintained after the stimulus is turned off (see Wolff, 1966a, for a detailed report).

Tapping various parts of the body repeatedly may arrest crying when carried out in rhythmical or near rhythmical fashion. While I have not compared the relative sensitivity of various body parts, tapping the spinal column firmly with the fingertip as if percussing the spine, is at least one effective method to arrest crying. Sometimes its effect lasts only for the duration of stimulation, sometimes prolonged tapping will keep the baby quiet long enough to let him go to sleep. The optimal rate of tapping seems to fall somewhere between 80-140 per minute; below this rate the infant 'breaks through' and begins to cry again; and it is very difficult to keep up a rate of more than 140 beats per minute without mechanical devices.

Swaddling is a very effective method to quiet a fussy baby, provided it is done by someone who knows how, and who sees to it that the baby is immobilized. When the swaddling is done unskillfully so that the clothing simply restricts the range of movement without inhibiting it totally, the procedure has a marked arousal effect and may provoke the 'mad cry'. The critical difference is probably that 'poor' swaddling increases the amount of *variable* proprioceptive feed-back, whereas 'good' swaddling generates a *constant* background of tactile stimulation.

Aside from rhythmical and continuous stimulations, isolated external stimuli will also interrupt crying temporarily. Picking the baby up to stop his crying is perhaps too obvious to be mentioned here. In a schedule of experimental stimulations which we have used to compare the effectiveness of different qualities of stimulation on crying, *picking up* has consistently been among the most effective, together with pacifier sucking and swaddling to stop crying. No doubt being picked up gives rise to a complex of cutaneous, visual, olfactory and kinesthetic stimulations which I have not analysed in detail. *Pressure* on the abdomen with the flat of the hand, or pressing the infant's hands on his own chest, is consistently effective for some babies, but not reliable as a general procedure.

Harsh sounds such as those produced by a rattle temporarily arrest a cry more often than the more pleasing sounds of a bell, an Audubon bird whistle or the human voice which during the first week is no more effective than other sounds. Similarly the flash of a bright light, touching the body, rubbing it, and even an actual pain stimulus like pinching, will stop the baby from crying for a moment. But all these are transient effects, and they seem to be non-specific alerting responses rather than coordinated responses to particular qualities of stimulation.

This account obviously does not exhaust either the sufficient causes of crying or the means to inhibit crying in the neonate; but the partial inventory of causes suggests certain generalizations which can be tested in greater detail: painful stimulation to the body surface or from the visceral organs, sudden excessive but non-painful excitation (in the physiological definition of pain), the disruption of sleep, the physiological disturbances associated with hunger (and thirst?), and cold are specific determinants of crying in the newborn infant. Similarly, noxious stimuli which are not painful in the physiological sense but have an 'unpleasant' quality (e.g., bitter tastes) will provoke an aversive reaction and may in some instances provoke crying. Whether or not the repeated removal of a pacifier should be regarded as a prototype of frustration remains uncertain, until its analogues at later stages have been explored. However, there seem to be events in the borderland between the physiological and the psychological which can provoke crying during the neonatal period.

The state of the organism must be included as a nonspecific co-determinant of crying since some of the specific factors I have listed (e.g., cold) may be effective when the baby is in one state, but ineffective under other conditions.

The social influence of the different cries on the parent is not nearly as specific in the human species as it is in lower species (see, for example, Collias & Joos, 1953; Thorpe, 1961). With some exceptions the mother's personal style (and hence her past experience) are far more important than the form of crying for determining how she will care for her crying baby. Mothers do not, for example, respond to the 'hunger' cry in any fixed pattern. Multiparous mothers (and others who have had experience in caring for children before they have their own) may or may not come when they hear the rhythmical cry; and if they come, may do one of several things depending on their general 'style'. Some always try a bottle first; others always check the diaper first, believing that wet diapers are irritating. But most experienced mothers seem to be guided in what they do by the events of the preceding three hours.

Primiparous mothers with no experience will come as soon as the baby starts to cry much more often than experienced mothers; and many are prepared to feed immediately, especially if they are not breast-feeding, and subscribe to a demand schedule.

The '*mad*' cry has a more peremptory and somewhat more specific effect on the mother than the basic cry. Even experienced mothers will drop what they were doing to check on their baby, but they do not seem alarmed and express tolerant amusement at this precocious expression of rage.

The parents' response to a *pain cry* is a dramatic exception to the general rule. Even nurses in the nursery who are accustomed to such sounds by years of exposure, may betray a need to do something by their actions, voice, and gesture. Mothers show the same need more dramatically when they hear the pain cry of their own infant. To test the impression that a pain cry has a particular peremptory effect on mothers, I have included the following experiment at least once in all my home observations: While the mother is in an adjoining room from which she can hear but not see her baby, I play a tape recording of the baby's basic or hunger cry, measure the delay before she comes, and record her behavior and verbal report about what she thought was the matter, explaining to her that I am testing her ability to distinguish her own baby's voice from those of others. Under the same conditions I play a tape recording of the baby's pain cry several weeks later, again measure the delay before she comes, and record the reactions when she discovers that her baby was not crying. For obvious reasons the experiment cannot be repeated too often without confusing the mother or wearing out my welcome; but even single pairs of tape recordings in different sequences (one pain cry and one rhythmical cry for each mother-infant pair) have shown a dramatic difference. In response to the pain cry most mothers immediately rush into the room looking worried, and once they have made sure the baby is fine they report a sense of relief, but little or no amusement with my games.

Another vocalization pattern that over-rides individual differences of maternal style, is the cry of the brain-damaged infant. This cry is typically shrill and piercing, and its fundamental frequency is higher than the normal cry of a healthy infant (650-800 cycles per second). Nursery personnel look for ways to keep such babies quiet, or else try to be out of ear-shot. Although I have observed no brain damaged infants in the home, mothers to whom I have played tape recordings of brain-damaged infants and who immediately recognize that it is not their child, find such cries very unpleasant to listen to. Plate 15 illustrates the spectrograms of (*a*) a brain-damaged neonate, (*b*) a 3-month-old infant with undiagnosed neurological disease; and (*c*) the cry of a normal neonate for comparison.

Two Weeks

During the second week the infant begins to respond more consistently to an interruption of feeding by crying. For a valid demonstration of the phenomenon one must select occasions of interrupted feedings when the infant was not crying before the feeding started, since a simple resumption of crying may otherwise be confounded with the

TABLE 10

Crying Provoked by Interruption of Feeding
(N = 12)

	Segment of Feeding		
	1st	2nd	3rd
Week			
I	0	2%*	0
II	17%	8%	0
III	32%	23%	3%
IV	18%	20%	0
VI	6%	7%	2%

* % of all occasions of interruption that provoke crying
when baby was not crying before start of meal.

direct response to the interruption. The vocal protest is most vigorous after the first interruption in a feeding, when the baby has taken only one ounce or less of formula. At the start of the second interruption, which usually follows after two ounces or more of formula have been consumed, the infant may or may not cry, and by the third interruption he usually does not remonstrate against the interruption. Some infants cry more consistently and vigorously than others, but all bottle-fed infants in this group cried at some time during the second week, in direct response to the interruption, and with increasing frequency in the next two weeks.

Table 10 summarizes the reactions of twelve bottle-fed infants to all interrupted feedings that were not preceded by crying (an average of four observations per week for each infant).

In bottle-fed babies, crying as the response to interruption lasts until the end of the first month or the middle of the second month. The four breast-fed infants who were observed beyond one month did not begin to protest to the first interruption until the end of the first month, but then continued to do so beyond the end of the second month. The relatively late appearance of protest cries among breast-fed babies was probably related to their considerably longer period of sucking before the first interruption and their drowsiness at the first break in feeding.

Crying as a response to being naked also becomes more obvious during the second week, and the inhibition of crying by placing a blanket or a diaper over the ventral body surfaces can now be demonstrated experimentally. While my sample of infants is too small for a statistical analysis of *sex differences*, there is a suggestion that girls are more sensitive to skin contact, cry more often when naked, and stop crying more easily when covered with textured cloth or redressed. By the end of the first month even a sensitive baby rarely cries while naked, since the events in the environment (the mother's movements and vocalizations as she leans over him) distract him and seem to draw his attention. As long as she remains in his field, the naked baby coos, kicks rhythmically and pursues her with what appears to be an expression of pleasure; but as soon as she leaves or breaks contact with him, he starts to cry unless he is first dressed or covered with a blanket.

Other causes of crying which were sufficient in the first week remain so during the second week; and the manœuvers which arrested crying before are still effective, but new interventions whose psychological significance is more apparent are added to the list.

The shift from the purely physiological to psychologically significant interventions is due partly to the infant's increasing capacity for alertness, and his expanding interest in environmental events. When objects are moved across the baby's visual field while he is softly crying, he stops to look and pursue the movement as long as the objects are within his range. All objects of sufficient size and brightness presented at the proper focal distance, seem to be equally effective in this respect. At least the infants in this sample have not stopped crying more consistently to particular visual configuration; and intensity of crying, or the degree of arousal, rather than the pattern of visual stimulation seems to be the critical factor that decides whether or not a baby will stop crying and pursue when presented with 'an interesting spectacle'. The quieting effect of visual pursuit on crying persists for a longer period than could be accounted for under the 'alerting response'. In some instances one can inhibit a fussy state long enough to induce a state of alert inactivity which will persist after the moving object is no longer visible (Wolff, 1965).

By the end of the second week the sound of the human voice arrests crying more effectively than a bell, a rattle, or an Audubon bird whistle, even when the voice is presented at a lower intensity or for shorter duration than other sounds. According to the results of our systematic schedules of stimulation, the voice is now more interesting than inanimate sounds although the human face still has the same effect on crying as any inanimate visual object of the same size and general shape.

Third Week

The state of the organism becomes a significant factor in cry provocation during the third week. Stimulus configurations which elicit only indifference or smiling when the baby is content may precipitate crying when presented while the infant is active or fussy. In the report on early smiling, I listed various stimulus configurations that consistently elicited smiling in three-week-old infants as long as they were alert and inactive; the list included a variety of inanimate sounds, the human voice, and 'pat-a-cake' (Wolff, 1963). When the same stimuli are presented to a baby who shows mild discomfort by diffuse activity and soft moaning, he starts to cry in a significant number of cases. The clearest indication of this relation between state and affective response is the fussy baby's response to a silent, nodding head. Although the silent face as yet elicits no smiling in the third week, it precipitates an immediate cry face or even full-fledged cry vocalizations when presented to the fussy baby, whether it is the face of the mother, a familiar observer, or a stranger. As soon as the face disappears, the baby stops crying; and by repeating this sequence until the baby gets desperate, one can demonstrate that it is a visual stimulus rather than an unknown factor which provokes the cry under the conditions described. The affective response at this age is not highly specific to the human face, and various complex inanimate visual configurations which evoke interest while the baby is alert can set off a cry when the infant is fussy, although objects like pencils or books have no effect.

The changes in behavior from the second to the third week

therefore suggest a shift from purely physical stimuli to events of psychological significance sufficient for cry provocation. The first indication was the response to frustration, already apparent in the first week. A second indication was the response to an interruption of feeding in the second week. Now the interdependence of state and affective response suggests that changes of state can significantly alter the meaning which the infant assigns (at a practical level) to a stimulus-event which we might view as being directly related to later 'social' events. Certainly the visual spectacle of a face can no longer be considered as a purely physiological cause of crying.

During the third week the infant discovers a new way of crying which many mothers identify as 'faking', implying by this that the infant has no distress but simply 'wants attention'. The cry is of a low pitch and intensity; it consists of long drawn out moans which occasionally rise to more explicit cries, and then revert to poorly articulated moans (see Plate 16). A mother will respond to the fake cry in one of various ways which largely depend on her general style and momentary disposition. More often than not she ignores such sounds until they become full-fledged rhythmical cries; at other times she picks the baby up to comfort him, or else changes his position so that he can see her while she works.

The morphological characteristics which distinguish fake crying from other patterns are of particular interest for studying the functional relation between cry and non-cry vocalizations: Non-cry vocalizations which are heard for the first time during the third week, always occur shortly before the infant starts to fuss; and while one can easily distinguish non-cry vocalizations from early crying by listening to the sound and looking at the baby, it is impossible to identify the point of transition on the spectrogram. Non-cry vocalizations as well as fake cries are longer in duration than rhythmical cries, but have the same fundamental frequency. What distinguishes non-cry vocalizations and fussy cries most from ordinary crying is the doubling or a halving of the fundamental frequencies in the middle of a vocalization, and their greater complexity of shapes, particularly in the terminal portion of the separate units. Rhythmical cries continue to show the downward curvature of frequency bands just before the end of a cry (see Plates 10 and 11), but the bands of non-cry vocalizations and fussy sounds often end as straight lines or upward flourishes with a terminal rise in frequency. At 3-4 weeks, between 50-75 per cent of spectrograms of non-cry vocalizations (except for high-pitched squeals), and 30-40 per cent for early fussy noises (including fake cries) no longer show the final drop in pitch, whereas 98 per cent of full-fledged cries still show it.

In Plates 17 a, b, and 18 a, b, I have compared samples of non-cry and early cry vocalizations of two four-week-old babies, selecting episodes in the transition from non-cry vocalizations (*a*), to early crying (*b*), to show how similar the morphological characteristics of these sound patterns are.

The functional relation of non-cry to cry vocalizations is of interest in that every new non-cry pattern seems to appear for the first time as the infant gets fussy, and shortly before he starts to cry. Once the baby has discovered a novel sound in this context he will also practice it while he is alert and apparently content; but until at least the end of the third month, vocal novelties appear as if they were discovered only in the context of moderate discomfort, became autonomous from a particular state by repeated practice, and then were incorporated into the ensemble of non-cry vocalizations.

As the patterns of non-cry vocalization differentiate, and it is easier to distinguish the various playful baby sounds, the first vocal 'circular reactions' also become apparent. New sounds which the infant discovered while fussy (gurgling at the back of the throat, high-pitched squeals, 'ga-ga', and 'da-da' sounds) are now repeated in cycles when the infant is clearly in no distress, and when the only apparent motivation is something like Piaget's *need to function* (Piaget, 1936).

Fourth Week

Under the appropriate circumstances, infants now show distinct food or taste preferences which are more complex than the neonatal reflex response to noxious tastes (dilute vinegar, quinine, etc.; Peiper, 1963). Around this time the mothers of bottle-fed infants supplement the milk formula with semi-solid foods, starting with a cereal preparation, and adding puréed fruits several days later. Although all infants in the group showed an initial reluctance to take any solid food, most of them took to the fruit with some enthusiasm after the first day, but continued to reject the cereal, grimaced and often cried as soon as they tasted it, yet stopped crying, pursed their lips and remained quietly expectant when they tasted the fruit. I have asked mothers to alter the order of presentation, to start with cereal on one day, with fruit on another day, and to alternate spoonfuls of fruit and cereal

H

on a third day; I have also asked them to vary the rate of feeding. All results point to the impression that the taste (or texture) of the food and not the order or rate of presentation are the significant factors; in most cases cereal provokes fussing or even crying, while fruit generally initiates quiet, expectant behavior unless the mother delays too long between spoonfuls.

One possible implication is that this indicates the first appetitive discrimination; the preferences are by no means fixed and several weeks later infants who at first protested, eat their cereal with a certain relish. Another implication is that 'bad tasting' food, which is not physiologically noxious, can provoke crying.

The meaning of laughter in babies is a topic about which there has been considerable speculation by developmental and philosophical psychologists. The concensus among empirical investigators seems to be that the laughter of the young infant is neither the expression of a 'pure' affect nor an extreme form of smiling, but expresses conflicting emotion (Washburn, 1929; Leuba, 1941; Ambrose, 1963b; but see Piddington, 1963, for a contrary view). Somewhere towards the end of the first month a number of the infants in this group started to chuckle and laugh consistently when tickled in the appropriate body area, in the appropriate manner; the sound spectrograms of this laughter provided some indirect evidence for the hypothesis that crying and laughter may have a functional relation.

Preliminary studies indicate that a gentle, firm and rapid scratching movement with the blunt ends of the fingers applied to the armpits, the groins or the abdomen, was most effective for eliciting laughter at this age. Tickling the sensitive areas of the face (for example, the nasal columnae), or the soles of the feet with a single hair or wisp of cotton, is a mode of stimulation which fits the physiological definition of tickling; but it evoked no laughter, only defensive flight movements and diffuse activity in young infants. Similarly, gently stroking the appropriate surface areas of the body with the flat of the hand evoked no laughter, nor did an otherwise adequate stimulation to the flat surfaces of the limbs or the back.

About a week after, tickling the most sensitive zones (arm-pits or groins) consistently elicits laughter, a baby can be 'primed' by first tickling the sensitive areas then shifting to other surfaces like the chest, the arms, or the thigh, and using the same manner of stimulation. In this way laughter can be perpetuated even though the zone stimulated evoked no laughter before priming. Not all of the infants laughed when tickled, even under the most favorable conditions; some showed a mildly negative reaction, others ignored the stimulus. Every infant of the group, however, started to *cry* when tickled in the proper manner while he was fussy, although it was impossible to make him cry in this way when he was alert and contented before stimulation.

The spectrograms of laughter were not sufficiently distinct from other vocalizations to permit a 'blind' diagnosis of laughter, but they were closer in form to fussing and early crying than to non-cry vocalizations: The frequency bands of most specimens of laughter *ended* on a downward slope like those of rhythmical crying, and the frequency bands of many of the specimens were simple straight lines with none of the complex variations in shape characteristic of non-cry vocalizations at this stage. (See Plate 19).

1-2 *Months*

After the fifth week the fussy baby no longer cries when he hears a human voice or sees a human face. Instead he stops crying, attends to the voice, and then remains content as long as he can either hear or see the person who has talked to him. By comparing the effects of human voice and other sounds, one can demonstrate that the voice now arrests mild crying more consistently than nonsocial stimulation and that the mere visual presence of a person not only inhibits mild crying but initiates a period of sustained alert interest.

Since any interesting visual spectacle, however, will sometimes arrest mild crying, it was important to isolate the specific effects of animate (human) objects from those of visual distraction in general, by comparing the babies' response to the *loss* of human and an inanimate object. I have routinely asked mothers to enter the baby's visual field while he is happily playing, to nod and talk, and then to disappear. Most infants tested in this way (ten of the twelve in the sample on which I am reporting) started to cry as soon as the person left the field, and stopped crying again as soon as the person reappeared. Such a sequence could be repeated for two or three trials in a single session, until the baby either lost interest or began to cry so vigorously that even the visual presence of the person was no longer effective. When only the first occasions of separation and reunion were counted, the affective responses to the loss and return of a human figure (onset of crying and arrest of crying) were statistically significant. There were no comparable responses of crying to 'loss' when

101

indifferent objects like a coat or a rattle were made to disappear from the visual field, and the human figures remained silently out of sight. Some of the infants started to cry when a favorite toy, particularly an animal, was removed even though they had not been playing with it before it was removed (see below). The critical factor in this case was the event of *being left* rather than the absence of a person: When a baby was (by my request) allowed to continue crying after he had been left, he usually settled down after several minutes, and resumed playing. At that point another temporary appearance and subsequent departure of a nodding, talking person started the crying all over again. In some infants this happens at the end of the fourth week, in others the sixth week; and two infants did not cry at all when 'abandoned'. For this demonstration I have only counted instances when the baby had been alert and happily playing by himself before the experiment started. Individual differences of sensitivity to being left are considerable; some babies cry invariably as soon as they are left – others only on certain days, or only the first or second time in a session. My sample is still too small to give more than a hint that those babies who spend most of their waking time with one or more persons (parents, visitors, children) are more sensitive than those who are alone during the day except when cared for. When one places a sensitive infant in a half reclining position (for example, in an 'Easy-Baby' reclining chair) so that he sees what is in front of him but cannot look to the sides, and slowly circles his chair so that he sees the person for a brief while, sees him disappear, sees him reappear, etc., the relation between being left and crying becomes quite clear. As soon as the person leaves (it does not have to be the mother), the baby starts to fuss and cry, and when the person reappears he stops. After three or more of such trials crying may reach such a pitch that it continues even after the person has reappeared.

I mentioned before that the continued presence of a person's back is sufficient to *prevent* some babies from starting to cry; but a person's back will not *arrest* crying which is already in progress. It seems to be necessary to face a baby to make him stop crying at this stage, but it is not clear whether actual 'eye-to-eye' contact is required in all cases, or whether simply a full face is sufficient since the observer cannot be sure that he has made 'eye-to-eye' contact with a crying infant. As long as the baby is only fussy or just beginning to cry, one can, of course, decide about eye-to-eye contact; and under these conditions it is easier to inhibit the baby's crying by staring into his eyes than by simply presenting the full face but looking away from eyes. Studies on the role of eye-to-eye contact in smile provocation (Wolff, 1963a) and these observations emphasize the importance of this communication between mother and child during the early months, say between the end of the fourth and the sixth weeks. Unfortunately I have gotten no further in objectifying 'eye-to-eye' contact. The mere fact that two individuals face each other while their eyes are open, or even look at each other's faces, is not sufficient to define eye-to-eye contact, since one can easily 'look through' another person by looking over his forehead or focusing on the bridge of his nose or on some imaginary spot behind his head. Nor is eye-to-eye contact a continuous staring into both eyes of the partner, since it is actually impossible to focus on more than one eye at a time, except at great distances.

By the fifth week most bottle-fed infants no longer protest to an interruption of feeding except when they have been very hungry. The decline in protests is paralleled by a growing interest in external events during the meal. When the bottle is taken away after the first one or two ounces, the baby may look attentively at the mother, the other children in the room, out of the window, or inspect his hands. The very fact that he now takes an interest in many new objects and remains alert during the whole meal makes him generally more resistant to crying. The same inhibition of crying by attention to the environment was noted earlier with respect to being naked. By presenting the baby who is about to start crying with an 'interesting spectacle' or something he can grasp, one can show experimentally that attention to external events inhibits crying for up to 25 minutes (see Wolff, 1965).

Between the sixth and seventh week, infants who are accustomed to have one particular toy animal always near them in the crib now act to the animal as if it had a special significance. When one stands behind a screen and removes the toy animal from the crib while the infant is playing with his hands or another toy, he starts to cry. When the toy animal is returned to its familiar place, still from behind a screen so that the observer remains invisible, or when the observer shows himself, the baby quiets down and resumes his previous activity. Such a sequence can be repeated several times in succession until the baby loses interest or gives way to rhythmical crying. Once the baby has started to cry because a person has appeared, talked, and disappeared again, the toy animal will frequently arrest crying so that the infant returns to his previous play or, if the animal is within reach, he grasps for it.

By no means all infants showed such an attachment as early as the second month; but the six who did, were clearly responding to the removal rather than the mere absence of the animal.When the animal was removed from the crib while the baby was asleep, he neither cried nor searched for it after he woke up. Various experiments on smiling and crying that compared the responses to toy animals and to other objects indicated that the infant's attachment was limited to objects which resembled the toy animal in shape, contour and texture. By the fifth month some infants would not be placated by any but the particular animal which they have favored.

The baby's non-cry vocalizations diversify rapidly between the sixth and eighth week, and now novel sounds are no longer discovered in a context of fussiness. The baby invents new noises while he is playing alone, including 'Bronx cheers', gurgling, and tongue games and then practices them in circular fashion. On the sound spectrogram these sounds are more complex, and to the ear the individual types of vocalizations are more discrete.

Exercise of new vocalizations is more prolific when the baby is not distracted by persons moving about in the room, so that the best recordings of novel sounds are obtained from behind a screen. The baby's private conversations can be interrupted by silent visual contact; at the same time one can initiate 'conversation' with the baby by imitating his vocalizations and encouraging him to talk even when he was previously silent. I have tested this effect by alternately nodding my head *silently* for five minutes, then *babbling* and nodding for five minutes, then nodding silently for another five minutes, etc., recording the session, and comparing the amount of baby vocalizations under the two conditions (whose sequence can be reversed systematically). In this way it is possible to demonstrate a significantly greater amount of vocalizations when the partner talks than when he is silent. A spectrographic comparison of the sounds made by the experimenter and the baby show that an adult cannot in any strict sense imitate the baby's voice pattern, and that baby vocalizations are not direct copies of the sounds adults make (see, for example, Plate 20; also Lenneberg, 1964). But once the baby has several discrete sounds at his disposal which he has practiced in circular fashion, one can demonstrate that the infant makes some effort to imitate the sounds he hears. When the observer, for example, introduces low-pitched *da-da* sounds which are a part of the infant's repertory, while the infant is making high-pitched squeals, the baby stops squealing and produces his own version of the low-pitched *da-da* sounds. When the observer then imitates the earlier high-pitched squeals, the infant resumes his own version of squealing. Even at this stage it seems legitimate within limits, to speak of vocal imitations, not in the sense of direct copies, but as an active 'accommodation' of vocal patterns which are already at the infant's disposal; the baby acts as if the adult's sound was sufficiently like his own to make him want to 'perpetuate' what he has heard (Piaget, 1936). This assumption is compatible with the observation that two-month-old infants for the first time show anything like 'infectious crying'. When I play a tape recording of the baby's own voice to him while he is alert and apparently content, he now often responds by getting excited and starting to cry.

2-3 *Months*

Crying after the adult or a favorite toy animal disappears becomes more apparent during this time, although none of the evidence suggests that the infant distinguishes visually between his mother's and another person's departure. He will not cry when his mother leaves as long as another person is present; and he cries as often when I leave as when his mother leaves him.

When all persons leave, or the toy animal is removed from sight and the baby begins to cry, he now sucks his hand or thumb with some consistency. This sequence of events can be repeated experimentally on all babies who (*a*) respond consistently to abandonment by crying, and (*b*) suck their thumbs. Until now the function of thumb-sucking was either non-specific or not apparent to direct observation; many babies sucked their fingers but as often when content or bored as when distressed. Between two and three months thumb-sucking seems to become a specific response to distress caused by psychological factors, especially by being left.

Teasing a baby by giving and removing the pacifier repeatedly no longer provokes crying. Most babies who in previous weeks had responded strongly when the pacifier was given and taken away repeatedly, now tolerate the procedure placidly. At the same time one can devise new ways to frustrate the baby, by offering him something which he can handle and bring to his eyes, taking it away after a minute or two, waiting a minute, giving it back, removing it again, etc. It will come as no surprise that one can tease babies in this way until they cry; if there is any merit at all to this procedure, it is only to demonstrate that the content of the frustrating conditions change with cognitive differentiation. What frustrates the infant depends in part on the sensori-motor capacities at his disposal, and on the meanings which objects have acquired in terms of his action patterns. Until the grasping of objects under visual control became a directed activity, for example, it was not possible to irritate a baby by taking the rattle from his hands (i.e., by opposing his grasp reflex). After hand-eye coordination has been practiced on suitable objects, experimental interruption of this activity becomes a sufficient cause of crying; once hand-coordination as such has become stabilized and is no longer practised in circular fashion, the baby's protest to its interruption is less intense, and in most instances provokes no crying. To be sure, one can always make a baby cry by taking *special things* away from him long after hand-eye coordination and the simple manipulation of objects has been thoroughly practiced. Babies who are 'addicted' to the pacifier will cry whenever the pacifier is taken away, long after rhythmical sucking has been fully stabilized. With the exception of 'special objects' for which such explanations do not hold, however, crying in response to 'frustration' depends to a large extent on the changes in meaning that objects acquire in the course of cognitive differentiation. A systematic study of the 'frustrations' of this kind which will elicit crying at particular stage in development would therefore contribute to our understanding of how cognition and affectivity interact in early infancy.

3-6 *Months*

The number of infants I have systematically observed beyond the third month is so small (five) that this section is at best incomplete.

As part of the study on the causes of crying, I have tried to pin down 'stranger anxiety' by tracing its ontogenesis. All efforts to frighten babies by wearing various facial masks have failed to provoke anything but indifference, interest, or smiling and happy vocalizations. This is true before as well as after the third month. Monster masks, contortions of the face into ugly grimaces, wearing the usual sun-glasses, etc., provoked no fear or crying until the end of the sixth month, with the exception of one mask made of clear plastic that transmits the color and gross features of the face but obscures any finer details. Three and four-month-old infants showed more than indifference to this mask although their reaction was not obviously fear, and they did not cry. Some turned their face away, others stared with wide open eyes and a 10-20 second complete arrest of random activity which gave the observer the impression that they were 'astounded'. When the same mask covering the face is presented to an unsuspecting adult, he or she responds dramatically and far more intensely than to conventional horror masks; individuals who have been frightened in this fashion report that the sight of the clear mask was something uncanny.

Infants (but not adults) also respond with doubt and certainly no smiling, to sun-glasses constructed so that the articulated eye holes are replaced by a continuous strip of translucent material, and the observer can look out but the baby cannot see the eyes. When wearing such glasses the observer has the impression that the infant searches for the eyes with an immobile face, then either smiles vaguely or looks away with an expression of doubt when he finds no eye spots.

To test 'stranger anxiety' more specifically, I have made it a part of the regular procedure during home visits, to introduce the baby to an unknown person once every month and to film his facial expressions and body movements. Until the end of the sixth month I have observed no response in the baby which would suggest stranger anxiety. All five babies responded to the stranger's visual presence, his silent nodding, and his nodding while talking in the same way as they responded to the mother or me. In one setting I had occasion to film the first encounter between a $5\frac{1}{2}$-month-old infant and a grandmother whom he had never seen. Without introducing herself to the baby the grandmother took over the feeding from the mother as soon as she came through the door, diapered and played with him, and the baby acted as if he accepted the stranger on a par with his mother; he took the feeding well, smiled, cooed, etc.

Quite different are the responses to familiar faces when certain of their elements are altered. The baby's questioning look to the clear plastic mask or to the special sun-glasses are examples of such distortions. Similar reactions arise in the course of natural observations. One five-month-old infant, for example, began to cry whenever he saw his *mother* wearing a bathing cap that covered her hair and obscured her hairline. Yet the same baby smiled in the usual manner when either I, or a young woman whom the baby did not know, wore the same bathing cap.

Another infant simply stared at his mother at $4\frac{1}{2}$ months whenever she removed her eyeglasses, and refused to smile to her vocalizations although he readily smiled to other people without glasses. Yet three of the mothers who usually did not wear glasses elicited no adverse reaction or doubt in their own babies when they put on ordinary eyeglasses. Another mother reported that she was silently weeping while feeding her five-month-old infant, and he refused the bottle as long as she wept. He simply stared at her until she had wiped away her tears, and then accepted the bottle readily. Mothers married to clean-shaven men have reported that their six-month-old infants fuss and cry when picked up by a man with a beard or mustache, but not when a clean-shaven stranger picks them up.

Although these diverse examples admit no easy solution, they suggest that a *distortion* of *familiar* facial configurations provokes a 'fear' response at this age, and that stranger anxiety, as it is usually defined, is at this age not a significant dimension of crying in the *natural setting of the home*. Yet the assumption that any distortion of the familiar face will provoke an adverse response is not sufficient as a general explanatory rule either, since the *removal* of glasses from the mother's face when the baby is accustomed to see it with glasses will provoke crying, but not the *addition* of glasses to a mother's face which is usually seen without glasses. It would seem that the *kind* of distortion and the *face-part* distorted are as important as the fact of distortion itself; and only a systematic analysis of the many possible variations will bring us closer to a general rule about the novelties in a familiar figure that provoke 'strangerness anxiety'.

Summary

It will be obvious to the reader that the preceding observations were no more than a preliminary report, and that while certain items were established with confidence, others were barely touched on. A comprehensive theoretical statement about the ontogenesis of vocalizations or about the implications of these observations for developmental theory would therefore be premature.

It became clear, however, that the range of causal conditions sufficient to provoke crying in the neonate is greater than has generally been taken for granted, and that very early in development the infant cries in response to environmental conditions which should be viewed as having a global *psychological* significance since they cannot be analysed in physical-physiological terms alone. While many of the primitive psychological causes differentiate in concert with sensorimotor intelligence, they cannot all be integrated within a 'purely cognitive' framework. Questions arose, for example, about the definition of *special* objects, *special* activities, and *special* distortions that provoked crying long after the baby had no more 'functional need' for them, and was thoroughly familiar with the novelties. Some of the differences between indifferent and special objects, activities, etc., paralleled the differences between human and inanimate objects, but the differential response to human and inanimate objects was never clear-cut. Similar considerations applied to the interventions that inhibited or arrested crying during the early months.

By at least the third week the *state of the organism* had become an important mediating factor between psychologically relevant stimuli and the infant's affective responses, so that it was no longer possible to speak of a one-to-one cause-effect relation between a fixed 'stimulus' and a specific affective 'response'.

The direct observation and spectrographic analysis of crying brought circumstantial evidence for the proposition that neonatal crying patterns are not entirely random expressions of distress; in selected instances one can infer the provoking cause from the morphological characteristics of the cry, and the mother is guided to some degree by these characteristics when she responds to her baby's cry. Direct observations combined with the analysis of sound spectrograms also gave some substance to the speculation that crying is functionally and morphologically related to the earliest non-cry vocalizations (Lewis, 1951); and cast some doubt on the supposition that crying and early speech acquisitions are entirely unrelated, or that the first non-cry vocalizations (generally viewed as the global 'precursors' of speech) begin *de novo* at one month, and then differentiate into refined lallation, babbling, and speech sounds, while crying follows its independent path.

Attachment and Exploratory Behavior of One-year-olds in a Strange Situation[1]

MARY D. SALTER AINSWORTH
and BARBARA A. WITTIG

This is a report of one facet of a longitudinal study of the development of the attachments of infants to their mothers throughout the first year of life. Visits were paid to babies in their homes every three weeks from three to 54 weeks of age. A visit usually lasted four hours. By the end of the first year, detailed data had been obtained about the behavior of each baby in the familiar environment of his own home – in routine situations, in play, and towards the familiar figures of his household, to whom, by this time, he had become attached. But it was desired also, to observe how the attachment to one of these figures his mother – influenced his behavior in a situation that was unfamiliar to him, and with this purpose he was introduced to a strange situation.

There were three aspects of his behavior that we particularly wished to observe in the strange situation: (*a*) his use of his mother as a secure base from which to explore the world, (*b*) his response to his mother's leaving the room, and to her return, and (*c*) his response to a stranger. At home few of the infants in this sample had shown any consistent distress in the minor separation situation of the mother leaving the room, and few of them showed any striking fear of strangers. It was expected that both separation anxiety and fear of strangers would be more intense in a strange situation. But the chief

[1] This study was supported by the Foundations' Fund for Research in Psychiatry through Grant 62-244. We wish to express thanks also to George D. Allyn and Edwin E. Ellis, who served as additional observers in the strange situation; to Eleanor S. McCulloch and Elizabeth A. Eikenberg, who played the unrewarding role of strangers; and to William C. Hamilton, whose skill under very difficult conditions made photographic records possible. We wish also to express gratitude to the pediatricians, through whose cooperation we obtained our sample of infants, and especially to the mothers and fathers, whose friendship and cooperation made the study not only possible but also productive and enjoyable.

purpose of introducing the infant to a strange situation was to observe his use of his mother as a secure base.

Blatz[1] was the first, to our knowledge, to describe the young child as using his mother as a secure base. He said that the dependent security a young child had developed in relationship to his parents served as a base from which he could venture out to brave the insecurity implicit in exploration of the world and in the acquisition of the skills and abilities that eventually form the basis for independent security.

Arsenian (1943) studied the behavior of young children aged 11 to 30 months in a strange situation. Those children who were left alone in a strange room with toys behaved in a highly 'insecure' fashion – screaming, attempting to escape from the room, moving in an agitated way, etc. Those whose mothers stayed with them in the strange room typically approached the toys and played with them. Harlow (1961) found that infant monkeys in an open field situation used their cloth surrogate mothers as a secure base for exploration, and also as a haven of safety when faced by a fear-arousing stimulus object. If the surrogate mother were present, the infant could approach the fear-arousing object, manipulate it, and even destroy it. In a field study of Ganda infants (Ainsworth, 1963) use of the mother as a secure base was noted.

Ainsworth (1963, 1964) proposed that a variety of behavior patterns mediated an infant's attachment to his mother, not only smiling, crying, sucking, clinging and following, as Bowlby (1958) had suggested, but also looking, reaching, approaching, vocalizing, and greeting responses of several kinds. It was also held that one of the most important criteria of a healthy attachment was ability to use the mother as a secure base for exploration. It was to investigate the development of these patterns of attachment behavior that the longitudinal study was planned, of which the present paper reports one facet. In contrast, Schaffer & Emerson (1964) used the consistency and intensity of protest in minor separation situations (such as when the adult puts the baby down or leaves the room) as his sole criteria of the intensity of attachment. In criticism of these criteria, it is held that

[1] The late William E. Blatz, Director of the Institute of Child Study, University of Toronto, was a gifted clinician and teacher, who established an oral tradition which stimulated and inspired many, and which contained much that he did not manage to commit to the printed word. Only now, many years since he first talked of the "secure base", can we refer the reader to his own writing on the subject (Blatz, 1966, pp. 35-43).

a high level of anxiety in a *minor* separation situation might indicate that a child is insecure in his relations with his mother as well as attached to her, and a low level of separation anxiety does not necessarily indicate that a child is weakly attached. It was hoped that the study of behavior of this sample of one-year-olds in a strange situation might offer definitive evidence in this controversy, particularly since so much first-hand information was available about the development of each child in the sample.

Method

Subjects

The sample consists of fourteen infants – seven boys and seven girls – from white, middle-class families. The sample was obtained through pediatricians in private practice, most of the parents having been contacted shortly before the birth of the baby. None of the mothers was primiparous. Two mothers held part-time jobs through part of the baby's first year; the rest were fulltime mothers. When they were introduced to the strange situation, twelve infants were within a few days of the median age of 51 weeks; two were older, one 58 weeks old and another 54.

Procedure

Two adjacent university offices were employed for the experimental room and the observation room, connected by two one-way vision mirror-windows. A microphone was placed in the experimental room to transmit sound to the room next door. In the experimental room the office furniture was pushed to the wall, leaving open floor space covered by a rug, in which there were three focal points – a chair for the mother at the extreme right, a chair for the stranger opposite, to the extreme left, and, at the apex of the triangle, furthest from the mirror-windows, a small chair, with toys on it, and other toys on the floor near it.

Four observers were used. The first observer dictated a narrative account into a tape recorder, which also picked up the click of a timer every 15 seconds. The second observer introduced the mother and baby to the strange situation, and then returned to the observation room to record her observations in a notebook, checking off the 15 second intervals. A third observer also recorded in a notebook, but, whereas the first and second observers focused attention on the child,

113

the third attended specifically to the behavior of the adults – the mother and the stranger. A fourth observer timed the duration of the several episodes and gave cues for the actors' entrances and exits. A photographer took a series of still photographs through the mirror-window. The stranger and the mother were instructed in advance about the roles they were to play. So that embarrassment and constraint could be avoided, a deliberate effort was made to structure these roles to conform to what the adults could do naturally. So that the mother would not be anxious about remembering the instructions, she was provided with a summarized version of the instructions to which she could refer if she wished.

TABLE 11

Episodes in the Strange Situation

Episode	Time	Entrances and Exits
1. Mother, Baby, Observer	30 seconds approximately	Observer leaves room
2. Mother, Baby	3 minutes	
3. Stranger, Mother, Baby	3 minutes	Stranger enters room
4. Stranger, Baby	3 minutes*	Mother leaves room
5. Mother, Baby	variable	Mother enters room, Stranger leaves
6. Baby Alone	3 minutes*	Mother leaves room
7. Stranger, Baby	2 or 5 min.*	Stranger enters room
8. Mother, Baby	variable	Mother enters room Stranger leaves

* Episode is curtailed if the baby is highly distressed

There were eight episodes in the strange situation, which are listed in Table 11, and summarized as follows:

1. *Mother, Baby, Observer.* The observer introduces the mother and baby to the experimental room. The mother has been instructed to carry the baby in, and is shown where to put him down – at the mid-point of the base of the triangle formed by the chairs, away from but facing the apex where the toys are. The observer leaves the room.

2. *Mother, Baby.* Three minutes. The mother puts the baby down, then sits in her chair and pretends to read a magazine. She has been told that she is to respond to him quietly if he seeks a response from her, and to reassure him if he needs it, but she is not to try to attract his attention.

3. *Stranger, Mother, Baby.* Three minutes. The stranger enters, greets the mother briefly, then sits quietly in her chair. After a minute has elapsed she is signalled to engage the mother in conversation. After another minute she is signalled to invite the baby's attention, gradually approaching him and attempting to engage him in interaction. Meanwhile the mother is to sit quietly and to talk only when the stranger talks to her.

4. *Stranger, Baby.* Three minutes. Another signal is given for the mother to leave the room as unobtrusively as possible, leaving her purse behind, on her chair, while the stranger distracts the baby's attention. The stranger then withdraws from active interaction with the baby, sits quietly in her chair, but responds to any advances the baby makes. If, however, the baby is distressed at his mother's departure, the stranger tries to distract him or comfort him, and, if this is successful, then she tries to re-engage his interest in the toys. If she is unsuccessful in comforting a highly distressed baby, the episode is curtailed.

5. *Mother, Baby.* Time is variable. The mother speaks outside the closed door of the experimental room, loudly enough for the baby to hear her. She pauses, then opens the door and stands in the doorway, hesitating for a moment, so that the baby has time to make a spontaneous response. Then she greets him and makes him comfortable for the next episode. She was not given more specific instructions, except that before she leaves she is to settle the baby on the floor again, interested in the toys.

6. *Baby Alone.* Three minutes. The mother leaves the room, after saying 'bye-bye' to the baby, and again leaves her purse behind her on her chair. In the case of extreme and prolonged distress this episode was also curtailed.

7. *Stranger, Baby.* In this episode the stranger's behavior varies in accordance with the baby's behavior both in this episode and in the previous stranger-baby episode. If he explored when alone with her previously, she is to approach him gradually to see how much close attention from a stranger he can tolerate, and to continue to interact with him for two minutes. If he did not explore previously, she is to allow three minutes for exploration, and then proceed to the two minutes of increasingly close interaction. But if he is distressed from having been alone, or becomes distressed, she is to attempt to comfort him. If she is unsuccessful in comforting him, the episode is curtailed.

8. *Mother, Baby*. The mother returns to the experimental room, pauses in the doorway for a moment, speaks to the baby, and finally picks him up to terminate the episode.

A case to Illustrate the Procedure

Before reporting how the observational records were analysed, one child's responses to the strange situation will be described as an illustration of the procedure. Brian – subject 10 in the tables – illustrates the generalizations that can be made about the sample as a whole, although there were marked individual differences.

1. *Mother, Baby, Observer*. Brian had one arm hooked over his mother's shoulder as they came into the room; he was holding on to her, grasping a fold of her blouse. He looked around soberly, but with interest, at the toys and at the observer.

2. *Mother, Baby*. After being put down, Brian immediately crept towards the toys and began to explore them (Plate 21). He was very active, picking toys up, then dropping them or moving them about, with vigorous movements. He crept around quite a bit, mostly on his mother's side of the room. Although his attention was fixed on the playthings, he glanced up at his mother six times, and smiled at her twice. She glanced at him covertly, from time to time, but their glances did not seem to meet. Once he threw a toy with a clatter at her feet; she moved it back towards him. Otherwise there was no interaction between them. Towards the end of the three minutes he blew into a long cardboard tube, vocalizing as though pretending it were a horn, and then he looked up at his mother with a smile, seeming to expect her to acknowledge his accomplishment.

3. *Stranger, Mother, Baby*. He turned to look at the stranger when she entered, with a pleasant expression on his face. He played with the tube again, vocalized, smiled, and turned to glance at his mother. He continued to play, glancing at the stranger twice. When the stranger and his mother began to converse, he continued to explore actively at the end of the room, and looked up only once – at the stranger. Towards the end of this minute of conversation he crept over to his mother, pulled himself up, and stood briefly, holding on to her knee with one hand, and clutching her blouse with the other (Plate 22). Then he turned back to play. When the stranger began her approach by leaning forward to offer him a toy, he smiled, crept towards her, and reached for it (Plate 23). He put the toy in his mouth. She offered him the tube and he blew into it again. He looked back

and forth from the toys to the stranger and did not look at his mother at all.

4. *Stranger, Baby.* He did not notice his mother leave. He continued to watch the stranger and the toys she was manipulating. Suddenly, he crept to his mother's chair, pulled himself up into a standing position, and looked at the stranger. She tried to distract him with a pull-toy. He approached the toy, and began to roll it back and forth; but he glanced again at his mother's empty chair. He was less active than he had been when alone with his mother, and after two minutes his activity ceased. He sat chewing the string of the pull-toy, and glancing from the stranger to his mother's chair. He made an unhappy noise, then a cry-face, and then he cried. The stranger tried to distract him by offering him a block; he took it but then threw it away with a petulant gesture. He gave several more little protesting cries, but he did not cry hard.

5. *Mother, Baby.* When his mother opened the door and paused in the doorway, Brian looked at her immediately and vocalized loudly, with a quality that could have been either a laugh or a cry; then he crept to her quickly, and pulled himself up, with her help, to hold on to her knees. Then she picked him up, and he immediately put his arms around her neck, his face against her shoulder, and hugged her hard (Plate 24). He then gave her another big hug before she put him down. He resisted being put down; he tried to cling to her and protested loudly. Once on the floor, he threw himself down, hid his face in the rug, and cried angrily (Plate 25). His mother knelt beside him and tried to interest him in the toys again. He stopped crying and watched. After a moment she disengaged herself and got up to sit on her chair. He immediately threw himself down and cried again. She helped him to stand, and cuddled him. For a moment he reciprocated in the cuddle, but then he threw himself down on the floor again, crying. She again picked him up, and tried to direct his attention to a squeaky ball. He looked at it, still holding on to his mother, with one arm hooked over her shoulder (Plate 26). He began to play, but quickly turned back to his mother with a brief cry, and clung to her (Plate 27). This alternation of play and clinging continued. After four and a half minutes, his mother, apparently not wishing to delay us, picked a moment when he was interested in a ball, and moved to the door.

6. *Baby Alone.* As she said 'bye-bye' and waved, Brian looked up with a little smile, but he shifted into a cry before she had quite

closed the door. He sat crying, rocking himself back and forth (Plate 28). He cried hard, but occasionally lulled a little and looked around. After a minute and a half the stranger was instructed to enter.

7. *Stranger, Baby.* Brian lulled slightly when he saw the stranger enter, but he continued to cry. She first tried to distract him, then offered her arms to him. Brian responded by raising his arms; she picked him up, and he stopped crying immediately. She held him in her arms, and showed him the pictures tacked up around the edges of the mirror-window (Plate 29). He looked with apparent interest; he held on to her tightly, grasping a fold of her clothing. Occasionally he gave a little sob, but for the most part he did not cry. But when she put him down, he screamed. She picked him up again, and he lulled.

8. *Mother, Baby.* At the moment that his mother returned Brian was crying listlessly. He did not notice his mother. The stranger half-turned and pointed her out. Brian looked towards her, still crying, and then turned away. But he soon 'did a double take'. He looked back and vocalized a little protest. His mother offered her arms to him. He reached towards her, smiling, and leaned way out of the stranger's arms and his mother took him. He threw his arms around her neck, hugging her hard, and wiggling with excitement. Then the stranger tried to attract his attention. Brian did not notice her advance until she touched him; he immediately clung to his mother and buried his face in her shoulder. His mother continued to hold him, and he cuddled and clung to her, as the episode ended (Plate 30).

Coding and Analysis of Data

The reports of each of the observers were transcribed independently and then collated. No formal estimate of reliability was undertaken although there was a high degree of agreement among reports. Three chief discrepancies were noted, however. A given behavioral item sometimes was assigned to one time interval by one observer and to an adjacent one by another observer. This was unavoidable since all observers tended to lag somewhat behind the action in their recording. When a discrepancy of this kind occurred, the first observer's record was used as the standard. Secondly, since the three observers were stationed at different points along the wall of windows, one might be able to observe the face and note a glance or smile while the others could not be sure of the facial expression. Therefore, visual orientation and smiling were accepted from the report of only one observer. Finally, the record of the first observer, who dictated a narrative report, was inevitably more detailed than that of the others who jotted their observations in writing; therefore, behavior items – usually minor – noted by the first observer but not by the others were nevertheless used in the analysis.

To facilitate statistical analysis, the behavior in each 15 second interval was coded. The frequency of a behavioral item was measured in terms of the number of units of time in which the behavior appeared. Thus, in a three-minute episode any behavior which was continuous or which occurred at least once in each of the twelve 15-second time-intervals, would be given a score of 12. In the case of episodes which were not exactly three minutes long, the frequency was prorated.

The episodes were compared one with the other in terms of the frequency of behavioral items. The significance of the statistical comparisons was estimated by means of a two-tailed sign test. All trends reported are significant at the five per cent level or better, unless otherwise specified.

Results

The following behavioral items were used as the basis for comparing episodes:

1. *Exploratory Behavior*

Exploratory locomotion, exploratory manipulation and visual exploration were considered separately. Exploratory locomotion included all locomotion, whether walking, creeping or crawling, except responses of approach to or withdrawal from persons, following the mother when she left the room, and random locomotion in the context of acute distress. Exploratory manipulation included all fine manipulatory movements, all gross movements such as shaking banging and pushing, and all movements involved in picking an object up, but excluded taking a toy from an adult, trying to open the door, obviously angry throwing and pushing, fingering of the clothing or body, and mere touching. Visual exploration included visual regard of all aspects of the physical environment except the mother and the stranger, but excluded prolonged fixation either while crying hard or while sucking. When the babies were alone with their mothers in Episode (2) they explored more, according to all three criteria, than they did in any other subsequent episode. (Table 12 shows the data for exploratory manipulation as an example.)

2. *Visual Orientation*

An analysis was made of the proportion of time in which the baby was oriented visually to the mother, to the stranger or to the physical environment, including the toys. When alone with their mothers in Episode (2), all babies were oriented to the physical environment a larger proportion of time than to the mother, although all but one

TABLE 12

Exploratory Manipulation

Subject	Episodes					
No.	2	3	4	5	6	7
1.	5.0	2·8	3·0	0	0*	0*
2.	5·0	3·0	1·7*	4·5	4·0*	0*
3.	1·8	8·8	0*	2·9	0	3·0*
4.	12·0	6·9	9·2	10·3	11·1	11·3
5.	0	0	0	3·0	1·7*	0*
6.	9·4	4·8	9·4	4·8	2·2	2·2
7.	10·3	6·3	8·3	6·0	10·3	4·5*
8.	10·0	7·0	0	4·8	0*	0*
9.	11·1	10·0	8·3	8·0	7·4	6·7
10.	12·0	6·5	5·0	6·0	0*	0*
11.	12·0	10·0	2·7*	3·5	0*	0*
12.	7·4	2·0	1·0	3·0	2·4*	0
13.	7·4	0	1·2	7·2	0	0*
14.	7·4	5·4	9·2	2·8	7·0	2·7

* Episode was curtailed.

Ep. 2 > Ep. 3 p = ·004   Ep. 2 > Ep. 6 p = ·004
Ep. 2 > Ep. 4 p = ·004   Ep. 2 > Ep. 7 p = ·004
Ep. 2 > Ep. 5 p = ·012

baby glanced at least once at his mother. After the stranger entered in Episode (3) all babies oriented visually to her more frequently than to the mother, although not to the exclusion of visual exploration, for this was more frequent in Episode (3) than in Episode (6), the baby-alone situation. In Episode (4) visual orientation tended to be towards the stranger, probably because of the frequency of her intervention, so that there was less visual exploration than in the baby-alone situation.

3. *Crying*

All kinds and degrees of crying were included in this analysis, from screaming at one extreme to a cry-face or unhappy noises at the other extreme. (See Table 13).

TABLE 13

Crying

Subject	Episodes					
No.	2	3	4	5	6	7
1.	0	0	0·9	12·0	12·0*	12·0*
2.	1·0	1·0	8·6*	3·0	10·0*	12·0*
3.	3·7	2·4	12·0*	12·0	11·3	10·5*
4.	0	0	0	0	1·0	0
5.	0	7·9	11·0	9·0	12·0*	10·3*
6.	0	0	0	2·0	8·7	9·8
7.	0	0	0	0	0·9	6·0*
8.	0	0	12·0	4·0	12·0*	12·0*
9.	0	0	0	0	6·5	0
10.	0	0	3·0	6·0	12·0*	9·6*
11.	0	1·0	8·0*	11·0	12·0*	12·0*
12.	0	0	12·0	6·0	12·0*	12·0*
13.	3·7	6·6	12·0	5·0	12·0	12·0*
14.	0	0	0	0	1·0	0

* Episode was curtailed.

In Episode (5), which was of variable length, the total number time units (up to but not exceeding 12) in which crying occurred was used as the frequency measure.

Ep. 2 < Ep. 3 n.s.	Ep. 2 < Ep. 7 p = ·001	Ep. 3 < Ep. 6 p < ·001
Ep. 2 < Ep. 4 p = ·004	Ep. 3 < Ep. 4 p = ·004	Ep. 3 < Ep. 7 p = ·001
Ep. 2 < Ep. 5 p = ·002	Ep. 3 < Ep. 5 p = ·022	Ep. 4 < Ep. 6 p = ·012
Ep. 2 < Ep. 6 p < ·001		

There was extremely little crying when the baby was alone with his mother in Episode (2), and only one child seemed to protest the strange situation even with her mother present and before a stranger arrived. In Episode (3) five babies cried a little, three of them minimally, when confronted by the stranger. The frequency of crying in Episode (2) is not significantly less than in Episode (3), but it is significantly less in each of these episodes than in any subsequent episode. Not all babies cried when their mothers left them with a stranger in Episode (4); and there was less crying than when the baby was left altogether alone in Episode (6). This suggests that the stranger in herself was not a significantly distressing feature of the strange situation.

4. *Responses to Mother's Leaving the Room*

Three types of responses were conspicuous: (*a*) 'regain behavior', (*b*) crying, and (*c*) other responses that seemed indicative of acute distress. For the purposes of one analysis a distinction was made between 'real' crying and the minimal crying of a cry-face or unhappy noises. 'Regain' behavior is behavior indicative of a desire to regain the mother. Strong regain behavior is an attempt to follow, which, of course, was frustrated by the closed door. Several behaviors were classified as acute distress behavior: random locomotion that resembled that of a little trapped animal; crying with detachment from the environment, with eyes closed or face hidden; rocking, and kicking the heels on the floor. In the statistical analysis the sign test was applied to mere presence or absence of each of these behavioral items in each of the two relevant episodes, (4) and (6). (Table 14 is shown as an example of this kind of analysis.)

In the first separation episode, (4), the only significant tendency was for the baby to show some kind of regain behavior, and in this episode weak regain behavior was more frequent than strong. Nine babies cried, at least to a minimal degree, with or without delay; four followed the mother to the door, including one who did not cry, and one went to the door screaming after she noticed her mother was absent; six showed acute distress.

In the second separation episode, (6), when the baby was left alone, all fourteen protested the mother's departure or absence, eleven with 'real' crying, three with unhappy noises, and most without delay. Ten babies attempted to follow their mothers. Seven went right to the door; five either banged on the door or tried to open it, either reaching vainly for the knob or trying to insert their fingers into the crack. Thirteen babies may be described as manifesting a strong reaction to the second separation, *either* trying to open the door *or* crying hard, usually with accompanying acute distress behavior. Only one child did neither, but even she gave a slight vocal protest and went to stand in front of the door. Two factors seem to make the response more intense to the second separation than to the first – the cumulative effect of the upsetting episodes, and the security which the stranger may have provided to some in the first episode.

Attempts to regain the mother appear to be even more significant when both episodes are taken into consideration, thirteen children displaying regain behavior on either one occasion or the other. Only one child did not; he cried inconsolably in both episodes. Eleven children showed strong regain behavior on either one occasion or the other. Some did not follow the mother until the second separation; others followed the first time but were overcome with acute distress the second time.

TABLE 14

Responses to Mother's Leaving Room

Subject No.	Regain Behavior		Crying		Acute Distress Behavior	
	Ep. 4	Ep. 6	Ep. 4	Ep. 6	Ep. 4	Ep. 6
1.	Strong	—	Min.	Real	—	+
2.	Strong	Strong	Real	Real	+	+
3.	Weak	Strong*	Real	Real	—	—
4.	Weak	Strong*	—	Min.	—	—
5.	—	—	Real	Real	+	+
6.	Weak	Strong*	—	Real	—	+
7.	Weak	Strong*	—	Min.	—	—
8.	Strong	Strong	Real	Real	—	+
9.	Strong	Strong*	—	Real	—	—
10.	Weak	—	Real	Real	—	+
11.	Strong	—	Real	Real	+	—
12.	—	Weak	Real	Real	+	+
13.	Weak	Strong	Real	Real	+	+
14.	Weak	Strong	—	Min.	—	—
	p=·012	p=·18	n.s.	p<·001	n.s.	n.s.
	Ep. 4 or Ep. 6 p=·002					

* Strong regain behavior, with attempt to open door.

5. Responses to the Mother's Return

Responses to the mother's return included approaching, stopping crying, smiling, clinging and withdrawing. Approach behavior included locomotion towards the mother, reaching towards her with lifted arms, and strongly inclining the body towards her with or without reaching. Two degrees of clinging were distinguished: (*a*) tight clinging, including hugging, sinking into the mother, grasping a fold of her clothing or part of her body, and holding on tightly with

123

the legs, and (*b*) holding on, in which the baby's arm seemed to exert some pressure against the mother, even though there was no clear-cut embracing or grasping. Withdrawal responses include walking away or turning away, averting the face, and, if held, struggling, stiffening or squirming to be put down. The relevant episodes for this analysis are (5) and (8).

All but two babies approached their mothers in Episode (5). Although the tendency to approach her also in Episode (8) was short of significance (p = ·18), all but one approached in either one or the other relevant episode. All but one baby stopped crying on his mother's return on either one or the other occasion, but there were enough babies who were not crying when the mother returned to make the trends non-significant when the episodes were taken separately. In each of the reunion episodes only four babies greeted the mother with a smile.

In Episode (5) there was no significant trend in regard to clinging. Nine babies were picked up by their mothers; only five clung tightly and two did not hold on at all. In Episode (8), however, there was a significant tendency to cling. Thirteen babies were picked up; twelve held on, and ten clung tightly. No baby withdrew from the mother in Episode (5), and only two did in Episode (8). In summary the significant responses to reunion with the mother were to approach in Episode (5), to cling in Episode (8), and not to withdraw from her.

6. *Responses to the Stranger's Entrance*

All babies looked at the stranger when she arrived in each of Episodes (3) and (7). In Episode (3) some smiled, some approached, some withdrew, and some merely looked. In Episode (7) the only consistent tendency was *not* to withdraw, and there were nearly significant tendencies (p = ·058) not to approach and not to cling.

7. *Responses to being Picked Up*

Two responses were conspicuous: (*a*) stopping or diminishing crying, and (*b*) clinging tightly. Episodes (5) and (8) are combined for the analysis of responses to being picked up by the mother. Ten babies stopped or decreased crying when picked up by the mother; nine clung tightly. But eleven did either one or the other (p < ·02). There was no consistent response to being picked up by the stranger. All but one baby was picked up by the stranger in either Episode (4) or in Episode (7) or both; seven decreased their crying or clung

124

tightly or both; but eight – with some ambivalent overlap – protested being picked up either by increasing crying or struggling or both.

8. *Responses to being Put Down*

Two conspicuous responses were made when the mother put the baby down, or when she merely attempted to release him: (*a*) crying or increasing the intensity of crying, and (*b*) reaching and/or tight clinging. In Episode (2) when the babies were first put down by their mothers, only one protested, and cried and clung. In Episode (5) behavior was variable. Nine babies protested being put down, crying or clinging or both; only five, however, showed the persistent effort to maintain contact that Brian did. Mothers of babies who had protested being put down in Episode (5) tended not to release them in Episode (8), so both episodes have to be considered together. One baby was picked up in neither episode; all the rest cried, or reached, or clung, or some combination of these responses in either one episode or the other.

None of the trends in regard to the stranger are significant, but it may be noted that seven babies protested when put down by the stranger, and three of these clung to her, trying to maintain the contact. To be sure, three babies showed ambivalence, first protesting being picked up and then protesting being put down.

Individual Differences and Case Summaries

In a sample as small as fourteen there has to be almost complete unanimity of response before a trend emerges as statistically significant. Despite the many significant likenesses within the group, there were nevertheless striking individual differences – as may be seen from an examination of the three sample tables. For the purposes of our investigation the individual differences are of even more interest than the group trends, since the major purpose of the strange situation was to highlight behavior that might not be perceived as clearly at home, and to relate this, if possible, to the baby's behavior in the home situation and indeed to his whole developmental history. Since there has not been as yet any but a cursory examination of the mass of data that has been accumulated for each baby, our consideration of individual differences must be brief and impressionistic, confining itself to the most striking points.

For the purposes of discussion the babies have been divided into three loose groups, largely on the basis of their responses to separation in the strange situation.[1]

Group A consists of four babies, three girls and one boy, who showed minimal disturbance upon separation – subjects 4, 7, 9, and 14.

Group B consists of six babies, five boys and one girl, who showed clearcut separation anxiety, but whose behavior retained some adaptive quality, which tended to break down only under cumulative stress – subjects 1, 2, 3, 6, 8, and 10.

Group C consists of four babies, three girls and one boy, who manifested clear-cut separation anxiety, but whose behavior showed maladaptive features of one kind or another – subjects 5, 11, 12, and 13.

Group B

Even in this middle group of six babies there are two sub-groups. One consists of Brian and two others – subjects 1 and 6 – who, in the first separation episode, showed relatively little disturbance, weak regain behavior, and some ability for positive interaction with the stranger, but who, in the second separation episode, showed marked disturbance. The other sub-group consists of two babies who were disturbed in the first separation, but who showed strong regain behavior in both separations and also some positive response to the stranger who tried to comfort them. The sixth child – subject 3 – is a special case. He was ill with a fever when he came to the strange situation, and much more inactive and fussy than he normally is at home. Nevertheless, his behavior on this occasion fitted him into Group B.

Brian – subject 10. Brian's behavior in the strange situation has already been described. His background will now be considered. His mother is outstanding for her delight in physical contact with

[1] Since this paper was prepared, 45 additional one-year-olds have been observed in the strange situation, making a total sample of 59. The criteria for distinguishing between groups have been refined. Group A is now distinguished from Groups B and C on the basis of three criteria: (*a*) relative lack of interest and effort in regaining contact, proximity, or interaction with the mother upon her return after an absence and relative lack of effort to maintain contact with her if contact is regained; (*b*) a strong tendency to ignore the mother upon her return or to go, turn or look away from her; and (*c*) a strong tendency to behave toward the stranger in an equally or more friendly manner than toward the mother. The degree of distress attributable to separation was discarded as a criterion for distinguishing between Groups A, B and C, although it was used as a partial basis for distinguishing subgroups within each of Groups A and B. On the basis of this new classification subjects 4, 7 and 14 were reassigned to Group B, although each to a different subgroup, and only one baby – subject 9, Joan – was retained in Group A.

him, and indeed for her delight in everything he does. She has been very sensitive to his signals, and, while not attending to every cry, she has been careful to intervene before tension builds too high. He has cried very little throughout his life, and his mother is skillful in soothing him if he needs it. His mother is too busy to give him un-limited attention, but each routine situation has been the occasion for intimate and prolonged interaction with much affectionate exchange and happy play. He was bottle-fed on a flexible schedule, but always with sensitive consideration for his preferences and for his own rate of intake.

He is attached not only to his mother but also to his father and to his three brothers, all of whom have had much interaction with him, in rough play as well as affectionate interchange. His mother kept him in his own room away from his brothers for the first three months of life. After that he spent his waking hours in the midst of family activity. He was not a 'floor baby', however, but was kept mostly in the playpen, even after locomotion had developed and he showed signs of wishing to explore.

From the beginning Brian was a very cuddly baby, sinking into the person holding him. Holding Brian is a gratifying experience, as his doctors and nurses discovered when he had a hospital experience of four day's duration at eight months of age. He showed the expected kinds of disturbance, but not to an extreme degree, and was the darling of the ward.

He is a friendly and responsive baby, not only cuddly, but also active, vigorous, curious and able to withstand knocks and bumps. He has invented games of delaying pleasure, and of being responsive to his mother without looking at her. His mean I.Q. on the Griffiths' Scale of Infant Intelligence was 115·4, with little scatter of scores among the five testings.

Susan – subject 1 – was classed in the same sub-group of Group B. Susan was 54 weeks old in the strange situation. She was outstanding in Episode (2) for the amount of interaction she had with her mother, repeatedly approaching her to play give-and-take games with the toys she found. In Episode (4) she discovered the empty chair, and started towards the door, but then was distracted by the stranger. She made one cry-face, stood watching for a while, then played the give-and-take game with the stranger. During Episode (5) she behaved like Brian, protesting every slight effort of her mother's to release her. When her mother left her sitting on the little chair she sat still screaming, and made no effort to get down. She was picked up by the stranger in Episode (7) but did not stop crying until her mother took her in Episode (8), when she stopped crying and sank into her mother, laying her head on her shoulder.

Like Brian, Susan has had much physical contact and interaction with a mother who finds her delightful – although Susan's mother is more selfconsciously progressive in her methods than Brian's. Susan has been permitted to develop more initiative and ability to look after herself than has Brian. After a period of breast-feeding on demand, Susan was encouraged to manage her own bottle and to feed herself table foods. She was a 'floor baby' even before she could crawl. She could control her own life very well – finding her bottle, napping, playing, or taking the initiative in interaction – all there on the floor. She is a charming, responsive little girl, and resourceful in inventing games to play by herself or with others – her parents, her brother, or visitors, who are frequent. Her mean I.Q. was 123·5.

Two little boys – subjects 8 and 2 – form the second sub-group of Group B.

Matthew – subject 8 – seems younger and more delicate than the two so far described. His legs seem weak, and he heaves himself about with his arms, his legs trailing helplessly. Nevertheless, he explored actively in Episodes (2) and (3), and smiled at the stranger when she approached. When he saw his mother leave, he cried with increasing intensity, and crawled towards the door. When the stranger picked him up, he lulled, clutching her, and protesting any shift of position. When his mother came in he cried and reached towards her, straining. His mother did not take him, however. When the stranger put him down he cried again, but his mother soon interested him in the toys. He began to smile and to play actively. When she left him for the second time he immediately began to cry; he tried to crawl to the door, but was so frantic that he went backwards rather than forwards.

Matthew also has had much physical contact with his mother. He was held most of his waking time until he was seven months old, and even after that his mother often held him rather than putting him in the playpen. Her games with him were tickle games, kissing games and other contact games. She tended to be overprotective, however, and generally encouraged passivity and discouraged self-help. His mother was very sensitive to his signals, except after she had put him to bed for a nap; then he could scream and she would not go to him. His mean I.Q. was 100·5, with little variation.

Summary of Group B. There is no doubt that all the babies in Group B, including subject 3, the sick baby, have established a firm, secure attachment to their mothers – and indeed to others as well, the father, siblings and other relatives. Two features stand out in their histories. All of them have mothers who delight in them, finding them a constant source of interest, pleasure and amusement, and who enter into frequent intense and prolonged sequences of interaction with them. In addition, with one exception – the sick baby, who might well have been in Group A had he not been sick – they have received much physical contact from mothers who enjoyed contact themselves, and who were not afraid of spoiling a baby by picking him up. Those in the first sub-group differ from the second in the greater amount of initiative they have been allowed in feeding or locomotion or both. Brian and Susan were less distressed when separated from their mothers, at least the first time, than was Matthew, but there is no evidence that they were less attached.

Group A

None of the babies in Group A cried in Episode (4), although they all showed regain behavior – weak in three cases. All smiled at the stranger, and were responsive to her. In the second separation episode they cried but relatively little, and all went to the door and banged on it or tried to open it. All were responsive to the stranger again in Episode (7). All greeted the mother upon her return, but two then went on with their play without making contact with her. Are these children less attached than the babies of Group B? In one case, and perhaps in three, the answer is 'yes'; in one case the answer is clearly 'no'.

Joan – subject 9. Of the four Joan seems the least firmly attached to her mother. Nevertheless in Episode (2) she glanced at her mother frequently, but never caught her eye. She played actively, but not as actively as at home, and one gained the clear impression that she wanted an audience. When the stranger arrived Joan got her audience; she seemed stimulated and showed-off. When the stranger advanced, she did not hesitate to play with her. When her mother left she looked puzzled and went to the door, but then continued to play. When her mother returned in Episode (5) Joan gave a half-smile and made no move towards her. When she left a second time, however, Jaon cried, followed to the door and tried to reach the knob. Then she turned back to play, less actively and with some grumbly vocalizations. She played with the stranger in Episode (7). When her mother returned, Joan approached her momentarily with a smile, but then turned away and had to be coaxed to come to her. When her mother picked her up finally, Joan accepted being held for a moment, then squirmed to be put down.

Joan's mother is an intelligent and charming woman with a professional calling. She feels torn between her desire to fulfil herself in her chosen profession and her desire to be a good mother to her three children. She has tried to resolve the conflict by practising part-time, and leaving Joan – the other children are in school – with a competent housekeeper. She is not altogether content with her compromise. She acknowledges that she does not give the children enough of herself, and yet during the periods when she has attempted to be a full-time mother she feels restless and dissatisfied. On the whole, she thinks that she gives Joan a better sample of herself now that she has picked up the threads of her work again than when she was trying to be a full-time mother, and she felt – and we agree – that Joan's tie to her was closer than to the housekeeper.

From the beginning Joan's mother claimed that she was a bad mother, attributing her shortcomings to the loss of her own mother in early childhood. She is an intellectual mother, charting her course by what she feels she ought to do rather than by any sure feel of Joan's needs and signals. She is not patient enough to hold a baby long enough really to soothe it, but she did hold Joan briefly when she remembered that she knew that this was a good idea.

From the beginning Joan, like another Group A baby, got into a vicious spiral. She spit up and she smelt bad. The more she spit up, the less inclined anyone was to hold her. But when she was 21 weeks old her paternal grandparents visited for several days, and gave her much cuddling and attention. Ten days later her I.Q. had risen to 128 from a previous 114. At this point she was able to sit alone and began to crawl. From then on she advanced rapidly. She was allowed the freedom of the house, and became a great explorer. Her parents and siblings found her more interesting and paid more attention to her. The spitting up gradually disappeared. At 54 weeks her I.Q. was 134 – the highest in the sample.

Perhaps Joan and two of the other three in Group A are in fact less strongly attached to their mothers than the children of Group B who protested separation much more strongly – although none of them is unattached. But the fourth baby in Group A is certainly strongly attached, although she was not distressed when separated in the strange situation.

1. Self-clutching by monkeys raised in social isolation.

2. Ventral-ventral clinging by pair of 'together-together' infants.

3. Unmothered infants arranged in 'choo-choo' pattern.

4

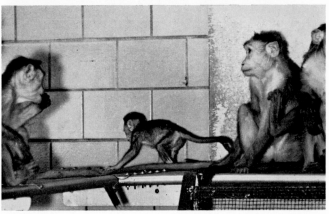

5

4. A group of bonnet mothers in characteristic *passive-contact* huddle. Note *cradle* by female at extreme left of picture and *enclosure* by female adjacent to her. Note also that while maintaining ventral contact infants are able to assume varying orientations.

5. A young bonnet in an early stage of a brief horizontal departure from its mother.

6. A bonnet infant taking a cabbage leaf from the hands of its mother. Initial acquisition of solid food often occurs by the infant taking part of the food gathered by the mother.

7. Another variant of *mouth-nipple-contact deterrence*, in which a pigtail mother presses her infant back against the shelf to prevent access to the nipple.

8. A pigtail mother actively punishing (*punitive deterrence*) her infant in an attempt to induce it to break contact with her.

9. Bonnet infant initiating *social play* while maintaining contact with its mother. The extremely frequent *passive-contact* behaviour of the mother provides early and repeated access to peers for bonnet infant.

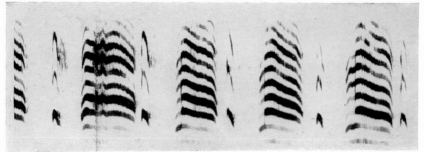

10. Sequence of 'basic' cries; 4-day-old healthy full-term male infant. Fundamental frequency, 350-450 cycles per second. (For this and subsequent figures, spectrogams were written at twice the normal speed. Vertical axis: frequency range from 0-7000 cycles per second; horizontal axis: time, 4·8 seconds of recorded vocalization).

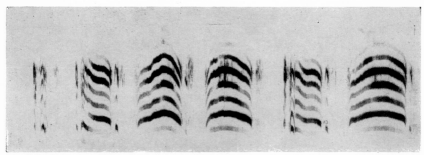

11. Same as Plate 10 – 6-day-old full-term female infant. Fundamental frequency, 300-400 cycles per second.

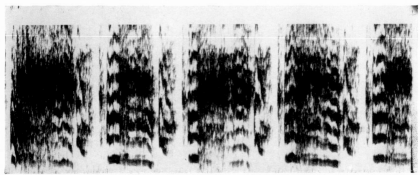

12. Sequence of 'mad' (angry) cries, in a normal full-term 4-day-old female after crying for 10 minutes and becoming increasingly excited. The black, fuzzy background reflects turbulence produced by excess air forced through the vocal chords.

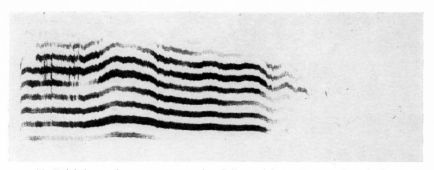

13. Initial vocal response to pain, followed by a 7-second period of silence in expiration.

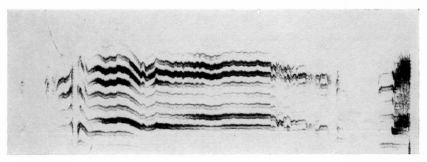

14. Initial vocal response after removal of a pacifier on which the baby was sucking and which had been given and taken away repeatedly. Although similar in form to the pain cry, this initial vocalization is not followed by a long silence in expiration.

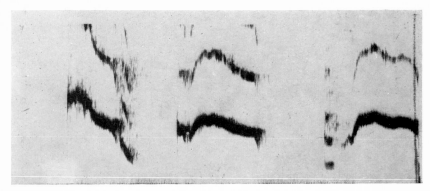

15a. Cry of 4-day-old, full-term infant with perinatal complications: rupture of membranes, 26-hour labor, anoxia at birth, marked lethargy during the first two days after birth and hyper-reflexia thereafter. Fundamental frequency, 650-700 cycles per second.

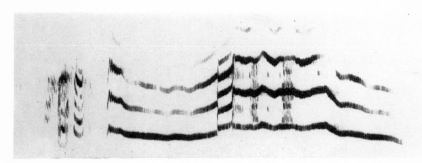

15b. Cry of 4-day-old full-term infant with many minor cephalic congenital malformations but no chromosome abnormalities.

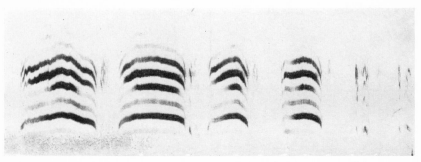

15c. Sequence similar to that of Plates 10, 11; for comparison.

16. 'Fake' cry or vocal signal not obviously related to distress, and not immediately followed by crying; normal 4-week-old male.

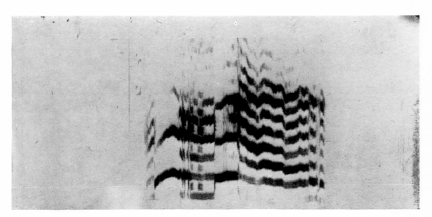

a

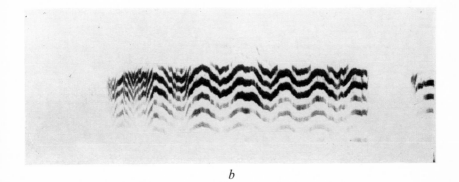

b

17. Transition from non-cry vocalization *a*, to fussing or early crying *b*, over a 3-minute observation.

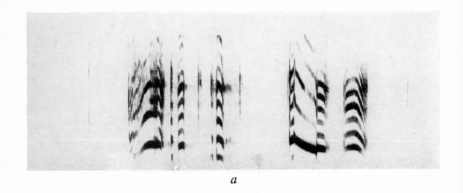

a

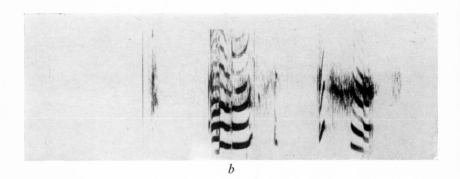

b

18. Transition from non-cry vocalization *a*, to fussing or early crying *b*, over a 3-minute observation.

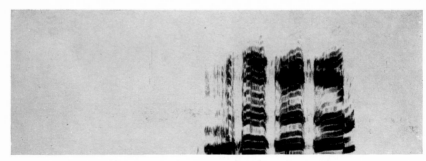

19. Laughter in response to tickling arm pit and abdomen: normal 5-week-old male.

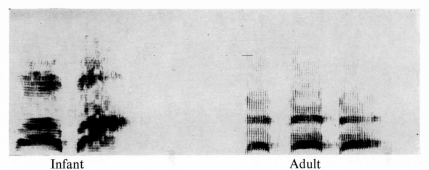

Infant   Adult

20*a*. Vocal 'imitation'.   Male adult's effort to imitate 9-week-old
female infant's lalling.

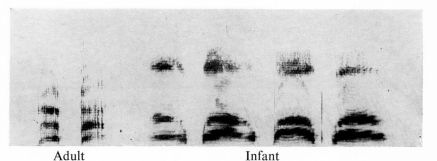

Adult   Infant

20*b*. Vocal 'imitation'.   Provocation of lalling in same infant;
adult makes baby sounds while infant is silent.

(Spectrograms written at normal speed; vertical axis: frequency
range from 0-4000 cycles per second; horizontal axis: time, 2·4
seconds of recorded vocalization.)

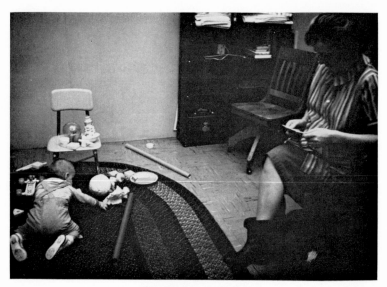

21. Brian explores.

22. Brian comes to
his mother briefly.

23. Brian responds to the stranger.

24. Brian hugs his mother when she returns.

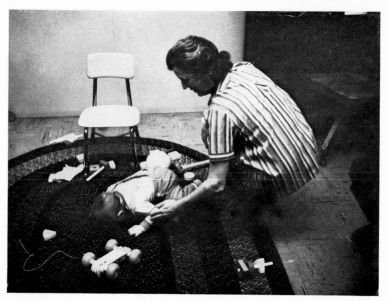

25. Brian throws himself on the floor when his mother puts him down.

26. Brian maintains contact with his mother.

27. He turns to her with a cry and clings.

28. Brian cries and rocks when left alone.

29. Brian is comforted by the stranger.

30. Brian clings when his mother returns again.

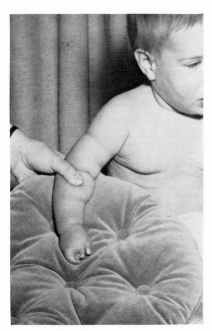

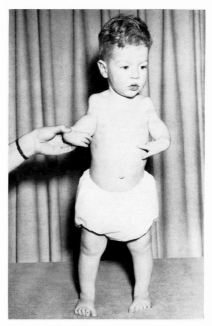

31. Pyc. Dystactylia and
syndactylia of the right hand.

32. Gil. Bilateral paraxal hemimelia by absence of radius.

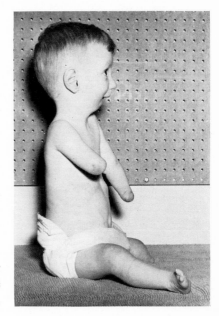

33. Rol. Dysgenesis of four
extremities. Hypoplasis of mandible
and aplasia of the tongue.

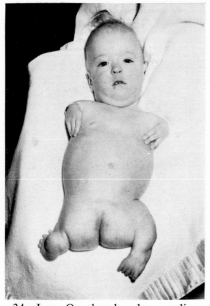

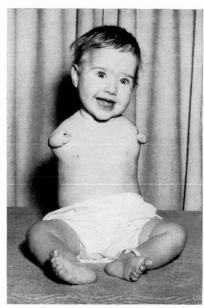

34. Jup. Quadruple phocomelia.

35. Lit. Bilateral phocomelia of upper extremities.

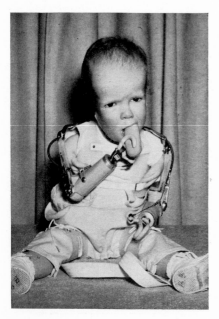

36. Beb. Bilateral phocomelia of upper extremities. Dysgenesis of the right ear.

Nora – subject 14 – was very active in Episode (2), and very excited by walking, which was a new accomplishment. She returned to her mother several times, however, and each time her mother's hand went down to meet her hand as it reached up slightly, in perfect timing. She went to the stranger twice in Episode (3), but to her mother three times. After her mother had left she played give-and-take games with the stranger. Just before her mother returned, she gestured that she wanted to be picked up, but when her mother entered she twisted round, leaning towards her mother with a great smile. She then approached her mother and reached to be picked up. Her mother held her a moment, but soon let her down. Nora indicated with a smile and a subtle lift of her head that she wanted to be picked up again. Then followed a period resembling Brian's Episode (5), in which she resisted any increase of distance, but she did not cry even though she clung. When Nora's mother left the second time she elaborated on the instructions. She said: 'Bye-bye, I'll be back soon. You stay here and be good'. Nora was good. She vocalized a slight protest, and stood at the door for a moment; later she went to her mother's chair and held on to it for a while; but she did not cry, and she played a little. She played with the stranger's bangles in Episode (7) and approached her mother eagerly when she returned a second time. While her mother was absent, she gave the observers the clear impression that she was waiting for her to return, and that she was by no means indifferent to her mother's whereabouts.

Nora's history is quite different from the histories of the other Group A babies. Like the mothers of the Group B babies, Nora's mother could interpret her baby's subtle signals with sensitivity. She responded with delight to Nora's positive signals and found her very entertaining and endearing. She was less responsive to distress signals, however, because she did not want to spoil her by picking her up or by feeding her on slight cues. There were three older siblings, and for Nora's first 18 weeks she spent much of her waking time closed up in her own room to protect her from overstimulation by the siblings. When she was taken up she was held most of the time – by her mother, her father, or her grandmother who lived most of the time with the family. The chief tension between Nora and her mother came during feeding, but much of this was resolved when she was given a bottle to take to bed with her and to manage by herself. Nora had much freedom to explore – but less than Joan. Her mean I.Q. for the first year was 127·4.

Summary of Group A. Nora is a child who seems as firmly attached to her mother as any child in Group B. She is the definitive case that demonstrates that there can be attachment without marked disturbance in minor separation situations. Joan, although bright and competent, may indeed be less strongly attached to her mother than the children of Group B. The other two children in Group A were intermediate between Joan and Nora. In regard to history, it is clear that Joan and these other two had, during one period or another of the first year, substantially less interaction with their mothers – or with anyone else – than had the children of Group B. Nora, however, seems to have had at least as much interaction as Matthew in Group B – although perhaps less physical contact. Although during her first quarter-year she was protected from overstimulation, she received more attention than Joan did – and more than did any of the others in Group A.

Group C

Group C divides itself into two sub-groups, the first consisting of subjects 5 and 12, who seemed very baby-like and helpless in the strange situation, and the second consisting of subjects 11 and 13, who, although certainly not helpless, behaved less adaptively than the children of Groups A and B, especially in response to the stranger.

Karen – subject 5 – arrived in the experimental room cuddling into her mother with her head down on her shoulder, the only child in the sample who showed no apparent interest in the strange room. After she was put down, she sat still, without budging, although she was quite capable of crawling, and she did not manipulate the toys at all. She looked unhappy when the stranger first entered, and became increasingly unhappy through Episode (4). When her mother got up to leave she went into a full-blown cry, stiff, red in the face and kicking her feet. The stranger picked her up, and, although Karen seemed a little less distraught when held than when put down, she was not comforted. When her mother returned and picked her up, Karen stopped crying and cuddled into her; but her mother put her down almost immediately and tried, with a frantic air, to interest the child in toys. Karen cried again, and, despite her mother's efforts to distract her, was still unsettled when her mother left the second time. She screamed non-stop, alternating between sitting rigid, kicking her feet, and hunching about in a random crawl. In Episode (7) her interaction with the stranger was as before. When her mother finally returned,

132

the stranger handed Karen over; but again the mother put her down quickly and tried to get her to play. She continued to scream. The observer intervened to tell the mother to pick her up. Karen snuggled in, and was soon able again to smile at the world.

Karen's mother is a warm and delightful person, but suffers from episodes of acute anxiety when she becomes fragmented and very tense. There are five children in the family, closely spaced – so, if the mother is a harried housewife, she has justifiable grounds.

For her first six months Karen was kept most of the time in her own room with the door closed. Her mother's policy was not to pick her up if she merely cried, but only if she screamed. But her screaming tended to be muffled by the distance and by the closed door. Moreover, her mother could tune her out, either not hearing her crying at all, or believing that she heard happy, singing noises. Karen would announce that she was hungry by screaming, but even after her mother acknowledged that it was time to feed her, there was often a long delay while she readied her food, and dealt with the interruptions provided by the other children.

When she was ill or teething it seemed that nothing pleased her. Her mother, not being able to find a way to comfort her, interpreted her persistent fussing as a desire to be alone. Although she protested being put down in the crib, she would eventually quiet there, whereas if she were kept up she continued to fuss. So her mother sometimes left her in her crib for several days at a time, getting her up only for necessary routines.

Sometimes, when the mother was in the mood for it, she engaged in long sequences of warm, gay, affectionate, and highly stimulating playful interaction. At such times she responded to Karen's every fleeting expression or subtle gesture. When so stimulated Karen became gay and active, and was capable of feats that were not in her ordinary repertoire of behavior. We gained the distinct impression that her play behavior was released chiefly by her mother's stimulation, and that everything that was given to Karen, whether food, warmth or play, was given according to her mother's timing and not her own.

At home she was usually more active than she was in the strange situation. But even there her exploration tended to be visual rather than locomotor or manipulatory, and she seemed a very passive baby. Her mean I.Q. was 110·8, and is as high as this because her mother participated in the test sessions and helped to evoke Karen's interest and activity.

Summary of Group C. The other three in Group C cannot be described here, except to say that one was even more passive than Karen, one – had been consistently over-stimulated at home, and the third was notable for a strikingly aversive response to strangers both at home and in the strange situation. They are diverse, but they have in common the trait of low frustration tolerance, and the experience that their own actions have no consistent consequences, because so much that happens to them is the result of the mother's timing, not theirs.

Summary and Discussion

The behavior of this sample of babies in a strange situation may be summarized as follows:

1. These babies could and did use the mother as a secure base from which to explore a strange situation, showing more locomotor, manipulatory and visual exploration when alone with her in Episode (2) than in any other episode, and crying less when she was present in Episodes (2) and (3) than in any subsequent episode.

2. They tended not to be disturbed by the presence of a stranger when the mother was also present, and to show minimal disturbance, if any, even when the stranger made advances. Even when the mother was absent they tended not to withdraw from the stranger, and some babies could either play with or be somewhat comforted by a stranger.

3. They responded to minor separation from the mother with decreased exploration and increased crying, but not necessarily with immediate and intense distress. Attempts to regain the mother were conspicuous. There was however a cumulative effect of the various episodes, so that a second separation evoked strong responses, either strong efforts to regain the mother or intense distress or both.

4. The most typical responses to reunion with the mother after a minor separation were approach behavior on the first occasion and clinging on the second occasion.

5. Before separation these babies did not protest cessation of physical contact, but after separation they showed a desire to maintain physical contact by either stopping crying or clinging tightly when picked up, and by either crying or clinging when put down.

Despite the satisfactory level of statistical significance of the group trends, the findings of this study cannot be generalized beyond white, middle-class American one-year-olds who have been reared much as these babies were reared. What was characteristic of these babies was not entirely characteristic of the Ganda infants (Ainsworth, 1963) or of Schaffer & Emerson's (1964) Glasgow babies. We are convinced that methods of infant care affect the development of attachment, and interact with biological growth processes to make for cross-cultural differences in the way attachment is manifested.

Nevertheless, the findings of this study, as well as the previous study of Ganda infants, support the hypothesis that one of the important criteria and functions of an infant's attachment to his mother is his ability to use her as a secure base from which to explore the world. This does not imply that a full-blown attachment must precede an interest in exploration. On the contrary, it is believed that the development of attachment interacts with the gradual development of competence through exploration and manipulation, one affecting the other. The infant's developing abilities provide him with new modes of interpersonal interaction, and it is at least in part through these that the attachment manifests itself and indeed through which it grows. Thus, for example, Susan's walking to her mother to play give-and-take games with her is a manifestation both of competence and attachment. Similarly, part of competence is social competence, and is undoubtedly influenced by feed-back in infant-mother transactions, as White (1963) suggests.

There is no doubt that the separation of a young child from his mother can produce distress and that, under certain circumstances, such separation can produce long-lasting adverse effects – as reviews of the literature amply document (e.g. Bowlby, 1951; Ainsworth, 1962). Moreover, distress even in minor and everyday separation situations is one criterion of an infant's growing attachment to his mother (e.g. Schaffer & Callender, 1959; Schaffer & Emerson, 1964; Ainsworth, 1963, 1964). This present study, however, supports the contention that distress in minor separations cannot be taken as the sole criterion of attachment. Among those in this sample who protested intensely when separated from the mother were some whose protests reflected strong attachment and others whose attachment was full of ambivalence or anxiety. Among those who responded with minimal distress were babies who seemed to have relatively weak attachments, but also at least one child whose attachment was strong – and secure enough to enable her to sustain a precocious equilibrium in a minor separation situation.

Although all of the babies in this sample responded to the mother differently than they did to a stranger, there was only one who showed

135

a consistently aversive response to strangers both in the strange situation and at home. The behavior of this sample as a whole demonstrated a remarkable acceptance of strangers without in any way diminishing the impression of attachment to the mother. Thus, although fear of strangers cannot be considered wholly unrelated to infant-mother attachment, this study suggests that stranger anxiety is in a one-to-one relationship to neither attachment nor separation anxiety – a view that has been previously advanced by Ainsworth (1963), Benjamin (1963), Schaffer & Emerson (1964) and Tennes & Lampl (1964).

The fourteen babies of this sample were disparate in many ways – both in details of behavior in the strange situation and in the way they had been reared – and still none could be described as lacking in attachment to the mother. Harlow's (1963) infant monkeys with motherless mothers who were extremely abusive or indifferent nevertheless attached themselves strongly. The development of attachment is not easily discouraged; it can be distorted, but it takes more deprivation than is represented in this sample to discourage its growth altogether.

Although all the babies in this sample were attached to their mothers in some quality and to some degree, it is obvious that the nature of mother-infant interaction differed widely. A cursory examination of the longitudinal data has suggested several variables in mother-infant interaction which seem to foster the growth of healthy attachment, while at the same time fostering the growth of competence: (*a*) frequent and sustained physical contact, especially during the first half of the first year, together with the mother's ability to soothe a distressed baby effectively through physical contact; (*b*) the mother's sensitivity to the baby's signals, but, even more important, her ability to time her interventions in harmony with the baby's rhythms; (*c*) an environment which is so regulated that the baby can derive a sense of the consequences of his own actions, and come to feel that what he does can have some consistent and hence predictable effect on what happens to him, so that the feed-back he receives promotes feelings of efficacy (c.f. White, 1963); (*d*) freedom to explore and to learn, first in a visual-motor sense and then later through locomotion. Finally, (*e*) these data suggest that a highly important interactional variable is the mutual delight the mother and baby take in their transactions with each other.

The Effect of a Strange Environment on the Behavior of Infants[1,2]

HARRIET L. RHEINGOLD

The strangeness of a stimulus affects behavior. In a strange environment, for example, many animals explore little and show 'emotional' responses (see Berlyne, 1960, and Welker, 1961, for reviews). Although the effect of a strange *person* upon the behavior of *human* infants has often been studied — most recently by Morgan and Ricciuti (see pp. 253-272), and Caldwell — the effect of a strange *environment* has less often been investigated. Of special relevance for the present studies are two reports; Bayley's (1932) that the strangeness of place and persons during psychological tests was one cause of crying in infants and Arsenian's (1943) that crying and 'autistic' gestures appeared in children, 11 to 21 months of age, when they were placed alone in a strange room.

In the animal studies, most of the subjects had been raised in laboratories and hence it may be assumed that they had experienced a restricted environment. Similarly, Arsenian's subjects were reared in an institution and thus, according to her, might have had less experience in strange environments than home children. When the studies to be reported here were begun, it was expected that human infants reared in normal environments – assumed to provide varied stimulation – would not be as distressed as organisms from narrower environments.

In a series of four experiments, the effects of a strange environment upon the behavior of different groups of infants approximately 10

[1] These investigations were supported by a Public Health Service research career program award (HD-23,620) and a Public Health Service research grant (HD-01107), both from the National Institute of Child Health and Human Development.

[2] I thank R. A. Helwig, H. R. Samuels, and M. Simner for serving as observers, and N. Bayley for the use of the Bayley Developmental Scales. I am especially grateful to H. R. Samuels for analysing the data.

months of age were investigated. This age was chosen as the earliest at which reasonably proficient creeping could be expected. In the first experiment, the strange environment was empty; in the second experiment, it contained toys; and in the third, it contained a person. For a different group of subjects in each experiment, the strange environment contained the subject's own mother. In the fourth experiment, the effects of the four conditions – empty, toys, person, and mother – were simultaneously examined in still other groups of infants.

The mother's presence was used to provide a contrasting condition; it was known from preliminary work in the laboratory that subjects at this age would creep around the room and not cry in an environment that contained their mothers. Arsenian's (1943) data, although the subjects in her study were somewhat older than those here reported, supported these observations.

The main purpose of the studies was to discover the effect of a strange environment upon the infant's behavior. A second purpose was to measure the effect of prior exposure to the environment *with* the mother upon subsequent exposure without her (the effect of familiarization). A third purpose was to measure the effect of prior exposure *without* the mother upon subsequent exposure to an environment now containing her (the persisting effect of a strange environment).

Two classes of responses to the environment were selected for study in each experiment: vocal behavior, which was considered to be a measure of emotional responses; and locomotor activity, which was considered to be a measure of exploratory behavior.

Experiment 1

Method

Subjects

The Ss were 10 normal white infants, 4 male and 6 female. They ranged in age from 9·1 to 10·1 months; mean age was 9·6 months. Mean D.I.Q. on the Bayley Infant Scale of Mental Development was 112, with a range from 104 to 126. The mean D.M.Q. on the Bayley Infant Scale of Motor Development was 114, with a range from 94 to 127. Their fathers had an average of 16·6 years of education; range was 11 to 20 years. Their mothers had an average of 14·9 years of education; range was 12 to 16. As a group, therefore, the Ss were somewhat above average in developmental status, and they came from homes of above average educational level.

The *S*s were obtained by telephoning mothers of infants born at the University of North Carolina Memorial Hospital. Rate of refusal was negligible. Age was the primary criterion for selection. The records of subjects were discarded only if they could not creep (three *S*s in this experiment), or if before the test was begun they did not easily allow the experimenter (*E*) to take them from their mothers (none in this experiment).

The Strange Environment

The strange environment was a room not seen by *S*s before the experiment (Figure 25). It was approximately 9 ft wide, 18 ft long,

FIG. 25 The strange environment. Infant is in the start cell;
the toys identify cell 52.

and 9 ft high. The walls were painted off-white and the floor was covered with an embossed white vinyl material. An electric baseboard heater of gray metal on the right wall was 4 ft wide and 7 in high. In general, the room presented a relatively homogeneous environment; there was little to attract *S*s' attention and nothing in it of an obviously fear-provoking nature.

The floor was marked by means of $\frac{1}{4}$ in -wide buff-colored masking tape into a matrix of 18 cells, each approximately 3 ft square. Lighting was provided by four 150-watt cove lights on the right wall; incident light at floor level was approximately 7 ft-candles. On the left wall there were two one-way vision mirrors, each approximately 3 ft above the floor; from these windows, observers (*O*s) outside the experimental room followed and recorded *S*s' behavior.

Procedure

On the day before the test, *S*s and their mothers spent an hour in the laboratory to adapt *S*s to the general environment and to *E*. Immediately upon first entry to the laboratory, each *S* was given a pretest: he was placed in a crib with three toys in a small examining room for 3 min, while *E* and the mother, in an adjoining room, observed his behavior through a one-way vision window. If an *S* cried before the end of 3 min the pretest was ended and the mother and *E* returned at once. The pretest was designed to insure that all the *S*s who could not stay alone in *that* environment would not by chance be assigned to one or the other groups. The *S*s who lasted three minutes were called 'tolerators'; the others, 'non-tolerators'. On the adaptation day, the Bayley Scales of Mental and Motor Development were also administered.

On the test day, *S*s were carried into the strange environment by *E* who talked softly to them and placed them in cell 22 (column 2, row 2 in Figure 25) in a creeping position, facing the long axis of the room. As a signal to time the trials, *E* said 'Start' when *S* was placed, then left the room, closing the door.

Duration of a trial was 3 min. At the end of 3 min, *E* entered the room, picked *S* up, and carried him to an adjoining room. The intertrial interval was 1 min. During the interval *S* did not see his mother, but *E* talked to him, showed him a toy, and patted him if he was emotionally upset.

The mother, when present, sat on a cushion on the floor in cell 52 (column 2, row 5), facing the infant. Each mother was told that she could look at and smile to *S* and could put an arm around him if he required support, but she was directed not to talk to *S*, play with him, or entice him to come to her; she was not, on the other hand, to push him away.

The Measures

Vocal Responses. From tape recordings of the infants' vocal responses two measures were calculated: *latency of crying* and frequency of non-distress *vocalizations*.

Latency of crying was the number of seconds from *E*'s placing of *S* in cell 22 until onset of *S*'s crying. Crying was defined as continuous, rhythmical, wailing sounds. Typically the onset was sudden, following a holding of the breath. The crying was often loud. It had the characteristics of a cry of pain and appeared to be as distressing for the infant to experience as it was for the observers to hear. As a response measure, it was used only for these acute sounds, and was sharply differentiated from such milder distress vocalizations as protests and fusses.

Frequency of *vocalizations* was the number of 30 sec periods in which there occurred discrete voiced sounds of a non-protest, often cheerful, nature.

All the measures reported are the average of measures made independently by the 2 *O*s. Observer agreement for each vocal measure yielded product-moment correlations of ·99.

Locomotor activity. On a plan of the floor drawn on paper, two *O*s traced *S*'s path through the room and recorded the second at which he crossed successive lines. From these timed tracings, three measures were calculated: *number of lines crossed, time to cell* 52, and *time in cell* 52.

Number of lines crossed was simply the number of lines *S* crossed or touched, including lines bounding the perimeter of the room. *Time to cell* 52 was the number of seconds from *E*'s placing of *S* in the test environment until *S* entered cell 52; it measured time to contact with mother. *Time in cell* 52 was the number of seconds *S* was in cell 52. When the mother was present, it measured time in proximity to, or in contact with, her.

Again, all reported measures are the average of the two *O*s' measures. The product-moment correlations of agreement between the measures of two *O*s were ·99 for lines crossed; ·99 for time to cell 52; and ·94 for time in cell 52.

A few words are necessary to explain that *S*s were removed from the room when they gave the distress cry and to point out the effect of their removal upon the other measures. Once an infant gave the distress cry, it was observed that he continued to cry without abatement. The longer he was allowed to cry, the less the possibility of calming him in the intertrial interval and therefore of carrying him through subsequent trials. Furthermore, it was observed that *S*s who cried did not creep around the room. They stayed in the start cell, lying on the floor, face down, or at most they crawled to the entrance door and *stayed* there. It follows then that when a *S* was removed, measures of locomotor activity were based on the assumption that, had he been allowed to stay, he would not have crossed any more lines. The data on locomotor activity are therefore less firmly based in reality than the data on latency of crying.

Duration of trial was longer by some seconds than latency of crying, because *E* waited to make sure that *S* would not recover spontaneously. As a measure, it was of course related to latency of crying.

Plan of Experiment 1

The ten *S*s were assigned at random to two groups, Group A and Group M, subject only to the requirement that each group contain an equal number of tolerators.

For both groups there were 5 trials, each planned to be 3 minutes in duration, with an intertrial interval of 1 min. For Group A, *S*s were placed in the strange environment for the first four trials without their mothers and for the next trial with their mothers. For Group M, *S*s were placed in the same environment but with their mothers present for the first two trials, with their mothers absent for the next two trials, and with their mothers present again in the last trial (Table 15).

The effect of the strange environment was measured by comparing the performance of the two groups in trials 1 and 2. The effect of familiarization was measured by comparing the performance of the two groups in trials 3 and 4. The persisting effect of the strange environment on responses to the environment now containing the mother was measured by comparing the performance of Group A in trial 5 with the performance of Group M in trials 1 and 2. In passing, attention will be drawn on occasion to the effects of experimental conditions *within* a group. Within-group effects were not tested but they offer additional confirmation of the findings.

Two measures, latency of crying and number of lines crossed, were subjected to statistical test. The Mann-Whitney test was used, and all *p* values are two-tailed. Other measures (e.g., frequency of vocalizations, duration of trial) are reported in the text or the tables but differences between them were not tested.

Results

Two trials of each experimental condition were planned in order to obtain a more representative sample of behavior. The results, however, showed a marked difference between the two trials in all experimental conditions except those in which the mother was present from the beginning. Where differences between trials occurred, the results of each trial will be considered separately.

Effect of the Strange Environment

The differences in performance between Groups A and M on trials 1 and 2 provide a measure of the effect of the strange environment.

In trial 1, four of the five Ss in Group A cried when placed alone in the environment. Mean latency of those who cried was 12·5 sec; mean latency for the group was 46·0 sec. (Table 15). In trial 2, all

TABLE 15

Design of Experiment 1 and Means of Measures

Groups and Measures	Trials				
	1	2	3	4	5
Group A	Alone	Alone	Alone	Alone	Mother
Latency of Crying	46·0″	5·6″	3·3″	0·3″	73·5″
Lines Crossed	4·0	0·6	0·7	0·2	7·6
Duration of Trial	86·5″	21·0″	7·0″	2·5″	157·8″
Group M	Mother	Mother	Alone	Alone	Mother
Latency of Crying	180·0″[a]	180·0″[a]	65·5″	45·0″	99·8″
Lines Crossed	15·9	13·7	6·5	1·9	6·8
Duration of Trial	180·0″	180·0″	87·9″	55·3″	180·0″

[a] Indicates that no S cried.

5 Ss cried with a mean latency of 5·6 sec. In contrast, no S in Group M cried at any time during trials 1 and 2. If, for statistical purposes, 180 sec is taken as a measure of latency for Ss who did not cry, the difference between the groups in latency of crying was significant ($p < ·01$).

Measures of vocalizations support the findings on measures of crying. No S in Group A uttered a vocalization of a non-protest nature, but all Ss in Group M vocalized one or more times in both trials. Specifically, Group M Ss vocalized during 3 or more of the 6 30-sec periods in trial 1, and during 2 or more periods in trial 2.

The findings on vocal behavior therefore indicate that a strange environment without the mother produced crying; with her, it did not. Her presence, instead, supported vocalizations of a non-protest nature.

Locomotor activity was minimal in Group A (Table 15). In trial 1 they crossed a mean of 4·0 lines, and in trial 2, a mean of 0·6 lines. Group M, in contrast, crossed 15·9 lines in trial 1 and 13·7 lines in trial 2. The difference between the groups on trial 1, although large, were not statistically significant; on trial 2 it was reliable ($p < ·01$); and on both trials combined, it was also reliable ($p < ·01$). The strange environment entered alone therefore inhibited locomotor activity; the presence of the mother in the strange environment supported it.

The responses of Group A on the whole differed markedly from trial 1 to trial 2; in trial 2 they cried sooner and crossed fewer lines. The responses of Group M, on the other hand, were similar from trial 2.

No *S* in Group A went to cell 52 in trials 1 and 2. In the absence of the mother, then, *S*s did not enter cell 52. All of Group M, however, went to cell 52. In trial 1 they took 30·5 sec to reach it and spent 97·7 sec there; in trial 2 they took 33·9 sec to reach it and spent 93·6 sec there. Once again, the behavior of Group M showed considerable similarity from trial 1 to trial 2, thus providing a standard with which to compare Group A's behavior.

Effect of Prior Exposure with the Mother

In trials 3 and 4, *S*s in Group A were placed alone in the strange environment for the 3rd and 4th consecutive times. Group M *S*s, in contrast, were placed in it alone for the first time, following two trials in which the mother had been present and during which they had an opportunity to become familiar with the strange environment. All *S*s in Group A cried, as they had in trials 1 and 2, and they cried earlier on each successive trial (Table 15). But now, 4 of the 5 *S*s in Group M cried in both trials 3 and 4. Latency of crying, however, was greater on each trial than Group A's on the same trials ($p < ·01$ for trial 3, $p < ·05$ for trial 4).

In passing, it can be seen that Group M on trials 3 and 4 responded much the same as Group A on trials 1 and 2.

Prior exposure *with* the mother therefore postponed crying, when compared with prior exposure *without* the mother; but at the same time the data also show that the strange environment when encountered for the first time by the infant alone produced a measure of distress.

144

Locomotor activity was also reduced for both groups in trials 3 and 4 (Table 15). Group A crossed less than one line in each trial. In contrast, Group M crossed 6·5 lines in trial 3, a performance that was reliably different from Group A's ($p < ·05$); they also crossed more lines in trial 4, but here the difference was not statistically significant. These findings show that prior exposure with the mother supported more activity on the first trial when alone than prior exposure without the mother. By the second trial, the effect of familiarization had disappeared.

Locomotion to cell 52 is also of interest here. As in trials 1 and 2, no S in Group A went to cell 52 in trials 3 and 4. Now that it is clear that Ss did not go to cell 52 if the mother did not occupy it, the next question asks whether Ss, who had gone to cell 52 when the mother was there, would go there in her absence. The data show that only one S went to cell 52 in trial 3, and that he stayed there for only 2 sec; none went in trial 4.

In summary, prior exposure with the mother had an effect – it postponed crying and supported locomotor activity. At the same time, the effect of being alone in the strange environment was marked: Ss of Group M cried now, although they had not in trials 1 and 2, and they crossed fewer lines.

Persisting Effect of the Strange Environment

How did the responses of Ss to an environment now containing the mother, after four trials alone, compare with the responses of Ss to an environment that contained the mother from the beginning? The differences in latency of crying and in number of lines crossed between trial 5 for Group A and trials 1 and 2 for Group M are large (73·5 sec versus 180·0 sec for latency of crying; 7·6 versus 15·9 and 13·7 for number of lines crossed) but are not statistically significant. Nevertheless, three Ss in Group A cried at a mean latency of 2·5 sec. Of these three Ss, two did not go to the mother.

The findings, then, are not straightforward. It is clear, however, that the performance of three of the five Ss was markedly affected; for them, there was a persisting effect. The mother's presence therefore did not dissipate distress and support activity in all Ss.

It may also be seen that Group M's performance in trial 5 was markedly different from its own performance in trials 1 and 2. Some Ss cried (latency of crying for the group in trial 5 was 99·8 sec) and they were less active (6·8 lines crossed in trial 5 versus 15·9 in trial 1

145

and 13·7 in trial 2). All Ss, however, went to cell 52 and reached it in less time than in trials 1 and 2 (16·9 sec versus 32·2 sec) and stayed with the mother longer (131·2 sec versus 95·1 sec). As a group they too showed the effects of being alone in the environment for the preceding two trials.

Some subject variables of interest, such as sex of Ss, and whether tolerator or not, will be evaluated later for the four experiments combined.

Summary

The results of this experiment show that a strange environment, of the kind studied here, inhibited exploratory behavior and evoked emotional distress. For a control group of Ss, the same environment containing the mother supported exploratory behavior and, instead of crying, evoked many non-protest vocalizations. When the mother was removed, this second group explored less and eventually cried, but they nevertheless explored more and took longer to cry than the Ss who had been placed in the strange environment without their mothers. Familiarity with the environment had an effect. Also, the mother in the environment did not uniformly inhibit distress and support exploratory behavior in all Ss, if they had first been exposed to the strange environment by themselves. The effect of the strange environment persisted. Lastly, successive entries into the environment were anticipated by many Ss who cried earlier and earlier.

Experiment 2

Because the strange environment by itself produced so much apparent distress and supported so little exploratory activity, toys were added to the room in this experiment. It was anticipated that the presence of toys might support behavior better than an empty environment and that their attractiveness might diminish the emotional response.

The number of trials in the strange environment without the mother was reduced from 4 to 2, because trials 3 and 4 for Group A in Experiment 1 added no new information on the effect of the strange environment. The design then was as follows: Group T (Toys) entered the room alone for trials 1 and 2 (Table 16). For trials 3 and 4, the toys were removed and the mothers were present in their place. Group M, on the other hand, entered the room with only the mothers present for trials 1 and 2 and then with toys instead of their mothers for trials

3 and 4. As a result, the effect of a strange environment which contained toys could be contrasted with the effect of one which contained the mother (trials 1 and 2 for Groups T and M). The effect of prior exposure with the mother could also be measured by comparing trials 3 and 4 for Group M with trials 1 and 2 for Group A. In addition, the effect of prior exposure without the mother upon responses to the environment when the mother was present could also be compared (trials 3 and 4 for Group T in contrast to trials 1 and 2 for Group M).

Method

Subjects

The *S*s were 8 normal white infants, 4 male and 4 female. They ranged in age from 9·6 to 10·0 months; mean age was 9·8 months. Mean D.I.Q. on the Bayley Mental Developmental Scale was 104; scores ranged from 96 to 114. Mean D.M.Q.on the Bayley Motor Developmental Scale was 106; scores ranged from 99 to 116. Their fathers had an average of 18 years of education, ranging from 12 to 23 years. Their mothers' education ranged from 12 to 17 years, with an average of 15 years. Subjects were obtained in the same way as in Experiment 1. The records of three other *S*s were not used; two could not crawl and one could not be removed from the mother before the beginning of the test.

The Strange Environment

The room was the same as in Experiment 1. In the toy condition, 4 colorful toys were placed on the floor close to the start cell; they were a pull toy containing marbles, a large plastic bolt with nuts, a large ball, and a string of wooden beads.

Procedure

Duration of trials was reduced from 3 to 2 minutes. Since the early onset of distress had markedly reduced the duration of trials for *S*s without their mothers, a shorter length of trial might serve to equalize duration of trials between the two groups. As before, two groups of *S*s were formed by random assignment.

In all other respects the experiment was carried out in the same way as Experiment 1. The same measures were used, and again all scores were the averages of the measures recorded independently by 2 *O*s. Product-moment correlations of agreement were ·99 for latency of crying; ·98 for periods in which vocalizations were heard;

·97 for number of lines crossed; ·96 for time to cell 52; and ·91 for time in cell 52.

Results

Effect of the Strange Environment

The responses of the two groups in trials 1 and 2 show the effect of the different environments.

All Ss in Group T cried in trials 1 and 2; latency of crying was 36·2 sec in trial 1, and 2·0 sec in trial 2 (Table 16). Group M behaved differently – none cried in either trial. Furthermore, no S in Group T

TABLE 16

Design of Experiment 2 and Means of Measures

Groups and Measures	Trials			
	1	2	3	4
Group T				
Latency of Crying	Toys 36·2″	Toys 2·0″	Mother 63·2″	Mother 62·8″
Lines Crossed	4·2	0·0	7·6	10·8
Duration of Trial	55·6″	2·2″	101·1″	90·0″
Group M				
Latency of Crying	Mother 120·0″a	Mother 120·0″a	Toys 120·0″a	Toys 66·0″
Lines Crossed	16·2	10·6	4·8	5·4
Duration of Trial	120·0″	120·0″	120·0″	115·0″

a Indicates that no S cried.

vocalized, but all Ss in Group M did; as a group they gave one or more vocalizations in 3 of the 4 30-sec periods in each trial. These findings indicate that, even with toys in it, the strange environment produced an emotional response. With the mother present, the same environment produced no distress but instead evoked vocalizations of a non-protest nature.

With so shortened a trial and with so much emotional distress, Group T crossed only 4·2 lines in trial 1 and none at all in trial 2 (Table 16). Group M Ss were much more active; they crossed 16·2 lines in trial 1 and 10·6 lines in trial 2. The difference between the groups was statistically significant ($p < ·05$).

The toys in the environment might have been expected to evoke some manipulation from Group T. Actually, the response was minimal. In trial 1, only one *S* manipulated a toy briefly before crying. Of the three other *S*s, one looked at the toys and two just touched one of the toys. In trial 2, none made contact with a toy.

No *S* in Group T went to cell 52 in either trials 1 or 2. All *S*s in Group M, in contrast, did go in both trials. They took a mean of 17·1 sec to reach the mother in trial 1 and of 36·8 sec, in trial 2. In trial 1 they spent 47·1 sec in proximity to the mother, and 71·9 sec in trial 2.

Effect of Prior Exposure with Mother

The performance of Group M in trials 3 and 4, when contrasted with that of Group T in trials 1 and 2, supplies a measure of the effect of prior exposure with the mother. Whereas all *S*s in Group T cried in trial 1, no *S* in Group M cried in trial 3 (Table 16). Moreover, three of the 4 *S*s vocalized, but not as freely as during the two preceding trials with the mother (for the group, vocalizations occurred in only one of the 4 30-sec periods). All *S*s in Group M, furthermore, manipulated the toys throughout the entire trial.

The conclusion, then, is that familiarity with the environment eliminated crying, fostered vocalizations, and encouraged manipulation of the toys; in every respect, they behaved differently from *S*s who entered the same environment without prior familiarization.

In trial 4, however, latency of crying was 66·0 sec (Table 16). Now, only one *S* vocalized and only 2 *S*s manipulated toys – and then for only part of the trial. The effect of familiarity had been dissipated.

Persisting Effect of the Strange Environment

In trials 3 and 4, Group T faced an environment that previously had occasioned distress but that now contained the mother. The group means show that Group T *S*s cried earlier in both trials than Group M in trials 1 and 2 (who in fact did not cry at all). They also crossed fewer lines in trial 3 than Group M in trials 1 and 2 (Table 16). These differences, however, although large, were not statistically significant.

Examination reveals the reason for the lack of significance. Two *S*s in Group T cried almost at once in both trials upon seeing their mothers and one of these stayed unmoving in the start cell. The other two *S*s did not cry, vocalized, went to cell 52, and moved about the room in a fashion similar to all *S*s of Group M in trials 1 and 2.

For the group, then, the effect of exposure to the strange environment did not persist. For two of the four *S*s, however, the effect was marked – they were emotionally distressed by the mother's appearance.

Summary

The strange environment, even when furnished with toys, proved to be distressing; *S*s cried early and tended not to move around the room. But, as in Experiment 1, the same environment with the mother in it, supported exploratory behavior and occasioned no distress. Prior exposure with the mother had an effect: *S*s did not cry, moved about, and played with the toys – for one trial; on the next trial they behaved as did *S*s without prior exposure. The appearance of the mother, after experience with the toys, produced distress in some *S*s but not in others. Toys in the strange environment, therefore, were no substitute for the mother, unless the mother had first been part of that environment. Even then, toys supported behavior for only one trial.

Experiment 3

Since toys did little to alleviate the distress caused by the environment alone and did not support locomotor or manipulative activity, the presence of a human being, it was thought, might serve *in loco parentis*. Typically, it has been observed that infants visiting the laboratory smiled freely to staff personnel. Therefore, it was expected that a person would support more exploratory behavior and produce less emotionality than the empty room alone or furnished with toys.

The person was a young woman, pleasant in appearance and in general accustomed to infants. She had not been previously seen by the subjects of this experiment.

Method

Subjects

The *S*s were 8 normal white infants, 4 male and 4 female. They ranged in age from 9·9 to 10·5 months; mean age was 10·1 months. Mean D.I.Q. on the Bayley Mental Developmental Scale was 107; range was 96 to 122. Mean D.M.Q. on the Bayley Motor Developmental Scale was 104; the scores ranged from 99 to 112. Their fathers' education ranged from 14 to 20 years, with a mean of 18 years. The education of their mothers ranged from 11 to 18 years, with a mean of 15 years. They were obtained in the same way as *S*s in Experiment 1, and were assigned at random to two groups, Person (P) and Mother (M). The record of one other subject was discarded because of fussing when taken by *E* before the beginning of the test.

Procedure

The experiment was carried out exactly as Experiment 2. Two *O*s independently recorded the same measures as in the previous experiments and the data reported are always the means of their observa-

TABLE 17

Design of Experiment 3 and Means of Measures

Groups and Measures	Trials			
	1	2	3	4
Group P	Person	Person	Mother	Mother
Latency of Crying	38·9″	8·0″	6·8″	—
Lines Crossed	0·1	0·0	0·8	—
Duration of Trial	47·0″	13·5″	51·8″	—
Group M	Mother	Mother	Person	Person
Latency of Crying	113·5″	120·0″[a]	44·0″	5·6″
Lines Crossed	5·9	16·1	2·8	0·2
Duration of Trial	120·0″	120·0″	79·9″	29·2″

[a] Indicates that no *S* cried.

tions. Product-moment correlations of their agreement on the two sets of measures ranged from ·97 for lines crossed to ·99 for all other measures.

The design of this experiment was similar to that of Experiment 2 (Table 17). For Group P in trials 1 and 2 the person was in the room, and in trials 3 and 4 the mother was in the room, instead of the person; for Group M, in contrast, in trials 1 and 2 the mother was in the room, and in trials 3 and 4 the person, but not the mother, was in the room.

When present, the person or the mothers sat in cell 52 on the cushion. The person and the mothers followed similar directions; they could look at *S* and smile to him; they could put out an arm to support

151

him as necessary if he stood near them; but they could not talk to an
S or play with him.

In this design, the responses of *S*s to the strange environment
containing a person could be compared with the responses of other
*S*s to the strange environment containing the mother (trials 1 and 2
for both groups). The effect of prior exposure with the mother upon
entering the same environment which now contained another person
would appear in a comparison of trials 3 and 4 with trials 1 and 2
for Group P. And, finally, the effect of prior exposure with the person
in the environment can be measured by comparing responses of
Group P in trials 3 and 4 with trials 1 and 2 of Group M.

Results

Effect of the Strange Environment

All Group P *S*s cried in trials 1 and 2; latencies were 38·9 and 8·0
sec (Table 17). In the M Group, by contrast, only one *S* cried – in
trial 1 at 94 sec; and none cried in trial 2. The difference in latencies
between the two groups was statistically significant ($p < ·05$).

Vocalizations were produced by three *S*s in Group M in trials 1
and 2 (during 3 or more of the 4 30-sec periods in trial 1 and during
all 4 periods in trial 2). Two *S*s in Group P also vocalized but only
in trial 1 and then for only 2 of the periods.

The strange environment containing the person therefore produced
an emotional response in all *S*s; once again, the strange environment
containing the mother, on the whole, did not.

Locomotor activity in Group P was minimal (Table 17); only one
S in trial 1 was judged by one *O* to have crossed one line – from 21
to 11 (that is, toward the door by which he entered). Group M however, crossed an average of 11·0 lines for trials 1 and 2. It can therefore
be concluded that the presence of the person in the strange environment all but suppressed locomotor activity and that, once again,
the presence of the mother supported it.

As in previous experiments, the second entry into the strange
environment without the mother proved to be more distressing than
the first. Group M, on the other hand, responded similarly on both
trials.

Again, too, no *S* in Group P went to cell 52. In Group M, 3 *S*s in
trial 1 went to cell 52 in 37·5 sec, and all 4 *S*s in trial 2, in 31·9 sec.
Duration of time in cell 52 was 61·8 sec for trial 1, and 48·1 sec for
trial 2.

Effect of Prior Exposure with the Mother

Group M cried in trial 3 when placed in the room which now contained the other person (3 Ss of 4). Latency of crying was 44·0 sec (Table 17), almost the same as for Group P on trial 1 ($p > ·60$). No vocalizations were heard during the trial. Mean number of lines crossed was 2·8. Although they crossed more lines than Group P on trial 1 (0·1 lines), the difference missed statistical significance ($p < ·114$).

The second entry (trial 4) was again even more distressing. All Ss cried at a mean latency of 5·6 sec. Number of lines crossed was 0·2. In none of these measures was their performance reliably different from Group P's on trial 2.

In trial 3, one S did go to cell 52; she not only entered the cell but seated herself in the person's lap. There she sat, unmoving, her back to the person, sucking her thumb. In trial 4, neither she nor any other S went to cell 52.

Two periods of familiarization with the mother, therefore, did not reliably alter Group M's response to the environment when it subsequently contained the person. In trial 3 they did cross more lines but the difference was not reliable. Still, one S not only approached the person but stayed in contact with her, a response not shown by any S in Group P.

Persisting Effect of the Strange Environment

All Ss in Group P cried in trial 3, that is, when entering the strange environment which now contained the mother (Table 17). Latency of crying (6·8 sec) was reliably different from Group M's on trials 1 or 2 ($p < ·05$), and even shorter than on their own first entry when the person was present (38·9 sec). Three Ss in Group P did not move out of the start cell, even with the mother present. The group mean of 0·8 lines crossed is therefore reliably different from Group M's performance of 5·9 lines crossed in trial 1 and 16·1 lines in trial 2 ($p < ·05$).

Trial 4 was not run because 2 Ss at the end of trial 3 were too distressed.

In this experiment, exposure to the strange environment containing a person affected the behavior of all Ss when they subsequently entered an environment containing the mother.

153

Summary

The presence of a person in the strange environment occasioned distress and inhibited physical activity. The presence of the mother supported behavior, as it had in Experiments 1 and 2. Prior exposure to the environment with the mother did not increase tolerance of the environment when it contained the person; and the effects of the environment continued to affect Ss adversely when the environment subsequently contained their mothers. All the measures suggest that the presence of a person in the environment was more disturbing for the Ss in this study than the toys had been for Ss in Experiment 2.

Experiment 4

In the previous experiments there was some evidence that toys were more effective in supporting behavior, and the presence of the person even more disturbing, than an empty environment. The main purpose of this experiment was to directly compare the effects of the three experimental environments within one design: the strange environment by itself, the environment containing toys, and the environment containing a person. In addition, to the extent that the procedures of this experiment resembled those of the other experiments, the results would serve to confirm the previous findings.

Method

Subject

The Ss were 24 full term infants, 6 in each group. They were randomly assigned to the four conditions as they entered the study, subject only to the requirement that each group contain an equal number of tolerators and non-tolerators.

The Ss were obtained in the same way as before. Of the 24, 11 were male and 13 female; 23 were white and one was negro. Their mean age was 10·0 months (range 9·7 to 10·5 months). Their mean D.I.Q. on the Bayley Mental Scales was 113·7, with a range from 98 to 133; mean D.M.Q. on the Bayley Motor Scales was 103·4, with a range from 88 to 125. Again, the educational level of the parents was above average for the group as a whole. Years of education for fathers ranged from 10 to 20, with a mean of 18 years. For the mothers, the range was from 11 to 18, with a mean of 15·5 years. On each of these subject variables, the four groups were markedly similar.

In addition to the 24 Ss in the study, the records of 3 other Ss were discarded because they could not creep proficiently, and 4 Ss were not run because they cried when E took them from their mothers before the start of the experiment.

Procedure

For the first two trials, Ss in Group A (Alone) were placed alone in the strange environment (Table 18). For Group T (Toys) in trials 1 and 2 the room contained toys; for Group P (Person) it contained a person; and for Group M (Mother) it contained the mother. In trials 3, 4, 5, and 6 it was planned that the mother would be present for all groups; that is, she was added to the environment for Group A; she replaced the toys for Group T, and the person for Group P; and nothing was altered for Group M.

Experiment 4 asked fewer questions and provided more direct answers. It focused on the differences between experimental conditions (trials 1 and 2) and since all four conditions were part of one experiment the differences could be directly compared. The effect of familiarization trials was eliminated. However, the persisting effect of initial trials upon subsequent trials in which the mother appeared could be compared. Furthermore, Group M would now provide a better standard for comparison with the other groups.

The conduct of the experiment was similar in most respects to that of the previous experiments. Three toys instead of the four of Experiment 2 were used; they were the same pull toy, beads, and the bolt-and-nuts of Experiment 2. The person was different from the one in Experiment 3, but again she was a young woman to whom infants in the laboratory generally smiled (although not seen before by Group P). Toys, person, and mother, in each condition, were placed in cell 52, a change made only in the case of toys in order to provide constant conditions. And, duration of trial was now 3 min as in Experiment 1.

The same measures of Ss' responses as in the other experiments were taken, except that vocal responses were calculated by 10-sec instead of by 30-sec intervals, to increase precision. This time, also, only one O recorded the number of lines crossed and the time at which they were crossed. The near-perfect agreement between two Os in the past permitted this revision. As a check, however, E, after starting Ss, observed through a one-way mirror in a room different from Os' and there dictated observations of their behaviour.

The Kruskal-Wallis test was used to test the differences between means and, again, all tests of significance were two-tailed.

Results

Data are available for all *S*s in only trials 1, 2, and 3. In trials 4, 5, and 6, more than half the *S*s of Groups A, T, and P could not be removed from their mothers at the end of trial 3 without exacerbating their distress, or could not be sufficiently calmed by *E* between trials 3 and 4. For Group M, in contrast, all trials were not only started but completed. This finding by itself tells a great deal about the effects of the experimental conditions.

Effects of the Strange Environment

All *S*s in Groups A, T, and P cried before the end of trial 1; but no *S* in Group M cried at any time during the trial (Table 18). Differences

TABLE 18

Design of Experiment 4 and Means of Measures

Groups and Measures	Trials		
	1	2	3
Group A	Alone	Alone	Mother
Latency of Crying	32·2″	0·7″	39·3″
Lines Crossed	3·3	1·0	1·8
Duration of Trial	68·5″	12·8″	104·5″
Group T	Toys	Toys	Mother
Latency of Crying	31·1″	0·7″	90·1″
Lines Crossed	6·0	0·8	5·0
Duration of Trial	81·3″	9·2″	158·0″
Group P	Person	Person	Mother
Latency of Crying	10·0″	0·0″	0·9″
Lines Crossed	0·7	0·5	3·0
Duration of Trial	58·3″	9·8″	150·2″
Group M	Mother	Mother	Mother
Latency of Crying	180·0″[a]	180·0″[a]	180·0″[a]
Lines Crossed	14·0	14·3	12·7
Duration of Trial	180·0″	180·0″	180·0″

[a] Indicates that no *S* cried.

in latency of crying among the four means were statistically significant ($p < ·01$). Although the latency of crying was shortest for Group P,

the means for Groups A, T, and P were not reliably different
$(p > \cdot 30)$.

In trial 2, all Ss except those in Group M cried almost at once.
They clung to E and resisted being placed in the start cell. As in
previous experiments, the second exposure provoked crying earlier.
And, although the latency for Group P was the shortest, as in trial 1,
the difference was small. The difference among the four means was
reliable $(p < \cdot 01)$ but, as before, the means for Groups A, T, and P
did not differ among themselves $(p > \cdot 30)$.

Once again, the strange environment produced crying except
when it contained the mother; but no reliable differences were found
among the three environments that did not contain the mother.

The occurrence of non-protest vocalizations tells the other half
of the story and by contrast supports the findings on the distressing
effects of the strange environment. Ss in Group M vocalized once
or more in 7·8 of the 18 10-sec periods in trial 1 and in 11·9 of the
periods in trial 2. Only one S of the 18 Ss in the non-mother groups
vocalized – an S in Group A vocalized during the first 6 periods
of trial 1. No vocalizations were produced by any of the 18 Ss in
trial 2.

In trial 1, fewer lines were crossed by Groups A, T, and P (Table 18)
than by Group M $(p < \cdot 01)$. Although Group T crossed more lines
than Groups A and P, the three means did not differ by statistical
test $(p > \cdot 10)$. In trial 2, the differences between Group M and the other
groups were even more marked $(p < \cdot 01)$, but again the other groups
did not differ reliably among themselves $(p > \cdot 50)$.

The data then show that locomotion was inhibited by a strange
environment – unless the mother was present. A second exposure
reduced the amount of locomotion still further; but Ss with their
mothers were as active on the second trial as on the first.

Of 18 Ss in Groups A, T and P only one entered cell 52 on trial 1.
In contrast, all of Group M entered the cell; they took 55·3 sec to
reach it and spent 61·2 sec there.

On trial 2, no S in Groups A, T, or P entered cell 52. Again, all
of Group M did; this time they took 19·2 sec to reach it and spent
103·7 sec there; thus, they reached the mother sooner and spent more
time with her than on trial 1.

The findings on trials 1 and 2, then, did not reveal a reliable
difference between the effects of the three experimental environments.

Persisting Effect of the Strange Environment

To measure the persisting effect of exposure to a strange environment, the responses of Groups A, T, and P in trial 3 (when the mother was present for the first time in their series) were compared with Group M's in trial 1. It will be recalled that no S in Group M cried then. Many Ss in the three experimental groups did: 5 in Group A, 3 in Group T, and 6 in Group P. The differences in latency of crying among the four groups (Table 18) were reliable ($p < \cdot 01$), but not among Groups A, T, and P ($p > \cdot 30$).

Duration of crying for the Ss of Groups A, T, and P who completed the session (that is, were judged to be not so distraught that they had to be removed) was calculated by the number of 10-sec periods in which any crying occurred. For Group A (3 Ss), the mean was 10·5; for Group T (5 Ss), it was 1·2; and for Group P (4 Ss), 7·0 periods. Thus, Ss of Groups A and P cried for longer periods of time on reunion with the mother than Ss of Group T.

The occurrence of non-protest vocalization, on the other hand, was highest in Group M. They vocalized during 7·8 of the 18 10-sec periods in trial 1; for Group A in trial 3 the number of periods was 0·3; for Group T it was 2·2; and for Group P, 3·0. Group M, thus, vocalized more than twice as often as the next highest group.

Groups A, T, and P crossed fewer lines than Group M in trial 1 (Table 18). The difference was significant at $p < \cdot 05$. Although Group T crossed more lines than the other two groups, there was no significant difference among the three means ($p > \cdot 30$). The mother's presence by itself did not support physical activity; it depended upon what had occurred before she appeared.

With the mother present in cell 52 for all groups, only 14 of the 18 Ss in Groups A, T, and P entered cell 52 – three Ss of Group A, and one S of Group P, did not. Again, all Group M Ss entered the cell, as they had in trial 1. Mean time to reach cell 52 for the 14 Ss in Groups A, T, and P was 13·7, 15·8 and 18·2 sec. Especially marked is the comparison of these times with the mean of 55·3 sec for Group M on trial 1. Furthermore, Ss of Group A, T, and P who went to cell 52 in trial 3 spent more time there (means were 132·7, 166·6, and 158·2 sec) than Group M in trial 1 (61·2 sec). Thus, they went faster and stayed longer.

The results show that the effects of exposure to the strange environment were apparent in the infants' responses to the mother's appearance. Fourteen of the 18 *S*s cried. They crossed fewer lines. Those *S*s who went to the mother crept faster and stayed with her longer than *S*s who had their mothers with them on the first trial. The presence of toys seemed to be least distressing: fewer *S*s cried; latency of crying was longer; more lines were crossed; and more *S*s entered cell 52. Nevertheless, on the two measures subjected to statistical analysis – latency of crying and number of lines crossed – no reliable differences were found among the three experimental conditions.

Summary

The results of Experiment 4 confirm the results of previous experiments. The strange environment – empty, with toys, or with a person – produced emotional distress and consequently inhibited locomotor activity. No differences were found among the effects of these different environments. When the mother was present in the environment, however, infants vocalized instead of cried and explored freely. The subsequent appearance of the mother for groups of *S*s previously exposed to the three strange environments resulted in behavior different in many respects from that of *S*s for whom the mother was present on trial 1: many of them cried, they vocalized less, they explored less, went to the mother faster, and spent more time with her. The effects of prior exposure were similar, however, among the three experimental conditions.

Additional Findings

The four experiments were sufficiently similar in purpose, procedure, and results to warrant pooling some of the data. Pooling serves two purposes: it reveals some effects most clearly and it permits the evaluation of some subject variables. Where appropriate, the Mann-Whitney test has been used to measure statistical significance.

Number of Lines Crossed

In the four experiments, the 31 *S*s who in trial 1 entered a strange environment without their mothers crossed a mean of 3·1 lines. The 19 *S*s who in trial 1 entered an environment with their mothers crossed a mean of 13·8 lines. The strange environment clearly inhibited locomotor activity ($p < ·001$).

Similarly, 19 Ss (in Exp. 1, 2, and 3) entered the strange environment without their mothers after familiarization trials with their mothers. They crossed a mean of 4.8 lines. The difference between the 4·8 lines and the 3·1 lines crossed by the 31 Ss who entered the environment without familiarization trails was small but reliable ($p < ·05$). Familiarization, it can be concluded, had an effect on locomotor activity.

Again, 31 Ss crossed a mean of 4·2 lines when their mothers were first introduced into the environment after two trials without her. When this finding is compared with the 13·3 lines crossed by Group M Ss in trial 1, the difference shows the persisting and inhibiting effect of exposure to a strange environment ($p < ·001$).

Time to and in Cell 52

In the four experiments, a total of 19 Ss entered the environment with the mother present on trial 1. Of these 19, 18 Ss or 95 per cent went to the mother. Similarly, in the four experiments, 31 Ss (on trial 5 in Experiment 1 and on trial 3 in Experiments 2, 3, and 4) entered the environment with the mother present, after exposure to it without her. Only 21 or 68 per cent of these 31 Ss went to the mother.

In trial 1, the 18 Ss of Group M took a mean of 37·5 sec to reach cell 52. The 21 Ss in Groups A, T, and P, in contrast, reached cell 52 in 17·6 sec, a reliable difference ($p < ·05$). Furthermore, Group M Ss spent 71·7 sec in cell 52; Ss in the other groups, however, spent 125·4 sec there. This difference was also significant ($p < ·01$).

Thus, a third of the Ss who had experienced an environment not containing the mother did not go to her when she appeared in the environment. Those who did go, however, went to her faster and stayed with her longer than Ss for whom the mother was in the environment on the first trial.

Effect of Sex

Sex was not a variable on which Ss were selected for the experiments or on which they were assigned to experimental conditions. Of the 50 Ss in the four experiments, 23 were male and 27 were female. This fairly even distribution of the sexes did not hold, however, within experimental conditions. Thus, of the 19 Ss in the four M Groups, 13 were male and 6 female; and of the 31 Ss in the other three groups, 10 were male and 21 female.

There was no difference of course on latency of crying measures between boys and girls in the M Groups on trials 1 and 2 – they did not cry. On trial 3, when Ss faced an environment without the mother, girls cried sooner than boys (84·6 sec in contrast to 105·0 sec), but the difference was not reliable. On trials 1 and 2 for Groups A, T, and P, latency of crying measures were very similar. Only on trial 3, when the mother appeared, did a difference occur. Boys cried at 18·0 sec and girls at 65·2 sec; this difference was significant at $p < ·05$.

Similar comparisons between the sexes were also carried out on the number of lines crossed. Again, on trials 1 and 2 for the M Groups, the number of lines was similar (e.g., on trial 1, 13·5 for boys and 12·8 for girls). Only one of the comparisons was significant: in trial 1, among the non-mother groups, girls crossed 3·8 lines and boys 1·8 lines ($p < ·05$).

In summary, the sex of the Ss appeared to have no consistent effect on their performance. Boys and girls responded similarly. Since sex was not a planned subject variable, a conservative attitude toward the two differences, of the many tested, seems warranted.

Effect of Pretest

As was explained under procedure, each S was given a pretest, and equal numbers of those who tolerated being left alone in a crib on the first visit to the laboratory were assigned to the experimental and mother groups. Within the four experiments there were 26 tolerators and 24 non-tolerators. Now, it may be asked if the tolerators and non-tolerators behaved differently in the various experimental conditions? When latency of crying and number of lines crossed were compared by experimental conditions, no differences were found between the performances of tolerators and non-tolerators.

Discussion

The four experiments agree in showing that a strange environment of the nature here used, produced distress and inhibited exploration in infants approximately ten months of age. When the strange environment contained the mother, even though she was permitted only a limited response by the design, infants showed no distress and moved about freely. The addition to the strange environment of toys or another person, in the absence of the mother, did not effectively reduce distress or support exploration. Although the data suggest that toys may have slightly ameliorated the effect of the strange

161

environment, and that another person may have exacerbated it, further testing did not confirm the suggestion.

The data also show that in some instances prior exposure to the environment with the mother – that is, familiarity with the environment – reduced distress and supported activity on subsequent entrances into the environment without the mother. This effect, although only temporary, appeared in two of the three experiments in which it was tested – when the strange environment was empty and when it contained toys, but not when it contained another person.

Exposure to the different strange environments without the mother affected the responses of the infants to the environment when the mother appeared in it in subsequent trials. Some infants, unlike those for whom the mother was present on the first trials, lay prone in the start cell, crying, and made no move to approach her. The other infants went to their mothers faster and stayed with them longer than infants for whom the mothers were present from the beginning.

Relationships between the Measures

Many of the measures in these experiments were obviously related. Latency of crying affected duration of trial ($r = \cdot78$). Number of lines crossed was also positively related to latency of crying ($r = \cdot66$). Early removal because of distress precluded the possibility of further locomotion, it is true, but observation forced the conclusion that crying infants did not move about. The measures of both Time to Cell 52 and Time in Cell 52 were derived from the timed measures of lines crossed. Furthermore, there was an inverse relation between manipulation of toys and locomotor activity. Lastly, vocalizations of a non-protest nature were of course inversely related to crying. On balance, the single measure which conveys the most information about the effect of the strange environment is latency of crying.

Nature of the Strange Environment

What were the characteristics of the room that were responsible for its distressing and inhibiting effects? The room certainly constituted a strange environment by definition – it was a room that no subject had seen before. There was, however, nothing in it of an odd, bizarre, or frightening nature. It was, to be sure, a bare environment, and its bareness may have contributed to its being different. On the other hand, the advantage of using a bare environment was that it could be precisely described and therefore would be reproducible. In these respects, it served as a standard value and, moreover, provided an environment to which new stimulus objects could be added.

The toys, as one set of stimulus objects, were known from preliminary observations to be attractive to infants of the age studied here. When they were presented together with the mother in pilot studies, they evoked sustained manipulation. That they did not function in the same fashion in the absence of the mother came as a surprise; so, too, did the failure of the person, the other stimulus object, to maintain normal behavior in the infants. Both the persons were laboratory personnel, accustomed to infants, and generally ready evokers of smiles in subjects.

The results show, however, that the infant's being alone in a strange environment offset the attractiveness of the toys and of the person. At least in the case of the person, the results suggest that she may well have been seen not as an attractive object but as a *stranger* in a strange environment.

Effects of Successive Trials

Two trials of each experimental condition were originally planned for the purpose of obtaining a representative sample of behavior. It soon became apparent, however, that the second of two trials, in any experimental condition that upset the child, upset him even earlier. Many *S*s began to cry as the door to the room was opened, and some were already crying in earnest as they were placed in the start cell. At least two explanations may be advanced: first, infants at this age are capable of such short-term memory and therefore anticipated the event; second, the practice of removing *S*s from the strange environment when they cried might have reinforced crying.

Two trials with the mother present in Experiments 1, 2, and 3 were planned for the purpose of providing familiarity with the environment. That it had an effect was apparent in Experiments 1 and 2. Nevertheless, further thought suggests that the attempt to familiarize the infants with the environment may have been attenuated by the *disappearance* of the mother and, even more so, by the *substitution* for her of toys or another person. By these alterations a familiar environment may have become less familiar.

Response to the Experimenter

All *S*s in the experiments allowed *E* to take them from their mothers before the beginning of the test. If they showed any distress, they were not used as subjects. The *S*s, thus, were infants who easily accepted separation from their mothers.

When the experimental condition produced crying, it was interesting to note that infants turned to *E* as they were picked up, and clung to her. All *S*s were sufficiently pacified by *E* during the intertrial interval so that the next trial could be instituted. When the next trial was a repetition of a condition which had occasioned distress, *S*s often clung to *E* and resisted being placed in the start cell. When an *S* lay, crying, in the start cell in the presence of his mother, he too came willingly to *E*, even though he would not go to his mother. These observations suggest that the infants became attached to *E*. They seemed to associate *E* not with the cause of their distress but with its relief, and they turned to her as the agent who would remove them from the emotion-provoking stimuli.

Instructive, too, were the responses to *E* of *S*s who entered environments in which their mothers were present from the beginning. Comfortable as they seemed in the test environment, they nevertheless came willingly with *E* at the end of the trial.

Response to the Mother

In these experiments the mother's presence constituted a major experimental variable. Her presence was used primarily to provide a set of reference points against which the other experimental conditions could be measured; the results uniformly justified her use for this purpose. In the presence of the mother, infants vocalized, did not cry (only one of 19 *S*s cried at any time in her presence on trials 1 and 2), and moved freely in the environment. The infants behaved much as they did in other rooms in the laboratory on the day before the test. The mother's presence, then, seemed to neutralize the strangeness of the environment.

The mother's presence had a different effect, however, on some infants after they had been exposed to the strange environment by themselves. Then, approximately a third of the infants became distressed. This is the more remarkable because the moment before, in the arms of the *E*, they apparently were not distressed. Not only did they cry when they saw the mother, but they did not creep to her. In fact, they stayed in the start cell and made no move to approach her. Some mothers volunteered that the infants were 'mad' because they did not go to the infants. Other mothers seemed to be upset and reacted to this behavior as though it were a rejection of themselves.

The records of the 10 *S*s who did not go to the mother were compared with those of the 21 *S*s who did go on a large number of variables (e.g., scores on the developmental scales, sex, birth order, age of parents, and whether mother worked outside the home). No reliable differences which might account for their behavior came to light.

One might surmise that the infants cried because their mothers did not speak to them. But this is not a sufficient explanation because other infants whose mothers were present on trials 1 and 2, and did not talk to them, did not cry. Also, it should be noted that infants exposed alone to the strange environment cried very quickly when they saw their mothers, before there was time for them to know that their mothers would not talk.

Although it was not the purpose of these experiments to study the attachment of infants to their mothers, the results do show the nature and extent of attachment at this age. Schaffer and Emerson (1964) also found that a specific attachment to a social object (usually the mother), measured by reports of the infant's behavior immediately after being left alone, reached a peak at 41 to 44 weeks of age – a finding in harmony with those presented here.

In studies in which acute distress is reported at separation from the mother (e.g., Schaffer and Callender, 1959), the distress has often been attributed solely to separation from her. When an infant is left in a strange environment with strange people, three sets of variables are operating simultaneously – a strange environment, strange people, and the departure of the mother. In the present studies, however, it is known that the departure of the mother occasioned no distress. Instead, the effect of a strange environment by itself was isolated for investigation. The results of the experiments show that it is a powerful enough variable in its own right to produce distress.

Conclusions

The findings of the studies reported here demonstrate that an unfamiliar environment had distressing and inhibiting effects upon the behavior of infants nine to ten months of age. Their responses resembled those reported by Arsenian (1943) for older subjects, aged 11 to 30 months, and thus show that the effect can occur in younger infants as well. Bayley (1932), too, found that strangeness (of the place and persons) during clinic visits occasioned most crying at 10 months of age. It is of course likely that even younger infants would

165

be affected by a strange environment, but for them locomotor activity would not be a possible measure.

Although the life experience of the subjects in the present studies was not a variable, the results show that the strange environment produced an effect upon infants reared in normal environments. It may be assumed that, unlike Arsenian's (1943) institutionalized subjects, these infants had been taken about by their parents. If the assumption is correct, the results then suggest that even with normally varied past stimulation a strange environment without the mother causes emotional distress.

The findings also show that human infants are as adversely affected by a strange environment as young mammals of other species. Like the young of dogs (Elliott & Scott, 1961) and of rhesus monkeys (Harlow, 1958), the human infant gives distress vocalizations. He does not, however, dash about, probably because at ten months of age locomotion is still effortful. More likely, though, he has already learned that crying by itself will prove effective in securing help.

The results show, too, that the presence of a familiar social object reduces the strangeness of a strange environment. Although it cannot be said that the environment is now familiar, it may be surmised that the strangeness is transmuted into novelty and as such supports the normal volubility and curiosity of children.

The emotional distress and inhibition of normal locomotor activity shown by the subjects of these studies leave no doubt concerning the sensitivity of infants at this age to a strange environment. The immediacy of their response illustrates the acuteness of their discrimination of places, things, and persons.

A Study of the Mental and Emotional Development of the Thalidomide Child[1]

THÉRÈSE GOUIN DÉCARIE

"L'idée du progrès reçoit, avec l'atroce aventure des tranquilisants,
le coup le plus grave depuis Hiroshima.'
Le professeur Merle d'Aubigné, de la Faculté de Médecine de
Paris.

The preliminary investigation reported here is taken from a larger longitudinal study (essentially of a qualitative nature) of 33 thalidomide children and their mothers. These children were all born in the Eastern provinces of Canada between January and December 1962[2] and their parents have qualified for assistance under the special program of the federal-provincial governments of this country. They were examined at the Rehabilitation Institute of Montreal, a highly specialized hospital for congenital and traumatic amputees, diseases of the brain and spinal cord with residual disabilities and other miscellaneous disabling diseases.

The goals of this long-term project are manifold: for the moment, let us emphasize only one of its essential features. We are trying to find out what kind of interrelationship might evolve between mother and child in the case of infants suffering from congenital malformations. To our knowledge, the thalidomide tragedy offers unique elements for such a research: (a) we have access to a population earlier than most investigators studying cases of congenital malformations (still in our opinion, this was too late; our youngest child was 17 months at the time of the first evaluation); (b) with the exception of

[1] This study is supported by the Canadian Council of Medical Researches and is a joint-project of the Institute of Psychology of the University of Montreal and the Rehabilitation Institute.
[2] One child, a girl with phocomelia of both lower limbs, was born as early as December 1961, the mother, a Canadian citizen, having obtained Contergan while visiting her own mother in Germany.

cases where the mother contracted rubella during pregnancy, it is the first time that the etiology of the congenital deficiency is known and that, in most cases, the deficiency itself is anticipated prior to the birth of the child. We assume that the fact that the cause was a drug, usually prescribed by a physician and taken orally to induce sleep or at least to reduce tension, might also influence in a specific way the subsequent relations of these children and their families; (c) we have the possibility seldom encountered in cases of severely handicapped subjects to study extensively both partners of the relationship. The children have already been evaluated once with a series of techniques (that I shall schematically describe), and they will be under observation over a period of years. The mothers have also been seen when the children were first hospitalized and the nature of their relationship will be systematically investigated in the coming months. The senior research assistant, Mrs Ethel Roskies, who is working on this half of the project, has borrowed Festinger's conceptual model (1957). The basic hypothesis is that the birth of a defective child arouses cognitive dissonance, placing the mother in a double bind situation in which she receives very contradictory messages from the implication of the 'defectiveness' and the 'my own child' connotations of the new-born baby.

The last step of the research will consist of course in putting together the two main sets of data: those relative to the children, and those relative to the mothers. Needless to say, such a project requires the constant collaboration of a team whose members belong to many disciplines (physiatrists, engineers, nurses, psychologists, prosthetists, psychiatrists, occupational therapists, social workers, pediatricians, etc.). Gratitude is expressed to all those who, for more than two years, have allowed the principal investigator to work with an absolute respect for the often impractical requirements of such a research and especially to my assistants for their unfailing enthusiasm. My thanks go particularly to Miss Monica O'Neill and Mademoiselle Réjane Rancourt who were responsible for the initial psychological evaluation of the 22 research-subjects and whose data I now wish to present and synthesize.

The thalidomide syndrome consists essentially in the absence or shortening of the long bones of the extremities such as the radius, ulna or humerus. Hands and feet defects can sometimes be corrected with plasters, but in cases of extreme shortening of extremities, prostheses are necessary. In a few cases of bilateral malformations of lower extremities, amputation of the feet was performed, a practice which appears rare in Germany and Great Britain (Ministry of Health, 1964).

'Usually both limbs are similarly deformed. Also notable is an accentuation of the nevus flammeus on the forehead, nose and upper lip. Wide-set eyes, low-set and occasionally deformed ears and depressed bridge of the nose are characteristic. A wide variety of associated anomalies, including malformations of the heart and

FIG. 26 Examples of several possible congenital malformations associated with thalidomide, from Blakeslee (1963).

digestive tract, are occasionally found, as are syndactylia and polydactylism.' (Blakeslee, 1963, p. 34).

In this paper, I have limited myself to the subsample of 22 children suffering from malformations involving either the upper extremities (hands and arms) or lower extremities (legs and feet) or both the upper and lower extremities. The severity of the malformation varies from a simple syndactyly to a quadruple phocomelia.[1]

Before describing *schematically* the main characteristics of our

---

[1] There is fortunately only one case of tetraphocomelia in the whole of our sample. The mental and emotional development of this child, Jup, constitutes a research in itself: one of our students, Mrs Gertrude Hill, has been working solely with this subject.

subjects, let me explain why we chose to concentrate this study on the cases of limb deficiency. Amongst the subjects affected by thalidomide, these are the children who present unusual methodological and theoretical problems. Let me focus on three of them formulating them in an interrogative fashion and inserting them in three different schools of thought. These are the points I would especially like to discuss with such a scholarly group as this one.

Problem number one: Of twenty-three articles bearing on congenital malformations associated with thalidomide and mentioning the intelligence factor, twenty-two express in a variety of ways what appears to be the universal belief: 'the intelligence of these children is, or seems to be, normal or above average.' Only one author challenged this statement; Illingworth writes: 'The effect which thalidomide has had on the child's intelligence is so far unknown, because there has not been time to assess it. It is obvious that it would be exceedingly difficult to assess the development of a limbless infant, yet one has seen statements that "thalidomide babies" are normal mentally. I saw one paper which purported to give the percentage of those babies who were mentally defective. As the figure given was considerably less than that of the population as a whole, the accuracy of the finding was questionable' (Illingworth, 1963, p. 42-43).

At the beginning of the research, we knew of no systematic evaluation of the intellectual development of these children. Since then, we have had contacts with Dr Helmut Strasser and Miss Gunhild Sievert of München who have worked independently on a much larger sample but on lines quite similar to ours (1964, 1965)[1]. We had to find ways of testing limbless children who had not yet reached articulate language. Most of the instruments at this level (be they the Gesell Developmental Schedules, the Cattell or the Hetzer-Bühler) are comprised mainly of items related to motricity or fine prehension. But how could locomotricity be evaluated in a child without legs, or eye-hand co-ordination in a child with no hands? Yet all those concerned with thalidomide babies were aware that no true rehabilitation was possible without the knowledge not only of the actual performance but of the learning capacities of these infants.

Problem number two: In a context radically different from the one of Baby Tests, Jean Piaget explains the growth of intelligence at the beginning of life by the gradual co-ordination of initially heterogenous and independent schemas, such as sucking, vision, kinesthesia, prehension, etc. One of his finest analyses (Piaget, 1936) shows how manual prehension

[1] Dr Mary E. Robinson, director of the Child Development Study of the Children's Hospital of the District of Columbia, Washington, has also been working with very young amputee children using selected items from the Griffiths, Bayley, Gesell, Cattell and Vineland (personal communication).

170

underlies the elaboration of the fundamental categories of intelligence: object-concept, space, time and causality (Piaget, 1937). But if prehension plays such an eminent role in the construction of the object-concept (and this concept determines the three others), what will happen, and we are not talking anymore of I.Q.s but of the structuring of intelligence itself, what will happen in the case of individuals lacking even the possibility of coordination between such essential schemas as sucking and prehension? How will such individuals reach, let's say, the last stage of object-concept and, will this acquisition appear at the expected chronological age or much later? A world without object-permanency is full of insecurity; would the thalidomide children live in such a world longer than normal children? We have always believed that even if Piaget is interested in what is universal and constant in mental functioning, the application of his theory to differential psychology (Gouin Décarie, 1953; Anthony, 1958; Flavell, 1963) could be extremely fruitful and one of the basic motives for this research (at least for the principal investigator) was the desire to test this important Piagetian hypothesis. As we shall see, this meant finding ways by which a child who could not grasp, walk or talk, could manage to convey to the experimenter his idea of the substantialization and localization of the vanished object and thus, allow us to place him in one of the six stages of sensori-motor intelligence.

Problem number three: The third problem was of course inspired by the ethological school and the stimulating re-interpretation of the nature of the child's tie to his mother by John Bowlby (1958). It concerns the emotional development of the thalidomide child in the absence of the behavior patterns of clinging and following.

If, besides sucking, crying, smiling, (and I wonder if Wolff's 'eye-to-eye contact' (1963, p. 122) should not be added here) clinging and following are instinctual behavior patterns that normally constitute basic elements of the tie of the human infant to his mother, what kind of attachment behavior will be observed in children for whom clinging (because of lack of arms) or following (because of lack of legs) is impossible? Will there by compensatory mechanisms? If so, from which partner will they originate? The mother? The child? Or through reciprocal adaptation?

These are some of the questions we asked ourselves. It remains for me to tell you how we went about trying to answer them and for you to judge what the answers are worth. I want to emphasize again before going on that this is but a *preliminary* report, but I do believe that one of the best features of such a meeting is the possibility of discussing here our trials and errors, our gropings rather than our well-proven discoveries.

171

The Sample

To describe in a satisfactory way a sample as heterogenous as ours, is a long and arduous process. We will present only the characteristics that appear relevant to the three problems under study.

Sex and Chronological Age

There are eighteen girls and only four boys. The subjects' ages range from one year 5 months to 3 years 8 months. Two-thirds of our sample (14/22) are between 2 years and 2 years and a half. Six children were less than 2 years while one subject, already mentioned, of German descent, was almost four at the time of testing (Table 19).

TABLE 19

Distribution of subjects according to sex,
Chronological Age (in years and months)
at the time of testing and hospitalization
(in years and months) (N= 22)

Sex	Age	Hospitalization
F	1 ; 5	0 ; 9$\frac{1}{2}$
G	1 ; 5	0 ; 8
F	1 ; 6	0 ; 6
G	1 ; 8	1 ; 4
F	1 ; 8	0 ; 6
G	1 ; 10	0 ; 6
F	2 ; 0	0 ; 6
F	2 ; 0	1 ; 6
F	2 ; 0	0 ; 5
G	2 ; 0	2 ; 0
F	2 ; 0	1 ; 3
F	2 ; 1	0 ; 3$\frac{1}{2}$
F	2 ; 2	2 ; 2
F	2 ; 2	1 ; 3
F	2 ; 3	0 ; 7
F	2 ; 4	2 ; 4
F	2 ; 4	0 ; 6
F	2 ; 5	2 ; 5
F	2 ; 5	0 ; 1$\frac{1}{4}$
F	2 ; 6	0 ; 2
F	2 ; 7	0 ; 3
F	3 ; 8	0 ; 3

Hospitalization

All of our subjects have been hospitalized at one time or another but the stay in hospital varies considerably irrespective of the age. Amongst the subjects that are between two years and two years and a half, four have spent all their lives in institutions, while the oldest subject of the sample (who is 3 years 8 months) has been away from home for only three months. (Table 19).

Malformations

An abbreviated description of the specific characteristic of the sample, that is the anomalies of the upper and/or lower extremities, is extremely difficult, since no two of the subjects present identical malformations.

Based on Webb's classifications (1963), Tables 20 and 21 give an idea of the distribution of our subjects in regard to their handicap.

TABLE 20

Classification of children's malformations according to degree of severity and to unilateral or bilateral limb involvement

Severity	Malformations of	Unilateral	Bilateral	Total
Least severe	Upper extremities	2	1	3
	Lower extremities	—	—	—
	Both upper and lower extremities	—	—	—
Intermediate	Upper extremities	—	3	3
	Lower extremities	—	—	—
	Both upper and lower extremities	—	—	—
Most severe	Upper extremities	—	10	10
	Lower extremities	—	1	1
	Both upper and lower extremities	—	5	5

The least severe malformations include minor defects of the limbs without complete absence of a part (Plate 31).

Intermediate deformities are varying combinations, which are not included in the other two categories, such as malformations below the elbow with limbs slightly shorter than average (Plate 32). In the most severe malformations, we may find the shortening of two or more limbs or even complete absence of a part (Plate 33).

TABLE 21

Upper extremity deformities classified by arm length, number of digits and side of the body affected

Arm length	Left side		Right side	
	Number of children with two or more digits	Number of children with one digit or no digit	Number of children with two or more digits	Number of children with one digit or no digit
Short	7	2	9	0
Medium	3	1	3	0
Long	8	0	8	1
Total	18	3	20	1

Choice of Techniques

To evaluate these severely handicapped children, we decided on a longitudinal method which will include, beside the initial evaluation, at least two follow-up periods. We used the following techniques:

(1) A specially devised system of observations of day-to-day behavior, divided in two sessions, one taking place in the ward, the second in occupational therapy;

(2) The Griffiths Mental Development Scale (1954);

(3) The Haeussermann Educational Evaluation (1958);

(4) The object-concept scale and the object-relations scale (Gouin Décarie, 1962).

What follows is a brief summary of the *first* data obtained with the Griffiths' test and with the two object scales. The analysis is limited to the three problems that are the focus of this paper.

Test Results: General Quotients and Developmental Profiles

We used two methods for scoring the Griffiths. The first general quotients and the first subquotients[1] were obtained without making

[1] The Griffiths is composed of the five following scales: A: Locomotor, B: Personal and Social, C: Hearing and Speech, D: Eye and Hand, E: Performance.

any allowances for the handicap: thus, the subject was penalized for every item he was unable to do because of the malformation[1]. The second score took account of the handicap in that any item below or at the chronological age of the subject, which, through a series of systematic observations, was determined as physically impossible for him, was automatically credited to him. Thus we have for each subject twelve scores, two profiles and, what we think might be a new measure of adaptation to the deficiency, the discrepancy between the scores obtained through the two methods. Because we believe that the score which takes the handicap into account best describes the child's true mental level (although this may be considerably

TABLE 22

Distribution of the 22 subjects according to I.Q.

Classification	Quotient	Number of subjects	Percentage of subjects
Superior	120–129	1	4
High average	110–119	2	9
Normal average	90–109	7	31
Low average	80–89	5	23
Borderline defective	73–79	4 ⎫	33
Mentally defective	below 73	3 ⎭	

higher than his actual achievement of course), we chose to limit ourselves in this paper to these second scores.

The mean developmental quotient is 90, with a SD of 16·91 and the median is 89 (Table 22).

'These scores show a distribution curve which is severely and positively skewed due to the fact that one-third of the subjects are concentrated along its inferior limits in the borderline and mentally defective categories. One half of the sample is situated within the normal limits and a very small number is found within the upper limits. There is no correspondence between the percentage of children found in any of the categories and the percentages found in the general average population, and the further one descends on the list, the more drastic is the discrepancy' (O'Neill, 1965, p. 90).

[1] This is the usual procedure and it was suggested by Doctor Griffiths to Doctor Helmut Strasser. The use of the two scoring methods that we have adopted does not imply any modification of the testing session.

Thus it seems that twenty-two optimistic authors were in the wrong and that Illingworth was nearer to the truth.

But even this statement has to be qualified, and one may ask before any hasty conclusion is reached whether there are any relationships between these general quotients and the three major variables of our sample: chronological age, degree of malformation and time spent away from home.

We have both older and younger children in all categories of I.Q.s and there is no continuous trend between the severity of the malformations (in terms of Webb's classification at least) and the general quotients. But a striking relationship appears when one compares

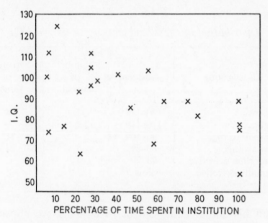

FIG. 27 Illustration of the relationship between the percentage of time spent in institution since birth and the intellectual quotient.

the time spent in institutions and the I.Q.s. Statistical calculation of the relationship between these two variables elicits a Pearson coefficient of correlation of ·76.

Figure 27 illustrates that amongst the children showing normal or superior intelligence, the time spent in institutions is smaller than amongst those who suggest mental retardation. There are four exceptions, where the low scores cannot be related to the length of time spent in institutions: the three children, who have an I.Q. below 80, present, beside the limb malformations, serious defects associated with thalidomide (facial paralysis, hearing defects, congenital heart malformation).

Thus it appears that when the environmental factor is taken into account, our sample (small as it is) can be divided in two groups: *group A* composed of what we call the family children, that is 14 subjects who spent an average of five months in hospitals and amongst whom, 10 are of normal or superior intelligence, the remaining 4 being below average, and *group B*, the institutionalized children (8 subjects) who have spent an average of twenty-two months and a half away from home and who, as could be expected, are all retarded, some slightly, others very severely.

At this point of the study, one could wonder if we were investigating, as planned, the effects of thalidomide on the mental development of

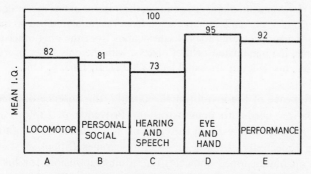

FIG. 28 The Griffiths developmental profile of the sample. The mean I.Q. is 85 with a SD of 13.86 while the median is 87.

the child or if we were not evaluating the effects of two different environments, home and institution, the effects of the latter having now been under scrutiny for more than a quarter of a century.

It is only when the five sub-quotients were compared to one another (that is the quotients of the five scales constituting the Griffiths) that another conclusion emerged: *regardless of the scoring method, regardless of the environment, there seems to exist a typical profile of the limb deficient infant and this profile is a rather unexpected one* (Figure 28).

The profile is not significantly altered if one divides the sample in the two groups: family and institution. This means that whatever the environment, the area of development most affected is language, although this scale, Hearing and Speech, (except for one case of tongue aplasia and two cases with hearing difficulties) is precisely

177

the one where we could expect the handicap to interfere the least. On the other hand, the Eye-Hand Scale[1] is the highest one in both groups.

This particular profile, which we think cannot be assimilated to any of the profiles discussed by Griffiths (1954), can be partially explained. We have a certain number of hypotheses as a starting point but they of course will have to be verified by further testing.

O'Neill hypothesizes that the relative elevation of the Eye and Hand Scale may be attributed to two factors:

'(1) interruption in the normal development sequence due to the limb deficiencies (either upper or lower) which especially interfere with loco-motor development, thereby resulting in the impetus in fine motor development. (2) lack of sufficient stimulation from the human milieu so that the child is forced to search for his satisfactions from the only other source available, the inanimate world of objects, with the only other instrument available, his deficient arms and hands.' (O'Neill, 1965, p. 136).

In the case of the institutionalized child, the absence of adequate stimulation needs no demonstration (Provence & Lipton, 1962), but it appears that even in the cases of home reared babies (and the fact is repeatedly stressed in other researches (Spock & Lerrigo, 1965) on handicapped subjects) the adult responsible for his daily care is not spontaneously inclined to compensate the infant's lack of initiative, and there is less interaction than with normal children. This could explain also the retardation in language development. Speech cannot be acquired without the presence of an *active talking* person.

The manner in which all these factors could interact requires further analyses.

Problem number two; As you know, in Piaget's view, the initial mental universe of the infants differs radically from that of the two-year-old child. It is not a universe of objects but one of 'perceptual pictures'[2]; these perceptual pictures are mobile, plastic, and are entirely centered on the action itself. It is a universe which has no permanent objects, no objective space, no time which establishes a relationship between events as such and no causality outside of the

---

[1] This scale, in the case of our sample, is falsely named because we granted such item as an D30 ('Can hold pencil as if to mark paper') even when this was done successfully with the toes, or with the mouth.

[2] Piaget does not talk about images to avoid confusion with mental images.

activity of the subject. Only gradually will things acquire the status of objects. What then is an 'object' for Piaget?

'What I call an object is a polysensory complex, i.e., something one can at the same time see, hear, touch, etc.; but a polysensory complex which in the eyes of the subject continues to have a durable existence beyond all perceptual contact' (Piaget, 1954, p. 59).

In other words, things become objects when they are conceptualized as permanent, substantial, external to the self, maintaining their own identity whatever the changes of position and remaining in existence even in the absence of direct perception.

In his work on the earliest stages of mental development, Piaget (1937) has used the different steps in the active search for the vanished object as criteria for the evolution of this object-concept. Thus, one can infer the presence of permanent objects in the infant's thoughts, when he searches *actively* for something which he no longer sees, touches, hears or smells: it seems obvious that if he continues to search in a certain way for an absent thing, he believes that it continues to exist somewhere in the external world.

The evolution from 'things' to 'objects' takes place gradually from the beginning of life to somewhere between 18-24 months: it corresponds partially to the six stages of general sensori-motor intelligence described elsewhere (Piaget, 1936). The object-concept, being a product of sensori-motor intelligence, is necessarily closely related to the gradual assimilation and accommodation of basic sensori-motor schemas such as sucking, vision and especially pre-hension. In the cases of children where some of these schemas are entirely missing, or if present, so deeply modified that coordination between them is impossible, it can be assumed that the evolution of the concept of the object would be different from what is seen in normal children.

On the basis of Piaget's observations, we had previously structured a nine point scale[1] of object-permanency which was administered to 90 normal babies whose ages ranged from three months to twenty months (Gouin Décarie, 1962). This scale consists mainly of oculo-manual items and allows the experimenter to locate a given subject at the beginning or at the end of any of the six rigorously ordered

[1] From now on, we are using the terms 'scale', 'item', in their widest meaning and outside of a rigid statistical context. It was never our intention to build a test. This holds true for the objectal scale further described.

stages of object-concept, that is from I a to VI b, 'a' representing the beginning of a stage and 'b' its terminal point.

Simply by administering this scale to our 21 subjects[1], and allowing them to use whatever ways they had to convey to us their knowledge of the displaced object (some children removed the screens with their mouth, others with their toes), we evaluated the level that had been reached in this particular dimension of intelligence.

The results were the following: 19 subjects, amongst whom was Jup, our case of quadruple phocomelia (Plate 34), reached the sixth and last stage of object-concept (VI b). Two subjects were below the sixth stage: one of them (Lit) having reached the second period of the fifth stage (V b) could find the vanished object if it had undergone not more than one invisible displacement. The other child (Jar) was still in the fourth stage (IV b), that is at the level of an active search, but without accounting for any visible displacement.

These two children were amongst the youngest of the group (one year five months), but age alone could not explain their performance: we had four other subjects, also less than two years old who had already reached the last stage. This means that even though severely handicapped and, in some cases, institutionalized since birth, all of our children between twenty-four and thirty-one months had reached the last stage of object-concept. Normally, this stage is reached between eighteen and twenty-four months. In the case of those children in our sample who were over two years old, we do not know when they reached this stage, but even if we assume the greatest possible retardation i.e. that this stage had just been achieved on the day of testing, the mean of the hypothetical delay does not exceed three months, ten days. Moreover, in the light of the fact that many of our children under 2 at the time of testing also had reached this stage, we have no reason to doubt that most of the older children had also reached this stage a few months prior to testing i.e. within the normal age range.

At first view, these data are surprising and contrary to our initial hypothesis: we had expected a very marked delay in the accession to the final stage of object-concept. A deeper analysis of the types of malformation in relation to the coordination of sensori-motor schemas offers some explanation of these initial results. If we use as a criterion of the functional use of the schemas, the capacity of the subject's hands (or digits) to meet one another in the mid-line, we

[1] One subject refused all of the Piaget's items.

see that it is easily done for 11 of the children. This remains possible, but with difficulties, for 8 other subjects: they can reach their hands and touch their mouth, nose, ears, but not their eyes, nor their hair, though these zones always remain accessible with their toes. There remain three children such as Lit (Plate 35) with no possibility of mouth-hand, hand-hand coordination. Amongst these three children, we find the two subjects who are below the last stage of object-concept and the child who refused to try the test. One must add that these children can reach the mouth with the help of a light and long object and even, in one case, hold such an object between the hands.

In other words, most of the subjects did not, in fact, lack the fundamental schemas required for the construction of the object-concept (though this was far from being apparent at first) and secondly, all of them could use substitute channels that led to such coordination as 'toes-mouth', 'eyes-toes', 'shoulder-chin-eyes', 'digits-toes', 'eyes-digits', etc. These results are in no way contra-dictory to Piaget's theory: the term 'schema' should not be taken in a restrictive sense and limited to an organ. In the normal child, prehension is mostly hand-prehension, of course, but the schema of prehension, like intelligence itself, has many different ways of reaching its goal.

I might add (in concluding problem number two) that the fact that the vast majority of our subjects had shown a remarkable development in regard to the conceptualization of the inanimate object is in complete agreement with the data obtained on the Griffiths' Test. Within the Griffiths, we saw that the highest scale is usually scale D, that is 'eye and hand', and it so happens that in the study previously mentioned on 90 normal infants, we had investi-gated the possible correlations between the six stages of object-permanency and the five subquotients of the Griffiths Scale. The highest correlation obtained was with scale D and it was highly significant.

Problem number three; This last problem refers to the emotional development of these children and more specifically to their object-relations. This term, considering what we were trying to investigate, seems more adequate than the expression: 'social relations' or even 'attachment behavior'. Social relations usually do not imply behavior patterns relative to inanimate objects, while attachment behavior

181

seldom refers to aggressivity towards the love object[1]; we believed, however, as postulated by the psychoanalytic theory of object-relations, that these are important aspects of the primary processes of socialization in the young child. This is why we chose to base our criteria of social development mainly though not entirely on indices that are especially meaningful in the context of the psychoanalytic theory.

Developmental psychoanalysis hypothesizes that, in the early stages, the evolution of object-relations can be expressed in terms of: (*a*) psychic structures, and particularly ego-development; (*b*) distribution and mode of libidinal and agressive cathexis; and (*c*) formation of the libidinal object. Using this theoretical framework, we had structured (simultaneously with the object-permanency scale) an object-relationship scale. This scale is an attempt to extend the theory operationally in that the behavioral characteristics of the developmental milestones are clearly defined and are elicited in standardized situations.

The indices vary greatly in complexity and reliability, some of them being analogous to well-known baby-test items while others such as one inspired by Spitz (1957, 1959) and Piaget (1945) have never, to our knowledge, been systematically experimented with[2]. Here we

[1] Ainsworth's excellent definition of attachment behavior 'Attachment behavior is behavior through which a discriminating, differential, affectional relationship is established with a person or object, and which tends to evoke a response from the object, and thus initiates a chain of interaction which serves to consolidate the affectional relationship' (1964, p. 51) would be very close to our approach if it read 'affective relationship' instead of 'affectional relationship'. Agressivity can be included in an affective relationship and we know that agressivity (rebuke, punitive measures, etc.) at a certain point of development provokes certain kinds of attachment behavior.

[2] To test for the presence of the seventh index: the semantic use of the gestural and/or verbal 'No' and 'Yes' (with or without an external model), we structured the following situation:

(*a*) The experimenter places in front of the child three lollypops of different colors and showing each one, asks him: 'You want one?' 'This one?' 'This one?' 'This one?'

If the subject does not immediately say *yes* verbally or by nodding the head, the procedure can be repeated 6 times with an actual offering of the candies.

If the use of the positive sign has not been elicited at this level, the experimenter can say: 'This one? Yes', matching his word with a nodding movement of the head (thus offering an auditory and visual model to the subject).

(*b*) The subject having indicated his choice of the lollypop (if the level of the verbal and/or gestural yes is not reached, he might do this with his hands or digits), the experimenter takes the lollypop and asks while beginning the throwing gesture: 'Shall I throw it away? Shall I?'

If the subject does not say *no* verbally or by turning his head from left to right

can only enumerate the general names of the behaviors which served as a basis for the construction of the scale:

(10) automatic or differential smiling;
(20) negative emotion upon the loss of a human being and/or the loss of an inanimate object;
(30) active manifestation of signs of affection;
(40) capacity to comply with requests and prohibitions;
(50) discrimination of subtle signs of communication;
(60) manifestation of jealousy without loss of the inanimate object;
(70) semantic use of the gestural and/or verbal 'no' and 'yes';
(80) self-restraint in the absence of the prohibiting adult.

Because of subdivision within the criteria, the scale finally yielded sixteen items which we hoped would allow us to evaluate a given subject fairly accurately in regard to his early social development. Of course, with such a technique, we did not expect a rigorous sequence, as in Piaget's stages of object-concept, where irreversibility of the stages is a fundamental aspect of the theory, but we knew that the order of some of the emotional behavior patterns is constant: automatic smiling always precedes differential smiling, the capacity to understand simple demands and prohibitions comes before the discrimination of closely related facial expressions such as the frowning and the surprised look.[1] We did expect the possible reversal of certain criteria such as the capacity to express jealousy coupled with an absence of manifestation of signs of affection.

The scale was administered to our twenty-two research subjects and a wide variety of protocols was obtained ranging from the absence of only one index to the failure of 13 of the 16 possible items.

---

and from right to left, the procedure can be repeated 6 times with an actual throwing of the lollypop.

If the use of negative sign has not been elicited at this level, the experimenter can say 'Shall I? . . . Oh no!', matching his word with a turning of the head from left to right and right to left.

One must note what type of response has been reached: gestural *no* with a model, gestural *yes* with a model, gestural *no* without a model, gestural *yes* without a model, verbal *no* with a model, verbal *yes* with a model, verbal *no* without a model, verbal *yes* without a model.

[1] This was already known to us because of the data obtained in the research with ninety normal babies. The objectal scale that is now referred to is simply an extension and a modification of this initial scale previously experimented with in this more extensive study. The last three criteria were elaborated by Réjane Rancourt so as to cover the age range from 20 to 30 months.

This is not the place for the detailed results and we shall only mention the major conclusion before going on with the problem of clinging and following. At the present level of analysis, our data show no relationship between the type of malformations and objectal development. A child suffering from severe malformations can show remarkable socialization, while a subject less handicapped may reveal a distressing lack of attachment to human persons.

This could mean that the absence of clinging and following in the cases of severe congenital malformations does not affect, at least in any specific way, the relationship of the thalidomide child with his love object, or, in other words, that these two behavior patterns which are usually believed to be universal are in reality not very influential in the primary processes of socialization. A closer look at our data qualifies such a clear-cut statement.

We had taken for granted that in cases of agenesis of upper extremities, there could be no clinging. This remains true of most of our subjects if we limit the definition of clinging to the grasping by the fingers accompanied by ventral contact with or without the bilateral enclosure movement of the arms (Mason, 1965); but if we extend this notion so that it means 'holding onto someone', we note that with the exception of Jup, the case of tetraphocomelia, all of the thalidomide children could cling. They do this mostly by embracing the adult with their legs but the small upper limbs and even the digits participate in the hold. Even Lit (Plate 35), who has only stumps, manages to hold on to her adoptive mother by her chin and shoulder, digging her head in the adult's neck and sustaining her weight with her legs. Beb, a severely emotionally disturbed child suffering from facial paralysis, lack of one outer ear and phocomelia of the upper limbs (Plate 36) has just begun, at two years, to cling actively. Up to now, she used to sit on the adult's lap, her head turned away from the person; now she approaches the sitting adult, face to face, pushes away whatever stands between her and the adult's waist (an apron, a hand bag, etc.) and completely envelopes one with her legs, the arms usually equipped with prostheses hanging limply. She stays firmly clasped supporting the whole of her weight even when the person rises from the floor or the chair to the vertical position. One has literally to unhook Bep and this is to her extremely frustrating, producing usually a violent tantrum that can last for more than an hour (one is reminded of the weaning tantrum on being put-down of Rowell's (1965) hand-reared baboon).

184

What seems of great interest here is the delayed reaction of clinging, in this subject. When we first saw Bep, she had been diagnosed as deaf and presented the psychological profile of a severely retarded child in all the fields of development except locomotricity and toe prehension. The tests clearly indicated nevertheless that the child reacted to sounds (Griffiths' tuning fork and bell, Haeussermann's graded sound blocks, etc.) but she did not respond to the human voice. She did not imitate human gestures on demand and had none of the typical responses before a mirror. The child had been institutionalized since birth. It is only after months of personalized care that the clinging behavior previously described appeared.

What we have said of clinging seems to hold true for following. We had also taken for granted that in cases of agenesis of lower extremities, there could not be any following: we have five subjects who present this type of malformation, which makes any comparison and generalization extremely hazardous. But within the restricted sample, all the children could follow and did so sooner or later. Sys, the only child with anomalies of the legs who was not placed in an institution, walked on her two feet, these being attached to limbs measuring eight and twelve inches, walking up and down stairs and following the mother around. Syr, though institutionalized since birth, had four different modes of locomotion and could follow one anywhere: the psychologist noted that she moved about: '(a) in her seat shuffling along with a kind of gallop crawl, (b) two hands together and two stumps together, (c) alternating left hand, left stump, and right hand, right stump, in a kind of coordinated creep, (d) standing on her stumps and holding on to wall and furniture'. Jup, with no arms and no legs, presents an unusual story in the development of motricity in general and particularly in regard to the capacity to follow. The visual motor orientation towards the human person, typical of the three-month-old baby, was (as could be expected) greatly delayed in her case, and it was only after establishing a rapport with 'a major mother figure' that Jup seemed to have discovered means of displacing herself without any prostheses, and finally finding ways of following the adult around.

The main steps of this evolution can be grasped through the systematic observations of Mrs Gertrude Hill:

March 2, 1965 – 2 years, 7 months: with upper and lower prostheses: plays 'hide and seek' by trying to find me visually where I last appeared but does not follow actively. Without prostheses: does not move on floor, prefers to be carried out and cries when put down. In my arms, she is practically motionless.

March 27: with prostheses: advances towards me for the first time as she spots me in corridor; follows up closely seeking bodily contact wherever I happen to move. Without prostheses: some movements towards me in crib; withdrawn and motionless at termination of session.

May 10: with prostheses: follows me closely from desk to drawer holding on tightly to my finger; when I loosen her grip, she 'freezes' and throws head back gazing toward ceiling.

July 19 – August 4: with or without prostheses: gradual widening of field of locomotion; increasing repertoire of 'cavorting activity', pursuit of objects across room; displaces herself on hip and side of head; the right side is preferred; the speedier the locomotion, the louder the vocalizations.

October 11: Being Thanksgiving, and no key to room BO9, Jup was given freedom to explore the hall which she crossed back and forth with dizzying speed, displacing herself on her right side: head, shoulder, hip or on her back: hips, back of head.

October 25: Exhibits distinct climbing behavior using whole body and the (rarely used) lower stumps.

January 1966: Acquisition of new lower prostheses seems to increase her autonomy and render locomotion more efficient in the vertical position.'

Brief (and selective) as they are, these observations lend some support to what was already suggested in the case of Beb, the child who manifested clinging only after personalized care had been initiated. In these children, the two behavior patterns of clinging and following, understandably enough, appeared much later than in non-handicapped children but to explain this delay simply by referring to the limb deficiency, does not appear entirely satisfactory: some subjects, though more severely handicapped than Beb, did nevertheless cling much earlier. For Jup, we have (unfortunately) no point of comparison, but it remains perplexing that in her case also, 'normal' behavior patterns emerged after attachment was already clear, and not the reverse.[1]

[1] In the case of this particular child, a learning theorist would probably explain the emergence of following through a process of learning that became possible only when the environment began to offer potent positive reinforcers. It would be fascinating indeed to analyze Jup's development *also* in this light. We completely agree here with Gewirtz (1961, p. 220) that 'Other potential unconditioned reinforcing stimuli, many perhaps even more potent than food

Is this specific of pathological cases or do we find something similar, in sequence at least, in any normal child? Or in other words, does the child become attached through clinging and following, these being instinctual behavior patterns of I.R.M. type as suggested by many authors? Or does the child cling and follow because he is attached?

This is not purely dialectical and reality might lie between these two alternatives: the child clinging and following because he is attached and becoming more attached through clinging and following.

I, for one, am inclined to believe that these two behavior patterns are the result of extremely complex processes both of a cognitive and affective order, closer to Piaget's circular reactions where there is a subtle interplay of assimilation and accommodation than to true innate release mechanisms. Also in the Piagetian line of thought, we could try to understand clinging and following by taking into account, as is necessary in any developmental psychology (on this subject, see a special number of *La psychologie française* (1965): La méthode génétique en psychologie), the whole of the evolution of the child: the end product throwing light on the genesis of the phenomenon. In this perspective, the sound of the rhesus infant can never be identified with the baby's vocalizations for one can only culminate in a system of differential signals (Hockett, 1959) while the other leads to symbolization and poetical thought.

It remains that we still know very little about the beginning, evolution and disappearance of clinging and following in the *normal* human infant. Bowlby, and many after him, frequently associate clinging and following with three other behavior patterns: sucking, crying and smiling, but our knowledge of the smiling response far exceeds our knowledge of clinging and following, or even of crying. . . .

And it might well be that further studies will show that the differences between these five behaviors are greater than their similarities, so that it would be impossible to characterize *all* of them as mainly instinctual behavior patterns.

and water, remain still to be studied for the case of earliest human learning'. In Jup's case, skin contact was certainly extremely important not only from the point of view of erotogenous gratification but as an immediate source of knowledge. In the same article Gewirtz also stresses (see note 6, p. 285) that the adult might have an important role to play as an agent that removes aversive stimulation; that was certainly true for this subject, Jup being unable to avoid noxious stimuli except by a closing of her eyes or a turning of her head.

The Longitudinal Course of Early Mother-Child Interaction - Cross-Case Comparison in a Sample of Mother-Child Pairs[1]

LOUIS W. SANDER[2]

The major content of this presentation will be devoted to three descriptions of the longitudinal course of interaction between mother and child pairs over the first 18 months of life. These three pairs are part of a sample of 22 mother-child pairs whose records are being analyzed as part of a naturalistic longitudinal study which has been going on at Boston University Medical Center since 1954. As research intensifies in the area of early mother-infant interaction, there is the opportunity to focus minutely on relatively small behavioral units. At the same time, there is a need to view these smaller units in their relation to broader interactional trends operating over longer spans of time. Empirical data of this latter sort is less frequently reported.

The descriptions which follow will not be a matter of three case histories of early development but will represent a particular approach to the study of interaction between mother and infant. They will illustrate a method of comparing certain sequences and trends in observational material across the sample of subjects. Both the approach and the method stemmed from our attempt to organize empirical data in the longitudinal study concerning the characteristics of the mother, the endowment of the infant at the neonatal level, the interactions between the two over the years of the study, and the systematic assessments of infant development and outcome. In

[1] This work has been supported thru USPHS Grants M898C_1, C_2; M-3325(C_1), (Formerly M-3923), M-3325 (C_2); K3-MH-20-505; and NAMH 1-925-00-561.

[2] Acknowledgment is made to the research associates whose team work made the longitudinal study possible. The data collection and analysis on the three subjects presented was particularly contributed to by Manon McGinnis, MSW; Ann Ross, Ph.D.; Ilse Mattick, B.A.; Gerald Stechler, Ph.D.; Abraham Fineman, M.D.

assembling these facets from the ground up, so to speak, we have had to deal with concepts about organization and the processes which mediate it. To do so we have turned to models from the biological sciences. This appeared to be an appropriate aspect of the work to mention at this conference, since it was Dr Bowlby's formulation of the nature of the child's tie to its mother that so vigorously stimulated the search for biological models which could be applied to early development. A further aim of this paper will be to illustrate the use we have made of ideas from biology.

The Interactional Data –
The Method of Longitudinal Course Comparison

Approach, method, and models have emerged together as we grappled with the task of data analysis posed by the longitudinal study. This was an exploratory, naturalistic yet an intensive, systematic multi-disciplinary investigation. It was launched by Dr Eleanor Pavenstedt, the founder of our Child Development Unit, for the purpose of providing clinicians with a clearer picture of the emergence of normal mother-child relationships. The clinician's view, on which so much work in Child Guidance Clinics depends, is usually based on anamnestic material furnished largely by the mother herself. The study was not designed to discover the causes of developing personality organization, but to describe systematically the ontogenesis of the infant's interpersonal relationships. It was a comprehensively detailed look, however, on a reasonable large sample of some thirty primiparous mothers and their families.

The problem of how to proceed with this complex data in order to make a cross case comparison of interaction and to communicate what had been encountered lay first in selecting the most salient interactional variables to focus upon in each pair. Although the longitudinal study was based upon and launched with a framework of psychoanalytic considerations, the attempt to apply this orientation directly in defining initial categories for analysis, led to classifications of primary data which often required a high level of inference. There was also a tendency for a certain circularity of reasoning, in which the variables that we wished to study as outcome, were being used to interpret the primary data.

The notion of a way to proceed arose from the experience of interviewing the study mothers in a systematic way every 6 weeks while we were, at the same time, studying the development of their infants. Times of stress tended to be followed by times of harmony. After following ten or fifteen of the pairs one could begin to anticipate the time of appearance of some of the important concerns the mother would express, or, on the other hand, feel relieved about. This gave the impression that we were watching a sequence of adaptations, common to all the different mother-infant pairs, although acted out somewhat differently by each. Each advancing level of activity, which the child became capable of manifesting, demanded a new adjustment in the mother-child relationship. A new equilibrium had to be reached. The problem was that there appeared to be a certain time scale on which these changes could be placed. If a pair had difficulty getting coordinated on one particular level, they presently were already struggling with the next before they had comfortably adjusted to the first. One could begin to appreciate, too, the difficulties this imposed in reaching the second adaptation. We became aware that we were looking at the substance of epigenesis in terms of interaction, that synchrony or asynchrony in this process was a highly important phenomenon.

This germinal idea has been gradually refined into a systematic way of studying our data of early mother-child interaction. The first step was to identify and define the sequence of adaptations. This effort was first published in a paper entitled 'Issues in Early Mother-Child Interaction' (Sander, 1962). In this, five levels of adjustment were identified in the first 18 months of life in the order of the temporal epochs which were appropriate to their negotiation. Table 23 lists these five levels and the time spans for each.

The next task was to identify component behaviors which could be teased out of the data in relation to the particular interactions of each epoch and which bore upon the adjustment being made. These categories constituted the evidence for or against the adaptation and degree of harmony which had been reached.

As one follows the mother-infant pair from the beginning, one can represent the degree of harmonious coordination which will be reached in any of the epochs as a particular open ended question, i.e., an issue, which is in the process of being settled for each individual pair. For the guidance of the data analysts, who were extracting and evaluating the material, these issues were worded as questions. They are listed in Appendix 1 (page 224), along with some of the observational and interactional categories. All evidence which could be discovered in the record, both for and against, was extracted for each category to provide a base from which the predominant trends for each span of months could be evaluated. As can be seen, these periods ranged from three months in duration to six months. Agreement

TABLE 23

Issue	Title	Span of Months	Prominent infant behaviors which became co-ordinated with maternal activities.
1	Initial Regulation	Months 1-2-3	Basic infant activities concerned with biological processes related to feeding, sleeping, elimination, postural maintenance, etc. including stimulus needs for quieting and arousal.
2	Reciprocal Exchange	Months 4-5-6	Smiling behavior which extends to full motor and vocal involvement in sequences of affectively spontaneous back and forth exchanges. Activities of spoon feeding, dressing, etc., become reciprocally coordinated.
3	Initiative	Months 7-8-9	Activities initiated by infant to secure a reciprocal social exchange with mother or to manipulate environment on his own selection.
4	Focalization	Months 10-11-12-13	Activities by which infant determines the availability of mother on his specific initiative. Tends to focalize need meeting demands on the mother.
5	Self-Assertion	Months 14-20	Activities in which infant widens the determination of his own behavior often in the face of maternal opposition.

between analysts on evaluations of trends, when taken in these large blocks and based on extensive and repeated documentation, is not impossibly difficult.[1]

[1] In order to test the repeatability of extracting and evaluating these items from the same protocol, two teams, working independantly, made separate complete sets of evaluations. Agreement and disagreement on 67 items was judged independently with the results given in Appendix 3, page 227.

This is a feature of the longitudinal study which is one of its greatest strengths, namely, that repeated observations at different times and under a variety of circumstances can reveal the redundant and consistent. In the same way, any deviation, once a trend has become established, shows up strikingly. The data collection schedule which was followed systematically for each pair is illustrated in Appendix 2 (page 226). The contacts were spaced at regular intervals every 3 to 4 weeks for the three to four years of most intensive sequential data collection. Besides the *variety* of contacts and their regular repetition, upon which we relied to give us a fair picture of the child in different situations and environments, objectivity was enhanced by (1) The use of tape-recorded interviews. Interviews followed an associative anamnesis in the first half-hour and a standard sequence of items in the second; (2) Standard situations of observations in the Well Baby Clinic, in the Developmental Tests, and in the Play Interviews; (3) For these observations we employed multiple observers (at certain observations, one for mother, one for child, and one for running sequence); (4) Observers were guided by pre-established observational categories; (5) Regularly repeated developmental tests.

This schedule has given the opportunity for unusual richness of actual experience with each subject, which provides a certain solidity to the *interactional picture*. Documentation is comparable in detail and completeness on 22 subjects through the third year of life.

A further feature of the material collected was that the study was designed to provide as wide a range of maternal character as could be found in the normal population of our prenatal clinic. The plan was that this selection would, in turn, spawn as wide a range and as gross a contrast in mother-child interaction as existed in this 'normal' population. It was anticipated also that this would make it easier to identify and to follow longitudinally unique individual idiosyncrasies. By following such variants to an outcome point, important factors in the developmental process could come to light. Indeed, it was probably largely because of this spectrum of subjects in the sample that our method of cross case comparison had any usefulness.

One could ask what the expected longitudinal interactional course is in a normal population when analyzed in the framework of this sequence of issues. One needs a basis – some yardstick – for evaluating the variations which can be found between any two pairs. If indeed, the average mother-child pair are negotiating five adaptations in the

193

first 18 months of life, the behavioral appearance of this sequence of achievements should look something like the usual course of events. In this sense, the 'usual course of events' would be part of the 'average expectable environment' (Hartman, 1939). We have used the following version as just such a yardstick in our data analysis. It is a picture which will be recognized easily as will be deviations from it.

(1) *First Issue*

In the first three months of life, there is usually achieved a stable regulation of such basic biological processes as feeding, sleeping, elimination. Usually by 4 to 6 weeks the primiparous mother has recovered from the delivery, has learned to read the important cues of her infant and respond to them in such a way that things settle down to a certain predictable routine. She begins to feel a confidence that she *knows* the baby's needs and can specifically meet them, while not jeopardizing her own needs and the remaining activities of her day. There is usually some sign of baby's preferential responsivity to mother or her ministrations by the end of this period. A positive and pleasant affect begins to pervade their interactions, especially with the appearance of the smiling response. (We have termed this first period that of initial adaptation or initial regulation).

(2) *Second Issue*

In the second three months, 4th, 5th, and 6th, the mother develops active reciprocations with her infant around the spontaneous development of smiling play. Both come to participate in this with delight and mounting expressions of exuberance as the period wears on. At the same time the principle activities of caretaking, such as diapering, dressing, or beginning of spoon feeding, are being accomplished more and more through a reciprocal coordination of the actions of each. Any one who has tried to feed a 5 months old his cereal knows the coordination it involves – and the effort needed by each to achieve it. We have called this the period of 'Reciprocal Activation' or 'Establishing Reciprocal Exchanges'.

(3) *Third Issue*

The third three months, 7th, 8th, and 9th, finds the infant beginning more vigorously to express his initiative in bids for attention, for social exchange, for motor, exploratory or manipulative activities, or to indicate his own special preferences. The mother attends to, reads, and responds to these activities with a certain respect for the specific and individually unique quality they are beginning to signify. As she does so, she makes it possible for the infant to experience success – or an interference – in achieving a result in line with that which he has specifically initiated. The adjustment of the mother to the child's increasingly precise and specifically intended activities may be scarcely discernible when an adequate level of reciprocity has been achieved in prior issues. However, in other instances, varying degrees of maternal ambivalence in respect to these new capacities leads to idiosyncratic patterns of interference mixed with reinforcement. For example, activities which are directed away from mother or independent of her wishes may tend to get blocked and those directed toward her be fostered or vice versa. We have especially examined interactions during this time in terms of initiations for social exchange and their success or failure to result in a reciprocal level of response. This period has been termed simply 'Initiative' or 'Period of Early Directed Activity'.

(4) *Fourth Issue*

In the fourth period, months 10, 11, 12, and 13, the advent of loco-motion and the extension of the capacity to direct one's own activity and express specific intentions by it, sets up the opportunity for the child to settle the extent to which mother is available to him. This is an availability specific to the child's bid – not just for care in general. This is a time when needs are recognized in great measure by the context of the situation in which they are expressed. For example, the simple knowledge of a mother that her child is still subject to stranger reaction will greatly facilitate her appreciation of her child's behavior at a time of distress, and suggest to her an appropriate response for it. In a sense, in this period the level of reciprocation depends on information, which exists in the adapted mother-child system, already having been built up through earlier achievements of reciprocity. This information of 'context' is an addition to the earlier individual characteristics of mother or infant on which reciprocation has been dependent so largely in prior issues. It is this specificity of familiar sequences and their context which is lost with separation from mother at this time.

One mother will be gratified by this special knowledge of her baby's needs and her capacity to act specifically upon them. Another mother experiences the child's directed and more specific demands

o   195

at this time as exceedingly threatening – something to be escaped from – or defended against. Ambivalent availability of mother, which may have been subtly evidenced earlier, may now be dramatized openly as limits begin to be set. If her limits are consistent and constructive, we find the mother has a certain confidence that if she yields to her child, still he will eventually turn away from her to wider horizons of his own. The pressure the child exerts at this time varies with the ambivalence of the mother in responding to him. If her availability is certain, he can turn to greater novelties; if she tries to run away, he is demanding; if she reacts to threat by aggression, his demand may provoke her attack or her surrender. We have termed this period from the 10th to 14th months, 'Focalization'.

(5) *Fifth Issue*

In turning then to 'wider horizons of his own' in the 14-20 month period, there emerges a new capacity of the child to assert himself and to widen his initiative to determine and select his directions of activity. When these directions tend to run counter to mother's wishes and household rules the issue of the degree to which this assertion will be successful is raised. In the usual instance in this span of months, these tender ventures are regarded with a certain affectionate condescension, often with a yielding for a time of a limit just drawn by the parent. The child's initiative, obviously, is not *all* in a direction away from, or contrary to the mother but is balanced by bids for reciprocation with *her*. The probability of success for the latter, he has been determining in the previous issue. Now this probability provides the context in terms of which he pursues his own inner intentions, and the independent plan of action stemming from them. We have termed the issue in the 14-20 month period that of 'self-assertion'.

It will be seen at once, that, if heretofore reinforcement and gratification have been connected with the achievement of a reciprocal exchange with mother, we are now encountering a new phenomenon. The appearance of success and gratification begins to become evident as the infant maintains his own aims even if they are in opposition to rather than in reciprocation with, the mother. Whereas separation before this period is reacted to as an upsetting event, now separation both physical and psychological begins to be produced at the iniative of the infant – or so we expect if all has followed the 'usual course of events'.

It is evident from this descriptive picture that we are focusing on certain broader 'formal' features of interaction for the evaluation of trend. These are features which can be represented in progressively more differentiated behaviors from the first to the fifth issue. They might be summarized in three words: initiation, reciprocation, and regulation. The emphasis is in distinguishing the level at which the infant is initiating his activity, the degree of reciprocal coordination achieved in the interaction with the caretaking activity, and the stability of regulatory harmony which prevails. In an observation in which the levels of activity are widely disparate between infant and environment, the question of who initiates is usually clear.[1] Equally clear to the observer of the mother-child interaction are the failures of the pair to achieve harmonious coordination or regulatory stability. On the other hand, behaviors which are smoothly mutual do not strike the observer with the same impact unless he has been following them from their more awkward beginnings. They can be easily taken for granted. Furthermore as one watches longitudinally the activities initated by the infant, he can note the progression in the level of these activities which become coordinated with the mother in reciprocal interactions. In this way interactions can be viewed as the arena of differentiation. Those activities initiated by the infant which become incorporated into this reciprocal coordination become differentiated from those which do not. That this should be so becomes even more reasonable as it is appreciated that stability of regulation for the infant, as the months pass, depends on this increasingly differentiated reciprocal exchange. The advanced levels include newly coordinated elements as well as features of old behaviors whose coordination has already been established at an earlier level. To put the same thing into the language of adaptation: as new capacities for activity appear in the infant's behavior, as he advances chronologically, fitting together or adaptation is reachieved between

---

[1] Spitz (1965, p. 12) has described this disparity of levels between mother and infant. In introducing the concept of development as a process of differentiation from an un-differentiated beginning he writes the following: 'An equally peculiar and perhaps unique aspect of the mother-child relation is that the psychic structure of the mother is fundamentally different from that of her child. The relation between such conspicuously unequal partners cannot be anything but asymmetric; accordingly the contribution of each of them to the mutual relationship will be dissimilar. Aside from the somewhat comparable relation of a human being with a domesticated animal (a pet for instance) such a high degree of disparity in two as closely associated and interdependant individuals is not found anywhere else in our social organization.'

infant and mother at each new level. The harmony or disharmony which prevails over time gives indication of the stability of this coordination. Under 'initiation', therefore, we describe not only *who* is initiating, but *what* is initiated, and the variety, vigor, directedness and timing of the acts. 'Reciprocation' likewise implies attention to its specificity, spontaneity, duration, and affective qualities. 'Regulation' includes the full twenty-four hours of the day and is evidenced in the basic functions of arousal and quiescence, and the evenness in maintaining or changing sleeping, feeding and eliminative behaviors, as well as the prevailing signs of distress or comfort which characterize them.

In the 'usual course of events' the transitions from one period to the next are so smooth that one is scarcely aware of the introduction of the new active capacities of the infant. In our particular population, which had its own special socio-cultural features and wide range of maturity in maternal character (Pavenstedt, 1965), these transitions were often abrupt and marked by considerable turmoil. The possibility of handling such variations systematically from epoch to epoch and giving them even crude evaluative assessments provides a means of exploring the relation of an individual child's adaptive experience to variables of later behavioral organization.

We can turn now to the description of the interactional course followed by the first of the three pairs. It will illustrate an actual instance in which our yardstick of the 'usual course of events' is closely approximated. It also illustrates the problem of assessing a prevailing trend in interactional data, in which behavior may vary from contact to contact often within considerable range. Evidence from systematic and frequent contacts under a variety of circumstances is one way of coping with this problem.

First Pair (Ellen and Mrs Q.)

Issue #1 (Months 1, 2, 3) *Initial Regulation*

It did take the first six weeks for this mother to get over the physical effects of the delivery and to establish with her baby a smooth and regular routine in which the mother could be confident. In the first six weeks there had been a mild depressive reaction and major concern of mother about damage to her own body. She had had excessive postnatal abdominal cramps and bleeding. She showed a curious concern with 'gassiness' in the baby by which she accounted for the baby's crying and alternately 'good' and 'bad' nights of sleeping. In the first weeks she left the baby at the breast for up to two hours at a stretch and soon developed painful nipples. However, after the obstetrician stopped the breast feeding at six weeks as a means of relieving the abdominal cramps and bleeding, which it did, there appeared consistent pleasure and contentment in the mother with the baby. The baby's sleeping became regular, smiling appeared, and reciprocal play with mother began to emerge. In direct observations mother was reported as deft, sure, and quick with the baby. She referred to the baby as a 'good baby', one who cried little, and was little bother, and showed little discomfort. One could see a steady improvement in harmony from the first to the last of the period.

Issue #2 (Months 4, 5, 6) *Reciprocal Exchange*

In the second period (4-6 months) this pair showed, outstandingly, a high level of mutual enjoyment in reciprocally coordinated inter-actions involving smiling, vocalization, and back and forth play. Father and especially mother-in-law contributed important additional amounts of play. On the incoordination side of the ledger during these three months, mother's consistent efforts to block mouthing of objects and finger sucking was the principle incoordination. The child was reported briefly as 'cranky' between 4 and 5 months, during a period when mother was working a few hours a day in a family business. At this time, Ellen's demand for social contact and play began and became clearly expressed. Mother readily let her house-work go to enjoy holding and playing with the baby.

Issue #3 (Months 7, 8, 9) *Initiative*

The third issue began early in this pair, therefore, i.e. at 4 rather than 6 months, and was highly successful of affective reciprocation. In the 7th, 8th, and 9th months, it was impossible to say in our observa-tions who predominantly initiated interaction between mother and child, so evenly balanced was this. It became even more enjoyable for the mother to reciprocate with these now more direct bids of Ellen for interaction with her. There was no pair in our sample which showed a more mutual exchange or a more spontaneous enjoyment. In addition, Ellen's increasing skill in object manipulation and motor development was a delight to the mother who often reinforced her vigorous bangings. Already at nine months mother repeatedly described her as having a 'mind of her own'. But it was with pride that mother described her as insisting on holding her cup and feeding herself, refusing help, etc. Mother was described, during this time, as talking a great deal to her baby, with reciprocal vocal imitations between them, and with the employment of mutual attention to distance communication. The variation in our sample of this dimension involving perception of focus of attention is quite distinct and of importance to assess in this third period since it plays so vital a role in the negotiation of succeeding issues. It is indeed an interactional bridge between the all or nothing world of direct contact and the coming interactional world of representation by language and symbol.

Mother often dwelt in her interview on the question of the one to whom the child went most. It seemed important for her to be the preferred one. On the negative side of the ledger, concerning the interferences or disharmonies, there was some excessive concern of mother to control biting by her infant, which we never could substantiate as more than occasional.

Issue #4 (Months 10, 11, 12, 13) *Focalization*

As has been stated, the fourth issue concerns the degree of availability of the mother to child-initiated bids. Ellen and her mother achieved the highest coordination in this respect. The following original notes of a Home Visit characterize the consistent picture: 'There was much contact between baby and mother, visual, bodily, and verbal. Initiative seemed mutual. Mother did not hover over the baby yet was always available when the baby would make the slightest gesture or noise which indicated to the mother that she wanted her. These indications were always quite direct. She would look at her mother, make a sound, and could say some words clearly. . . . The tone of the child's voice or the direction of her look seemed to give the mother her cues'.

On the dissonant side of the ledger, there were continuations of overconcern with the child's biting or hitting out in anger when frustrated by mother. When the child became angry or hit out, mother angrily yelled and the child yelled back again angrily. Reciprocation existed even here. This frustration appeared often a part of a new kind of teasing interference by mother. The teasing was mostly centered about mother's interfering with an object the child was engrossed in manipulating, i.e., an involvement independent of the mother. Again in the overall picture this held a very mild and tempered place and was not a major obstacle which countered the mainstream of initiative in this instance as it did in the next pair to be described. Mother seemed both pleased, and yet somewhat threatened, by the child's autonomy. It seemed to tie in with Mother's sensitivity in regard to whom the child preferred. She preferred mother when tired or at bedtime but stayed easily with others. When she obviously enjoyed being held by the visitors on a home visit, mother would test out whether Ellen would leave them and come to her. If not, mother would pretend to leave the apartment or actually go away to the neighborhood store for a bit during the visit, or threaten to give the child to the visitor. When she did so leave the child alone with home visitors at 14 months, there was no protest or distress on the part of the child who continued to play with the visitor. Mother attributed this to the fact that she had not put on her coat as she left, for if she had, she maintained, the child would have protested. That is, the usual signal for separation was not present. One could also suggest that it was not necessary for this child to test mother's availability by this time in this context, that it had been already established by mother's response to a large number of trials over previous months. The ability to tolerate separation did not reflect here a lack of attachment but a predictable stability of regulation. The importance to the mother of a preferential one-to-one relationship was obvious. It was as though mother tested during this period as we might have expected the child to have tested.

It was at the end of the fourth period, near 14 months, as the child achieved walking and was showing an ability to be apart from mother with a strong investment in her own independent course of action, that the mother became pregnant again.

Issue #5 (Months 14-20) *Self-Assertion*

The course of the fifth period between 14 and 20 months was colored by the mother's pregnancy. The predominant trend in the material confirmed mother's ability to allow Ellen autonomy and to regard her new capabilities with pride. In the developmental test situation Ellen showed this independence and self-assertion with the tester, insisting on manipulating the items in her own way rather than as suggested by the tester. She also showed her ability to work on her own task persistently and with intense involvement, without turning to mother for help and without being overwhelmed by frustration in the face of obstacles. As a matter of fact, Ellen had repeatedly excluded the mother in her attempts from time to time during the test to get Ellen's attention. The assertion of the child was evidenced in such observations. It was also evident in the clashes stemming from activities the child initiated and which the mother interfered with, such as Ellen's grabbing for the visitor's pocketbook, or insisting on peeling wrappers off the crayons in the Clinic. In the latter instance the child refused to yield her crayon to mother's active efforts to wrest it from her. In the subsequent observations of crayon situations, peeling was returned to by Ellen and accomplished now without further attempts of mother to block it.

On the incoordination side of the ledger were continued examples of mother's teasing intrusions into Ellen's play and a period of irritability when mother was depressed. This was between the 3rd and 5th months of this second pregnancy, when Ellen was 17-19 months of age. Mother began again to bleed intermittently, gave evidence of concern whether she would be able to carry the baby, was unable to do her housework, and left the child for longer periods restrained in her feeding-chair or carriage. There was one report from the mother, during these weeks of depression, that Ellen was not wanting the mother to leave, and was demanding to be held and played with. The mother, in a way that was unusual for her, said she now was not in the mood for this. Our social worker, who visited the mother at this time in order to get her to keep her clinic appointments necessitated by the bleeding, found mother just sitting on the front steps with Ellen strapped in the carriage at one side. Both looked disheveled and solemn. Mother said she had just been sitting there for hours. However, depression was a matter of a few weeks and as a consistent trend this behavior was not borne out in repeated contacts. An example of mother's unusual irritability at the time of depression occurred during a home visit. It shows, however, the strength with which Ellen tended to maintain what she initiated. The child was in her feeding-chair and the visitor was conversing with mother, who was apparently paying little attention to Ellen at the moment. Ellen was exploring the chair for crumbs and mother suddenly got up and angrily demanded, and wanted to remove from Ellen's mouth, a crumb which she had just picked up. Ellen yelled in rage and mother yelled back and then said to the visitor, 'That's what she does when she doesn't get what she wants . . . that's when I have to hit her' –

but she didn't and Ellen kept her crumb. Taken alone, this example would miss the more numerous observations of Ellen's usual success in initiating interactions with her mother in which the same highly sensitive reciprocity and pleasure was present as had been customary in previous issues.

The reason such material has been included is not to introduce confusion into the picture but to illustrate as fairly possible the kind of thing one runs into when a detailed account of an actual life history is available. Contradictory and ambivalent behavior is simply what the infant is confronted so often with in his encounters with real caretakers. It is one of the reasons why we have been interested in data over longer periods for evaluation and have tried to stay with the complexity of the material, while attempting to esti-mate predominating trends. We have attempted to estimate the degree to which an enduring coordination is achieved in respect to particular levels of activity which the infant can initiate. This is something which is essential also for the infant to do. If his behavior is to be organized on the basis of a predictable feedback to the activities he initiates, then the pressures which the toddler exercises by his assertions in the fifth period, and in the months which follow, may go a long way toward clarifying for him the extent of his mother's earlier and more subtle contradictions.

In summary, Ellen's interactional profile showed the achievement of a stable and harmonious regulation in the first period, after an initial period of difficulty; a high level of affectively mutual reciprocal exchange in the second period and a very evenly matched initiative for social contact with a high degree of maternal availability in the third and fourth periods; and finally the appearance of independent directions of interest and investment, which could be maintained in the face of the mother's opposition.

As we move on now to the descriptive accounts for the second and third pairs, two contrasting variations from the yardstick of a 'usual course of events' will be illustrated. Further illustrated also will be the way trends are compared between pairs in terms of the evaluations of success or failure in the negotiation of the five issues.

A paired comparison of interactional course can carry a step further the exploration of the emergence of organization through the inter-actional process. As we compare, in these two pairs, the interplay of initiation, reciprocation and regulation, we will be following the progress of the infants as they struggle to differentiate[1] their repertoire of adaptive behaviors.

The relation of organization of behavior to mother-infant inter-action can be illustrated by experiments on the development of behavior in animals. There is an interesting parallel which exists between the sequence followed in our five 'issues' and the steps in the longitudinal course of suckling behavior in mother cat-kitten interaction as described by Rosenblatt *et al.* (1961). When the initia-tive taken by kitten or mother in achieving feeding coordination is traced, initiative passes from mother cat to the kitten after a period of mutuality or reciprocal coordination. In Harlow's account (1963) of the maternal affectional system in monkeys, coordination was described in terms of maternal activities in a contrived cage situation. This shift in the mother's role was identified in three steps as 'attach-ment', 'ambivalence' and 'separation'. In humans, the initiation of activity in the interaction between mother and child in our adaptive 'issues', whether or not the interaction accomplishes a fitting to-gether by reciprocal coordination, ordinarily rests in the first two issues with the mother predominantly. It is more a 50-50 proposition in Issues #3 and #4, and becomes highly related to the child's initiative in the 5th and later periods. At this point it is a matter of selection for the infant whether he turns toward the mother or away from her. It was possible with the kittens in the experiment by Rosenblatt *et al.*, to study the effects of separating the kittens from the mother at various points in this transition and to see the steplike progression of experiences necessary for the normal organization of kitten behavior in the feeding situation. If the repertoire of inter-actional adaptive behaviors between individuals in the various animal species is built through the experience the infant has in achieving coordination with the mother during a sequence of stages

[1] For those who regard personality development from the approach and point of view of the embryologist (i.e., in terms of emergent organization), the problem of the process by which differentiation takes place occupies a key position. The formulation of this point of view in the study of personality development has been represented in the orthogenetic principle of Heinz Werner (1947). Here development is portrayed as proceeding from the less differentiated to the more differentiated – the differentiated units becoming articulated and hierarchically integrated. Our question concerns the process by which differentiation takes place and by which articulation and hierarchic integration are effected. Inter-actional phenomena should indicate, even mediate this process, and so provide an avenue of access for investigation. Detailed paired comparison between individual records offers a method of study in addition to the correlation of outcome variables with interactional trend evaluations.

of shifting initiative, then it should be possible to study the organization of interpersonal behavior from the same point of view. In the human, however, being unable to manipulate the interaction at different points in the chronology as in animal experimentation, we must wait for naturally occurring experiments to reveal relevant relationships. These can come to light in paired comparisons when there is a systematic framework for comparison which includes chronological sequence.

The comparison of the second and third pair in respect to our yardstick of the 'usual course of events' illustrates variations in the dimensions we have been discussing initiation, reciprocation and regulation.

B. Second Pair (Ned S. and his Mother)[1]

The adaptive task for this pair concerned the problem of fitting-together encountered by a vigorous, aggressive, garrulous mother who was a compulsive housekeeper, and an infant, who although he showed good spontaneous motor activity in the first four days of life also gave the appearance of a certain frailty particularly in irritability to stimuli. As a neonate he tended to turn away from tactile rooting and sucking stimuli, cried when he was picked up and showed an easily fatigued sucking with frequent spitting up. These difficulties seemed to clear after the first 4 days.

Issue #1 (Months 1, 2, 3) *Initial Regulation*

The first period showed the reverse of the expected increase in coordination between infant and mother over the first three months. Things appeared to go most smoothly in the first six weeks with increasing difficulties after that time. The mother had habitually managed her anxieties by controlling her environment. This was easy for her in the first 6 weeks when Ned was sleeping for long stretches and she could count on sufficient time to get her housework done as well as time to respond to him. She was reported to be keenly perceptive of the infant and attentive to detail. Feeding observations repeatedly described her handling as smooth, warm, and comfortable. This is an illustration, I think, of the problem in trying to assess adaptation

[1] Some of the interactional material for this pair was described in a previous publication (Sander 1964) in which a particular focus was brought to bear on the interplay of maternal character evaluation and infant endowment in understanding the adaptive course which follows in the 'issues'.

by examining only small segments of time. Adaptation and regulation imply a stability over the full span of time. Difficulties began at the end of the first month, when Ned began falling asleep regularly after taking $\frac{1}{2}$ to $\frac{3}{4}$ ounces of feedings which appeared to observers to be comfortable, well-modulated ones. He would awaken again in one or two hours, hungry and crying. For a number of weeks the mother strove heroically to maintain a demand-feeding schedule which was evidence of her basic devotion. However, the irregularity so disrupted her characteristic way of coping with her compulsive needs, that it threw her into increasing distress, anxiety, and finally some depression after two and a half months. At this time she felt she simply could no longer neglect her husband's needs, and the demands of her house to meet Ned's schedule of discomforts. Ostensibly to decrease his dependency she began to avoid picking Ned up and enforced separation for one to several hours per day while she completed her housework. She often placed him across the street in the carriage where she could see him from the window, or would put him in another room where he could cry it out. She described spells in which he 'screamed to exhaustion'. By the end of the three-month period Ned began to scream whenever the mother left him in the crib. He would awaken from his nap screaming, as his mother described it, 'as if something was gone'. Thus 'separation' can exist even when mother is present and 'separation behavior' can be interpreted as having another meaning than strength of attachment.

Mother's principal aim in interaction was to quiet the baby and one could see her plan to try to train him out of his demands. Mother relied heavily on the bottle as a means of responding to Ned and she was never observed during this first period to stimulate the baby in order to arouse him or to get him to respond to her. There were none of the little early reciprocations evident between Ellen and her mother. Only later did we become aware of how important it was for this mother that her baby sleep so that she could have time of her 'own', and that her initiative be not compromised by his. She reported later then that she had used the feeding period to watch television as she held baby and bottle. Finally, while attempting to help the mother in the third month to achieve some regularity in the feedings, the pediatrician discovered that the mother had not changed the amount of the feeding in spite of the increase in weight and size of the baby. She was still using a 4 ounce bottle and was not letting the infant finish the bottle at a feeding. She was keeping out some, as she explained it, so that she would have it handy in case she needed it between feedings to quiet him. When it was suggested that she use an 8 ounce bottle and allow the child to take as much of it as he wanted, improvement followed at once and a predictable four-hourly schedule was finally reached in the fourth month, a month behind our schedule. This illustrates the longer time spans in adaptive regulation which may not come to light when viewing interaction more microscopically.

Issue #2 (Months 4, 5, 6) *Reciprocal Exchange*

In respect to the second period, Ned's smiling response emerged rapidly at two and a half months of age. The charm of his smile and his readiness to respond delightfully to a social interaction even by 12 weeks was outstanding. Over the next 2 months Mrs S gradually succumbed to this irresistible influence, at first interacting with Ned by voice and eye at a distance. Finally, in the fifth month, she not only allowed herself to be involved by him but spontaneously picked him up and held him or reached out to initiate play with him herself. This play was in the form of little games rather than direct smiling. Their relationship gradually became more harmonious and activation more mutual. There was achieved a reciprocal, nicely modulated body positioning as mother held her baby, which appeared to be gratifying to both. Reciprocal vocalization was also described and observed. The mother referred to this as a secret language which only she and her baby understood. Toward the end of the period, certain reciprocal games such as peek-a-boo, were reported and a good reciprocal quality was present in much of the routine care interactions, furnishing delight and satisfaction to the mother. The issue was judged as negotiated at this point, although the mother's affect, unmistakably revealing pleasure, pride, happiness, and gratification in her baby, never showed the qualities of expressed joy or exuberance. The over-all impression was of a prevailing matter-of-fact atmosphere.

There remained, as an undercurrent however, the same prominent ambivalence, in respect to demands, that had been reported in the first period. Mother complained in her six months interview that Ned was 'draining me dry' by his bids for social involvement, with subsequent complete disruption of her housework schedule. She said at this time that she had gotten so that she avoided looking at him when she went by his play pen so that she would not 'get stuck with him' in an involvement. Periods of enforced separation continued and he was now restrained in the carriage outside by a harness. Mother reported, at 5 months, that he 'cried himself sick' in tantrums upon separation from her, and had cut himself with the straps in his struggle against the harness. During this time the child developed outstanding social responsiveness and an excellent reciprocal interaction with the father. This remained excellent for the most part throughout, and is an important part of the wider view of his interactions.

Issue #3 (Months 7, 8, 9) *Initiative*

At the end of the sixth month as the third period was opening, mother suddenly decided to solve the problem of Ned's demands for involvement with her as well as a new problem: that of his refusal to go to sleep alone, by beginning to work outside the home on a 3-11 p.m. shift. Concurrent with the increased absence of the mother, Ned's reaction to separation became exquisite and intense. Tantrum behavior was frequent and he even refused to go to sleep for his morning nap. Faced with the virtual impossibility, under these circumstances, of resolving the issue in reciprocal adjustments, the mother oscillated: as a means of managing the screaming which arose when he was put down for the morning nap, she would lie down with him until he fell asleep; on the other hand, when he had a tantrum on being put in the now restrictive highchair she resorted to slapping him. Here is another level of ambivalence – a gross one.

After she had been at work some weeks, having left the major task of getting Ned down for the night to her husband, she suddenly gave up the job to take full charge again in the home. This occurred after she found her husband was handling the matter by letting Ned fall asleep on the couch in the den, while he watched T.V. She felt Ned was being allowed to get away with it: 'To me that was the end', said she. Mother won the violent struggle over restraint in these months and clearly indicated her avowed intention in this matter to win, saying, 'Ned has to learn that *he* doesn't win, that *we* win'. The defeat of his initiative to get his mother to respond to his bids was unquestioned. Interestingly enough, in the times during this period which she set aside to be with him as part of *her* plans – such as to bring him to the clinic for an afternoon of observation – there was much of the same comfortable mutual relationship that had developed before in the 5th month – but it was on *her* terms and time, not *his*. In the evaluation of Issue #3 in this instance, definitely less than the usual degree of success attended the efforts Ned initiated.

Issue #4 (Months 10, 11, 12, 13) *Focalization*

In respect to the fourth issue, Mother remained clearly determined not to yield to Ned's demands and her compulsive schedule retained its priority. An observation in the home at 12 months reported the mother and child as having 'lost contact' with each other. Reciprocal interactions and communications had largely disappeared from the observations by the 14th month, as had the child's once charming affect; he began to show the listless withdrawal that dominated the next six months. The mother's complete control of her own availability was never in question, although there was never, at the same time, any further physical separation. There was a clear failure in this pair then to negotiate an Issue #4, either during this period of 10-13 months, or later.

Issue #5 (Months 14-21) *Self-Assertion*

In the fifth period there was an increasing tightening of mother's control and an increased plasticity in Ned. Mother was pleased that his demands were lessening and at first seemed not to notice the development of a wan listlessness and an affect of persistent sadness and whining. She didn't mind lying down with him now to put him to sleep, or the rituals at meal time before he would eat. At about 18 months, after mother punitively inhibited his masturbation, which had been increasing rapidly, he developed a remarkable spontaneous withdrawal of investment whenever anyone became successful in securing his involvement to manipulate an object. Later in this period mother was observed frequently trying to initiate play with him by stimulating him in contrast to her usual aim to quiet him. She even went so far, during a home visit, as to run a bat up his pant leg to his genital area while he was lying in his usual withdrawn way, stretched out on the floor at her feet. Nevertheless, she remained unsuccessful in achieving an exchange with him.

Tantrum behavior, frequent before 14 months, gradually disappeared and there was an eating inhibition, certain eating rituals, and a persistent sleep disturbance, increasing frequency of colds, bouts of diarrhea, and finally in the 21st month a nocturnal choking spell for which he was rushed to the hospital.

Here we see a situation in which, in the first period, there were major difficulties in basic regulation, early affective reciprocation was not fostered by the mother although it finally emerged in the second period, in the presence of a highly responsive, almost irresistible child. Even this threatened mother's sense of being the one to determine her own involvements. Mutually shared initiation of contact was not achieved in the third period, nor was her availability determined by him in the fourth period. This was part of mother's clearly conscious intention and we see him in the fifth period withdrawing from an active effort to organize his world, and developing increasing physical symptoms.

I think it is important to bring out here that this mother loved her child. She was not out to destroy him as *her* child – to this day she refers to him as she must have wished him to be – 'my Ned'.

C. Third Pair (Bud and Mrs E.)

We can now turn to the pair with whom we shall contrast Ned's course. The mother in this instance was a conscientious, attractive-appearing girl, but quiet, shy and reserved, almost to the point of somberness. She kept herself well in control in anxiety-provoking situations and showed a capacity to endure without complaint. If there is a role for the so-called normal feminine masochism in childrearing, its usefulness may become evident in this instance.

Mrs E. was a very effective housekeeper, in the sense that she kept a neat and well-organized home, but, in contrast to Ned's mother, did this with one hand, so to speak, without the slightest complaint or sign of burden. She refused our offers of home nursing help after the delivery and her time seemed unusually free to attend to her baby.

The infant, Bud, had sustained a clear perinatal anoxia as a complication of the delivery. He required some 15 minutes to establish a regular breathing pattern and showed in the neonatal exam a general hypertonicity of the legs and an occasional limb tremor, both of which persisted well into his first year of life.

Issue #1 (Months 1, 2, 3) Initial Regulation

There were two chief sources of anxiety in the first three months for his mother. The paramount problem was in respect to his poor feeding behavior and the second was his developmental retardation, which became evident by eight weeks. In this latter, he showed a developmental course which was consistent with our 8 other subjects who had sustained perinatal anoxia, Stechler (1964). The feeding problem had started almost from birth and was manifested by his taking very small quantities at a given feeding, rapidly going to sleep on the bottle and reawakening after a short period of time hungry for more food, the same situation grossly as with Ned. However, between Bud and his mother, coordination and regulation steadily improved over the three-month period. After the first ten days, in which mother had tried to increase his intake by stimulating him and felt nervous and concerned about his low intake, she spontaneously recognized her anxiety and decided that she might be adding to the problem by her tension during the feeding. She decided that these frequent small feedings were characteristic for him and that she should accept it and make the feedings as relaxed and happy as she could. From then on things steadily improved. It was three weeks before he slept for a three-hour stretch at night. At one month of life he was taking about three ounces at a feeding and by two months he could sleep for a $5\frac{1}{2}$-hour stretch and take five ounces at a feeding. Although in our observations at six and 12 weeks, he was described as tense and fussy, and was reported by mother to have a fussy period of two to three hours per day, mostly around dinner time, mother always described him as a good baby, not colicky and not difficult to care for. In our observations during this time, mother seemed to want to be in constant visual contact with him when he was awake. She always held him so that she could look at him, engaged in extensive gentle talking to him, and put him to sleep by rocking him. She felt confident she knew his different cues, knew when he was 'faking', and also that he knew her and would quiet for her. We felt she was highly predictable as to the kind of response she would offer him in respect to his various state changes.

The developmental retardation, which was the second problem, became evident in the later part of the first period. It was the source of an increasing anxiety in the mother after the feeding difficulty abated. The retardation consisted chiefly of delayed social perceptual responses and delayed adaptive development in response to, and in approach to, materials.

Issue #2 (Months 4, 5, 6) *Reciprocal Exchange*

In respect to the second issue, the appearance of the smile was late – eight weeks. It was not obtained first by mother, but by father and aunt, who used somewhat stronger stimuli than mother. But Bud at this time was not a very alert or perceptually organized baby,

and his developmental difficulties were becoming more apparent
to Mrs E. In the undercurrent of concern which often popped
through to the surface, mother seemed to be torn between a basic
capacity for a warm, easy-going relationship with her child and a
need to deal with him in such a way as to foster development, particularly fine motor development. She was quite accurate in her
perception of his difficulties and worked very hard to overcome these
deficits by imposing a kind of training on him, endlessly encouraging
and urging him to reach for, grasp and manipulate objects. In the
6-month developmental test the tester makes the following observation:

> 'If left alone, he was tense and rigid, whether moving or still. If
> he was still, the tension was manifest in his muscle tone, with rigid,
> extended limbs. During periods of movement, the total arm and
> wrist movements were sharp, jerky, abrupt, and uncontrolled,
> and were unsuccessful in achieving the object, a small red cube,
> that was quite obviously the goal of his activity. One could tell
> that this was the goal of his activity by the intense visual concentra-
> tion upon the object and the sudden activation of his limbs and the
> movement and struggle of his entire body towards that object.
> (The observer generalizes): I doubt if I have ever seen a baby in
> whom there was such a wide discrepancy between his desire to
> achieve a particular goal, such as securing an object, and his total
> inability to do so.'

The hypertonicity of his legs gave him advanced scores on some of
the items such as pull to standing, so that the total test picture was
irregular. When his difficulties began to clear up in the seventh month
a much lighter mood prevailed. Nevertheless, during the 4th, 5th,
and 6th month period mother developed many ways to play with Bud
and establish a back and forth exchange. Mrs E. is not an articulate
woman, but she gave a spontaneous description of interaction with
him, illustrating her appreciation of what we refer to as reciprocal, or
back-and-forth exchange from a tape recording: 'Well, he'll go
uh-uh – and I'll talk to him. I'll say, "What are you telling me? A
story?" – something like that.' If you screech to him, he goes ah –
like that and I'll do it and then he'll do it. Then I'll do it and we'll
keep on going back and forth. And when Ralph comes home, I said,
"See, he can do it! And after I do it, he'll do it." – but he wouldn't
do it.' Mother reported to us how she employed reciprocal play to

capture his attention in order to manage him while changing or dressing him. At about three months after the feeding difficulty was largely resolved and mother was confident about his nourishment, she began propping his bottle. He was very slow in accepting solid feedings and did not give up his night bottle until the 7th month, but mother, in sensing his cues and pacing herself, did not try to hurry this progress. There was no evidence that she was compelled to be with the baby at all times. From very early she had gone out of an evening with her husband, leaving the baby despite the fact that he did not always respond well to this. In fact she seemed to note with some pleasure that he didn't do as well without her. However, when she was with him, she seemed always observant and attentive to him, perhaps overly so. He was in addition much involved with reciprocal play with father and aunt over these months.

Issue #3 (Months 7, 8, 9) *Initiative*
During the third period, mother's need to 'train' abated, when Bud developed initiative to reach, grab, manipulate, and secure a social response from her. His development on tests remained about one month retarded during this period. As part of her eagerness to promote his reaching out, she was completely permissive to the activities he initiated during these months, facilitating them whenever she could. She continued to be active in involving him in a great many reciprocal games. In repeated observations it became difficult to tell who initiated contact with whom, so mutual was it. There was no evidence in the record of failures of one to reach and involve the other. The baby was, at this time, now a predominantly visually organized baby and, as with Ellen, the third period saw a well developed distance responsivity and the use of distance reciprocation by voice and facial cue. For example, during the developmental examination at nine months, mother sat as usual where she could see him, and frequently tried to make contact with him. The observer writes, 'A few seconds later, they caught each other's gaze again and she played a little game with him, nodding her head and talking in a tender way'.

However, he was not a very appealing baby, appearing pale, flabby, and heavy jowled, with clumsy, awkward stiffness and serious mien. Stranger reaction, which began at seven months, was unequivocal, but mild. His first separation anxiety began at $7\frac{1}{2}$ months with protest on his mother's leaving the room. Her effort was to minimize this experience or separation for him whenever she could.

Issue #4 (Months 10, 11, 12, 13) *Focalization*

Mother's strong desire to gratify Bud and to facilitate his motor development, coupled with her alertness and sensitivity to his cues, contributed to the completeness of her availability to him during the 4th period, and the negotiation of the issue of 'focalization' in our interactional sequence. Mrs E. never appeared disturbed or upset by Bud's demands during this period but seemed unambivalently to feel that it was her role to respond to them to give him what he wanted. She did this in a gentle and giving, although at times in a teaching and controlling manner. Most of the interaction from mother and child was of the visual and social-verbal level, with relatively little physical contact. This mother was able to maintain a certain continuity of reciprocal interaction with him by means of this well-developed distance channel and because of this she was capable of dividing her attention. For example, while engaged in conversation with the visitor, she was constantly aware of his activity and could maintain contact with him. Here is a new level of interaction important to the negotiation of this issue. On this level mother's 'availability' can be mediated by the child's perception of the mother's focus of attention on him.

Although Bud experienced a high degree of frustration in mastering standing and walking, which we saw as a sequel to his early neurological findings, mother did not attempt to minimize his task. She often responded to his plight by some vigorous stimulating play which further heightened his effort by adding a new twist to his interest or anticipation. As be became able to creep and walk, he vigorously launched himself into exploration in directions away from his mother, moving into Issue #5 in a very charming and playful way.

Issue #5 (Months 14-20) *Self Assertion*

He developed distinct self-assertiveness in the 14-20 month period, especially in the home situation where he had pretty much the run of the place, getting into the pantry, breaking knick-knacks and climbing over the furniture. He insisted on feeding himself. In the clinic he showed less vigor of exploration of materials, being chiefly pre-occupied with the observers and not particularly eager to invest in the materials. However, in time, he was observed in a certain single track testing of limits as he would repeatedly run down the hall against the express wish of the mother, continuing what he had begun, in direct opposition to her 'No'. During this span of time, mother's position pretty much was that he was too young to understand and be limited and that she was not the kind of person prone to struggles, preferring to avoid them unless absolutely necessary. In other words, Bud determined to a degree where the limits would be.

The interpretation of the material during this period was, to some degree, complicated by the birth of a sister when he was $18\frac{1}{2}$ months old. After this, some of his demanding control of mother increased, in which he reasserted her availability to him at his expressed wish. There is the observation, during a feeding of the new baby, in which he completely displaced the baby from the mother's lap and gained sole possession of it himself. This may have been, in part, a regression and, in part, have reflected her lessened ability, at this time, to deal as effectively with his demands. But it certainly describes his assertion with her. It is only toward the very end of the 5th period that the mother became concerned over his continued victories, expressing apologetically that it was her inability to limit him that was at fault. Only at about 21 months did he develop temper tantrums as his aims were frustrated. At this time he was beginning to show intense pressure to have things his own way, which, for the first time, began to be evocative of an expression of anger in the mother. This is, however, ushering in the next period during which we look particularly at data concerning intentional and provocative expression of aggression vis-à-vis the mother. This is the reverse of attachment behavior and although this is a vital phase in the total picture, it is one which we shall not be examining in this paper. By 20 months the outcome of the issue of self-assertion remained clear in Bud's data, as did the relatively mild degree of tension which this behavior elicited in the family.

There are two levels of *outcome* in respect to which these interactional evaluations are being studied. The first concerns the course in each child of the intentional acts of aggression and defiance toward mother in the 18-36 month period and the manner in which this clash abates. These events will not be taken up here, but they culminate often in dramatic episodes, the picture of emerging regulation. Here are spelled out ambivalent undercurrents which may have revealed themselves by only subtle clues in the earlier interactions.

A second outcome assessment has been obtained on these subjects during their first year at school. Although designed around a separate research problem, the data furnishes a careful description of classroom behavior. The data collection has been carried out by a new team under the direction of Dr Eleanor Pavenstedt and includes a two- or three-day period of classroom observations in the fall and in the spring, interviews with teacher and with mother, a home visit, and psychological testing. Data collection was completed at the end of the spring term 1965 and analysis of it is still underway.

Many questions are raised at once as to which classroom variables should be studied in relation to the interactional evaluations of the first 18 months.

The summaries which follow, of our three children, are based on documentation from all the school outcome data. They were prepared by a data analyst[1] who has been working independently with this material over the past two years. He did not participate in the data collection of the longitudinal study and was unfamiliar with the earlier material on the subjects. The descriptive accounts are based on his detailed analysis of the organization of the child's *attentive* behavior as recorded in the classroom observational data.

In respect to *Bud's* behavior in the classroom, he writes: 'Most striking is his intense interest and involvement in work and mastery of tasks. His attention is strikingly on his work. Attention to teacher, with lack of attention to peers are both related to the primary focus on work. The attention to the teacher is not very personal but rather is that he understands that she is teaching and explaining and his attention is to the task of mastery. He is very alert to what is going on and comprehends easily, and as a result is very conforming. Physically he seems well-coordinated, though perhaps over-controlled and not showing a free-flowing grace. There is a great capacity for control and surprisingly little evidence that this costs anything in terms of decreased function in any other area. He seems greatly relaxed. Motor behavior is controlled and directed in the service of work. The time when it is least controlled is the way he stands up out of his seat when raising his hand eagerly. He shifts from one activity to another while manifesting the ability to attend more than one thing at a time and to be finishing one thing while already starting on another. He is very much an achiever, constantly striving for mastery as well as for approval and recognition. He attacks things with intensity. There seems to be relatively little competitive element in his motivation and his need for mastery is not based on competition with peers. He is appropriately independent of the teacher and

---

[1] Dr Padraic Burns who participated in the school follow-up study as a Special Research Fellow in the Boston University Division of Psychiatry.

even his intense involvement in subject-matter seems, by the time we saw him, independent of stimulation by her. He maintains an appropriate distance from her, as she does from the class. In all the rankings which have been obtained thus far on the study children in respect to overall adaptation, attention deployment, and learning in the classroom, he has been given top ranking.'

Ned, on the other hand, is described in the summary of his classroom behavior as a 'passive withdrawn boy who maintains a barrier between himself and the teacher. One function of this may be to protect himself, but another, by his mute unresponsiveness to the teacher's efforts to reach and motivate him, is to aggravate her to the limit of her tolerance. When the teacher is near or talking to him or the class he avoids her eye and when she does get and hold his attention he responds with frozen impassivity. Sometimes when he should be working and she is at a distance he will watch her as if to keep track of her whereabouts. In spite of this he still seems able to comprehend most of what she says, but his learning is secondarily hampered by the immense tension he is under which expresses itself as a constant distraction by internal stimuli, resulting in wiggling, hand-mouth stimulation, and generally prevents him from concentrating on anything. He shows a very short attention span and high distractibility at all times. He spends much of his time being distracted from work, although there are longer periods of staring and day dreaming. He brings home "F's" in most of his subjects, just doesn't do his work in school. He dawdles over it at home, but is not *ever* aggressive about this refusal.'

Ellen turned out to be one of the most flexibly adapted of all the children in the school situation. She was described in her summary as follows: 'She shows more spontaneity and affect than most first graders which gives her the appearance of lively intelligence. She loves interaction of any kind, getting much pleasure from her many peer interactions, but loving praise from the teacher as well. She has the most difficulty in following requests to be quiet and to talk less with peers. Otherwise, she adjusts well to limits. She knows easily and clearly what is expected and what she can get away with. As her desire to adhere to the teacher's demands increase over the year she exerts more conscious effort and becomes less spontaneous. There is always a striking inner directed or inner motivated quality to her behavior. She is very interested in her work and is not dependent on the teacher, but enjoys interaction with her and is stimulated to learn by her. Her attention in class is usually task-oriented, though motor discharge is at high level. It is controlled, in nature and direction, so as to be permissible, but there is much body twisting, scratching, and occasional mouthing and finger sucking. She pays good attention when *she* is interested and especially when it offers an opportunity to interact. She can be easily distracted by external stimulation, but she controls this and can then return to work easily and can at times concentrate without interruption. She seems only to really strive for achievement when she is interested in what is going on. Her skills are good though not top. She does not get upset

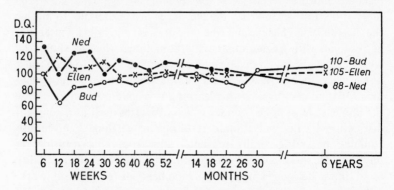

FIG. 29 Scores represent Gesell test results at ages specified in the abscissa for our 3 subjects. The score at 6 years is a WISC I.Q. The Gesell results are described in detail in a publication by Stechler (1964).

about failure and is not competitive with her peers but is interested in what they are doing.'

Inasmuch as developmental testing was carried out on all subjects at regular intervals from 6 weeks of age, the trends in the test scores of our three children have been included. These are graphed in Figure 29.

The questions we are asking concern the *process* by which these strikingly different patterns of behavioral organization came to be established. The way we are proceeding to study these questions is by having a framework for cross-case comparison, comparable longitudinal observational accounts for evaluation, and naturally occurring experiments arising from the range of subjects selected for the sample. We need also new models of developmental organization which will bring more precise focus on the variables and the relationships between variables which are the most salient.

218

Discussion

There have been several aims in presenting these three accounts of the longitudinal interactional picture over the first 18 months of life. The first was to provide empirical data which would constitute a broader interactional context for the smaller and more localized components of behavior that are being studied in the mother-infant interaction.

A second aim was to stimulate a consideration of the methodological problems involved in defining and evaluating longer trends in directly observable interactional data encountered in early life.

A third aim has been to convey some of the thinking which has been stimulated in this attempt to investigate process in interaction and to explore relations between early interactional experience and later consistencies in function.

It was mentioned at the beginning of this chapter that research approach, methods, and models have developed together as we have proceeded and that conceptualizations from basic biological sciences have been most helpful. A few words in conclusion about some of these useful ideas may serve to bring coherence to the presentation.

We have felt new modes are needed if one is to focus attention on interactional phenomena and to specify the salient dimensions. The interactional sequence depicted by the five 'issues' can be conceptualized as the interplay of two basic models. One concerns adaptation and the other, information-processing. At the level of the more primitive living systems these two models may operate as one and the same, but at the level of postnatal ontogenesis in the human infant, it is more useful to apply them as an interplay of two models. The interplay centers about the relations of each to 'regulation', a pivotal consideration in the maintenance of living systems.

The first of these two, namely adaptation, has been frequently referred to in the body of the paper. Since, however, the term adaptation is used loosely and often carries more than one meaning, certain essential points should be clarified. Adaptation has been used here as the concept in its evolutionary sense. As such it has been formulated concisely and lucidly and its application to ontogenesis detailed in a paper by Paul Weiss (1949).[1] Drawing on his extensive investigations of embryo genesis, especially of the nervous system, Weiss depicts the processes of adaptation taking place between tissue components

[1] In a previous publication (Sander 1964) this view has been applied in a paired comparison of two mothers, with contrasting character organizations in respect to aggression, as they negotiate the five issues.

219

as they are differentiating. In this formulation one is looking not just at the individual component, but is considering a field or system which is maintained by the interactions or exchanges between component subsystems. The 'active tendencies' of each of these components are emphasized and given a central role.

The reciprocal coordination or fitting together of these active tendencies is achieved by the adaptive process through modifications in the tissue components participating in the interaction. These modifications stem from their 'elastic' and 'plastic' properties.[1] Weiss points out that in ontogenesis the necessary modifications are chiefly quantitative ones, and relatively small in degree. They give great precision to the fit and are effected through direct 'on-the-spot' interplay of the active tendencies in question. The rough prefit between components, which provides the approximation in which these finer adjustments can occur, derives from phylogenetic evolution.

The adapted state is reached in the system when reciprocally coordinated interactions of 'active tendencies' can endure over time and when they are 'harmonious with the conditions for existence' of the participants. These conditions include influences vital to stability of regulation. Endurance over time in evolutionary adaptation represents a span of stability long enough to complete the reproductive cycle. In ontogenesis enduring stability in the adaptive field between two elementary tissue organizations establishes them in a new unit of the next order, e.g., an organ system. Such stable systems can then interact in this adaptive process to provide a next level of integration, e.g., an organism. Thus hierarchical order as well as articulation of elements entails these basic aspects of adaptation. Organization and adaptation are inextricably related.[2] This is a relationship made clear in Piaget's introduction to his sensory-motor theory of intelligence (1936), in which he concisely summarizes the matter as follows:

---

[1] A similar notion appears in other formulations of developmental process. For example the yielding and resisting properties of tissues subjected to 'shearing forces' as conceptualized by D'Arcy Thompson and described by S. Escalona in explaining some of the background for her developmental views (1959, pp. 8-13). The modification of behavior via the 'invariants' of assimilation-accommodation (Piaget, 1936) might be another example.

[2] One of the difficulties with our usual concept of psychological organization is that we tend to think of it in terms of the individual. The essential feature of the biological view is that organization is a characteristic of a system and cannot be considered as a property which can be maintained separately. These points are dealt with in general systems theory (Von Bertalanffy, 1952) and the organismic approach (Goldstein, 1939).

'From the biological point of view organization is inseparable from adaptation. They are two complementary processes of the same mechanism, the first being the internal aspect of the cycle of which adaptation concerns the external aspect.'

The external aspect of the cycle concerning the nature of interactions involved in adaptation has been elucidated to some extent by Weiss's formulation. The internal or organizational aspect has been in a similar way illuminated by the information processing model.[1] Piaget anticipated many of the essential features of the information processing model, for example in his conceptualization of schemata, their emergence, and modification by new experience.

This is a model which has been widely applied to the organization of functions in biological systems and especially to their regulation. It is not within the scope of this paper nor the competence of the author to take up this body of concepts in any detail. Inasmuch as it has been of great help to us in appreciating the crucial relationship of 'regulation' to the emergence and organization of behavior it should be touched upon briefly.[2]

[1] References to the information processing model are widely represented in the literature of a number of disciplines. Most influential in this study have been discussions of concepts by D. MacKay (1955, 1956); of concepts and neurophysiological applications by Miller *et al.* (1960) and Pribram (1963); application to physiological controls and regulation Yamamoto and Brobeck (1965) and the review by J. McV. Hunt (1961).

[2] One of the basic notions is that the system possesses inner criteria to which new inputs are matched. A certain 'error signal' results if there is a mismatch. This activates effector apparatus which can then carry out activities to reduce the error signal. If these activities repeatedly require certain modifications necessary to achieve a match (e.g., on encountering consistent features of the environment) the modifications become part of the inner criteria. The criterion (or schema) then comes to represent the organism-environment relationship more precisely. Miller *et al.* (1960) have expressed these points in their concept of the TOTE unit as the basic unit of behavior. The cogency of the information processing model for the developmental process has been suggested by D. MacKay (1956). He proposes that an inner criterion on which an error signal is based must itself have an ontogeny, differentiating more specifically from earlier more global routines. The information-processing model provides a means of visualizing the organization of a self-modifying system, which can take a changing relation to environment into account in terms of changes within itself as it maintains goal direction. In his application of the model to an understanding of neurophysiology and especially the regulatory function of the brain stem, Pribram (1963), emphasizes the optimal response of the system when such change takes place relatively slowly and by small increments. This provides an optimal 'error signal' to which the system is best suited to respond. The concept of an error signal optimal for acquisition of new behavioral schemata sheds further light on the picture we have drawn of regulation and its relation to the sequence of interactional behaviors encountered in the five issues.

One of the features provided by a successful reachievement of regulatory stability on advancing levels is to maintain smaller degrees of variation or mismatch in the interaction. Information processing can be more optimally carried out under such circumstances by the manipulative activities of the infant organism. The larger increments of stressful excitation which go with interactional asynchrony and dissonance tend to promote protective withdrawal and defensive reactions in the infant rather than his active manipulative approach. Furthermore it is essential that the initiative of the infant be free to manipulate selectively the very interaction itself with the mother. In the information processing view, through this manipulative process, the variations which are experienced in the interaction would tend to be brought into some predictable relation to the actions which the infant determined. Reciprocal coordination in this view would involve a particular feedback to a particular configuration of activity initiated, that is, specificity would be a critical feature.

In a context of stability of regulation, one can assume an option, on the part of the infant, to exercise selectivity in initiating new variations of manipulative activities in reducing the error signal occasioned by the small degrees of variation and novelty which would characterize a regulated system. In a context of regulatory in-stability this option would be lost in the necessity to restore or main-tain basic regulation. The smaller degrees of novelty could not be attended. The extent to which reciprocal coordination is achieved at each level would determine both the task of regulation that is imposed on the system and the selectivity optimal for new organiza-tions of activity to be tried out or integrated.

From the point of view of the information processing model, the infant's selective initiative to employ advancing capacities for activity in manipulating his environment provides him with an increasing repertoire of schemata or TOTEs. Eventually these will include those interactions with the mother necessary to mediate his own regulation.

It is in Issue 1 that the mother comes to 'know' her baby as *she* initiates variations of her own in her caretaking procedures in order to determine what 'works' and what doesn't in stabilizing the baby's regulation.

It is in Issue 3 on the other hand that the child himself must begin to experience reciprocation as produced specifically at his own initia-tive and at the time he designates. It is precisely the freedom of the infant to initiate exploratory and manipulative variations, which can be so sensitively interfered with or facilitated during this period.

It is in Issue 2, in the period of 'establishing reciprocal exchanges' that we see the affective display of delight and joy in both participants of the interaction when a back-and-forth specific reciprocal exchange has been achieved. This extends from smiling play to a host of little back-and-forth games in which one learns to match the other's actions. The specificity of this match becomes familiar to both. Joyful affect may come to operate as an indicator of specificity of fitting together. This is suggested also by the next step in the child's organization of his behavior. In the 6- to 9-month period the same effect of delight begins to mark the child's success in manipulating objects to fit what he has intended to reproduce. It is possible that this affect later becomes a signifier of reciprocal fit in interpersonal interactions.

From the investigation with kittens mentioned earlier it was suggested that we are looking at a shifting *equilibrium* of *initiative* in the interaction through which the kitten is organizing its behavior step by step in ever more independent degrees. One thing is certain, such a shift can be compromised by the human in many more ways than the animal perhaps can even imagine with the more stereotyped set of caretaking behaviors available to it.

There is only so much that can be usefully dealt with under the general rubric of the organization of behavior. It should be obvious that we have limited ourselves here to interactions of the first 18 months of life and have discussed them on the level of the organization of 'behavior'. The events of the second 18 months of life must be considered in respect to a next level of organization namely, that of 'personality'. Although it is built upon the foundations of the first 18 months and can be approached via the same interactional principles mother-child interaction in the second 18 months involves important new and additional capacities in the child. When these are followed in our longitudinal material and ordered in terms of the concepts we have presented, we suspect that bridges to more familiar personality theory can be outlined. This must be left for future work to determine.

APPENDIX 1

Examples of Categories Guiding Extraction of Data from Records

ISSUE 1 – INITIAL ADAPTATION – MONTHS 1, 2, 3.

'To what degree in the interaction between mother and child will the cues of the infant and/or his state be met by a specifically appropriate response on the part of the mother?'

Categories:

(1) *Examples* of appropriate and inappropriate interaction in respect to specificity, timing, modality, intensity, appropriateness, consistency.

(2) Sequence – that is, whether infant or mother has priority in initiation; nature of interaction initiated.

(3) Regulation – extent and duration of comfort or distress in infant and mother (achievement predictable schedule of feeding, sleeping, elimination).

(4) Evidence for preferential responsivity of infant.

ISSUE 2 – ESTABLISHING RECIPROCAL EXCHANGES – MONTHS 4, 5, 6.

'To what extent will the interaction between mother and child include reciprocal sequences of interchange between them, that is, back and forth alternations of activity and response?'

Categories:

(1) *Examples* of sequences of affectively reciprocal back and forth smiling play – frequency – vigor.

(2) Reciprocal co-ordination in other activities (and with other people). Extent to which reciprocation characterizes interaction? Non-reciprocation?

(3) Regulation – extent and duration of comfort or distress in infant feeding, sleeping, elimination.

(4) Amount and quality of separation.

ISSUE 3 – INFANT'S INITIATIVE TO DIRECT HIS ACTIVITY – MONTHS 7, 8, 9.

'To what degree will the initiative of the infant be successful in establishing social contact with the mother, especially in the form of a reciprocal interchange with her?'

Categories:

(1) *Examples* (success and failure) initiation of social contact with mothers, especially reciprocal sequences.

(2) Facilitation or interference with child's initiative (respect shown his specific preferences).

(3) Reciprocation of attentive and distance signals.

(4) Motor manipulation and co-ordination.

(5) Amount and quality of separation.

ISSUE 4 – AVAILABILITY OF MOTHER ON INFANT INITIATIVE MONTHS 10, 11, 12, 13.

'To what degree will the infant succeed in his demands that the mother herself fulfill his needs?'

Categories:

(1) Extent of infant demands *for* maternal response, extent of activity directed *away* from mother.

(2) Extent of maternal response (availability) frequency, specificity, affect.

(3) Use of attentive and distance signals for maintaining availability.

(4) Special devices used by child to secure maternal availability.

(5) Child's preference for mother in presence of others.

(6) Amount and quality of separation.

ISSUE 5 – SELF ASSERTION OF INFANT – MONTHS 14-21

'To what extent will the child establish self assertion in the interaction with mother?'

Categories:

(1) Extension and vigor of motor and manipulative exploration.

(2) Vigor of child in consummating his own intentions against interference – extent of child's yielding.

(3) Attitude of mother to child's self assertion and to his victory – extent of parental yielding.

(4) Behaviors of negativism, possessiveness, exhibitionism, tempertantrums.

(5) Progress of toilet training.

(6) Progress in ability to separate from mother; through own activity?

APPENDIX 2

Schedule of Contacts

Prenatal

Six to twelve tape-recorded interviews with the mother.

Psychological testing of mother and formulation of her character structure.

Interview with subject's own mother and/or husband.

Home visit.

Obstetrician's prenatal clinic record.

Social Service index.

Screening conference and final prenatal conference with formulation of maternal character structure.

Predictions of postnatal course of mother-child relationship.

Delivery and Lying-in

Observation of delivery.

Obstetrician's account of delivery.

Immediate postdelivery observations of child.

Daily observations, tests, and movies of child in lying-in period, including an eight-hour observation on fourth day.

Daily report of visiting nurses' observations in first fourteen days at home.

Post-natal conference with assessment of endowment of child and further prediction at approximately six weeks.

Postnatal to 18 months – a rotating schedule of

Home visit every six weeks.

Tape-recorded interview with mother every six weeks.

Well-baby clinic with pediatrician's examination report and

Developmental testing (Gesell and Hetzer-Wolf Tests) at same well-baby clinic (both every six weeks).

Postnatal: 18 to 36 months

Pediatrician's well-baby clinic four times per year.

Developmental tests (Merrill-Palmer or Gesell) four times per year.

Tape-recorded interview with mother six times per year.

Home visit six times per year.

Play sessions with child six times per year.

Two 'intensive weeks' at six-month intervals, beginning at eighteen months, comprising three play sessions with child in a ten-day period plus a tape-recorded interview with mother.

APPENDIX 3

Inter-analyst Reliability of Descriptive and Inferential Statements of Issues[1]

	++	+	O	−	− −	
Issue 1	10	4	1	0	0	15
2	11	2	1	0	0	14
3	5	2	0	0	0	7
4	8	6	2	0	0	16
5	7	5	0	0	3	15
Total	41	19	4	0	3	67

[1] Frequency of statements judged to be of high (+ +) and moderate (+) agreement, and those judged to be of high (− −) and moderate (−) disagreement. 'O' refers to those statements in which comparison was not possible.

Caretaking Settings, Background Events and Behavior Differences in Four Israeli Child-rearing Environments: Some Preliminary Trends

HAVA B. GEWIRTZ[1] and JACOB L. GEWIRTZ

Introduction

A method has been developed and described which is currently in use in an investigation of environmental stimulation, infant behaviors, and the contingencies between stimuli and behaviors in caretaker-infant interaction (J. L. & Hava B. Gewirtz, 1965). These contingencies imply conditioning opportunities as well as acquired stimulus control. The purposes of this investigation, which has been carried out in diverse Israeli child-rearing environments, can be described in terms of five overlapping aims:

1. *To define caretaking environments* for infants in functional terms, by identifying the stimuli impinging on infants in each environment, the incidence of their behaviors, and the sequential contingencies between the environmental stimuli and those infant behaviors.

2. *To compare diverse caretaking environments* in terms of the analyses at this level of stimulus, response and interchange (as under Aim 1). The environments compared are: the residential institution; the collective settlement (*kibbutz*); the single-child middle-class nuclear town-family (i.e., for the 'only' child); and the multiple-child middle-class nuclear town-family (i.e., for the 'youngest' child).

3. Within and across environments, *to compare the stimuli provided to infants and the incidence of infant behaviors at four successive age points* in the first year, i.e. at 8, 16, 24, and 32 weeks of life. Similarly, the interchanges between these behaviors and the environmental stimuli provided are to be examined at the successive age points.

[1] The first author's work on this project was supported by Grant MH-06779 from the National Institute of Mental Health.

4. *To develop methods for abstracting the elements of the interaction sequences* (chains) emerging from the dyadic interchange between stimuli and the behaviors of the infant. Those stimuli are provided for the most part through parent or 'upbringer' behaviors. And,

5. As a corollary of Aim 4, *to consider the learning implications of the stimulus-response contingencies* that are afforded infants in the different environments at the different age points. These contingencies have implications for the *acquisition* of responses and for (already) *acquired stimulus control* over responses.

In this paper, a sequel to our preliminary methodological report, we shall examine more closely some extensions of our method. In so doing, we shall present illustrative data from the four child-rearing environments selected for study. In addition, we shall detail the beginnings of a method for abstracting out the sequential details of the flow of interaction between the infant and each of the significant adults in his environment.

Background for Selection of Environment and Age Groups

The four environments studied, selected in part because of the circumstance of our presence in Israel at the start of the study, afford a 'natural laboratory' for the examination of the range of stimulus conditions available in different child-rearing settings.

Environmental Groups

The *residential institution* has been a focus of considerable interest for many years because the routine rearing conditions assumed to be provided in the typical institution were often pictured as having an unwholesome impact on the behavior and development of its residents and of those children who had spent considerable portions of their early lives there.

The middle-class *nuclear family* would appear to represent a point along many theory-relevant dimensions at an opposite extreme from that of the usual residential institution because of its low caretaker-child ratio and the typically exclusive and continuous responsibility of the single caretaker-mother for her infant.

Conditions affecting the behaviors of children in both the residential institution and the family have been described (for the most part in terms of differential caretaker roles and the degree of caretaker dedication or attachment to their charges) in global trait terms or in

230

the terms of a clinical picture arrived at informally (see, e.g., Provence & Lipton, 1962). Such descriptions are often plausible. Nevertheless, with perhaps one partial exception (Rheingold, 1960), there has been little attempt to specify the conditions provided infants in those settings or the patterns of infant responses (both immediate and long term) in the context of those conditions. These are the stimuli, the responses and their interchange required for a functional analysis.

The unique setting for the raising of children found in the more than 200 collective settlements or *kibbutzim* in Israel has for years intrigued observers in the behavioral sciences. The *kibbutz* has been typically described more in sociological or anthropological terms (e.g., Spiro, 1958) than in the terms of a functional psychological analysis. For instance, there has been interest in the role of the child's parents relative to that of his regular caretaker-upbringer (*metapelet*). Until the present time little or no attempt has been made to specify the stimulus conditions provided children which characterize the *kibbutz* as a child-rearing setting, and as compared, say, to the more conventional family environments; nor has much of an attempt been made to follow in detail the pattern of daily responses of the *kibbutz* infant. But even apart from an interest in the unique character of the *kibbutz*, as a child-rearing environment it falls within the dimensions of social stimulus conditions used in our study. The multiple caretaking and the age-homogeneous peer group in which the child is reared in the *kibbutz* provide points of similarity with the residential institution, while the active presence in the child's life of important family members, and especially his mother who has a major feeding role during much of the child's first year in the *kibbutz*, appears more similar to the pattern prevailing in the nuclear town-family.

In the residential institution as in the *kibbutz*, the infant's peers are typically part of his immediate environment, and all are under the care of the same professional caretaker(s). Hence, the division of the middle-class family sample into *single*-child and *multiple*-child families would permit a differentiated assessment of the stimulus conditions associated with the setting in which a single mother caretaker is continuously responsible for her infant; in the first case he is her 'only' child, and in the second, the 'youngest' of her several children. Moreover, the gross variable of *birth order* might be analyzed at the level of stimuli and responses into its functional components through such a comparison. For example, a newborn infant would inevitably displace his siblings by virtue of the finite caretaking capacity of the

231

one available mother. And we would expect conditions for a 'youngest' child to differ considerably from those for an 'only' child (see, e.g., J. L. & Hava B. Gewirtz, 1965). Lastly, if the observations could differentiate between the single-child and the multiple-child family environments (which would seem far more similar to each other than either would be to the institution or to the collective settlement), the observational method itself would receive a degree of validation.

In summary, then, the environment of the nuclear town-family single- and multiple-child, that of the collective settlement, and that of the residential institution, may be thought to represent points along some complex continuum of social stimulation from the vantage point of the child being reared in them.

Age Groups

Foci for descriptive information about the character of each environment and about the changes in the infant's behavior with age are provided by the 8-, 16-, 24-, and 32-week age points. Moreover, the age variable allows us to index selected changes in behavior which could, in part, be an outcome of cumulative effects of systematic differences in environmental conditions. Thus, if infants at a young age exhibit relatively homogeneous behavior patterns in environments which provide different amounts and types of stimulation, but then in their behavior draw apart increasingly with age, such findings might suggest that (among other things) differential learning opportunities had been provided in these environments.

The behavior concepts for performance and learning phenomena provide keys for an understanding of the impact of recurring contingencies in the environment on systematic changes in response strength in early human life. At the same time, also, such concepts offer us the means for identifying an organism's functional environment. That is, an analysis in conditioning terms can facilitate the identification or isolation of the relatively few events, out of the very many which constitute an environment, that actually can and do function as stimuli for an organism, and, hence, that can have a systematic impact on behavioral development. On this basis, the utility of a corollary of the conception of learning can also be evaluated. The assumption involved is that it is of limited predictive utility simply to note the types or frequencies of environmental events offered infants; rather, it is particularly important to take into account the circumstances under which given stimuli are provided to them, and in particular, whether these stimuli, together with the infant behaviors, enter effective contingencies for the acquisition and maintenance of behavior strength.

Method

Some General Methodological Considerations

First, the independent variables used in this study are not taken to be the age and environmental group membership of subjects per se, but rather as they are *reduced* to patterns of environmental stimulation and as they are involved in *contingent* relationships with infant behaviors (see Gewirtz, 1961, 1968a, 1968b). It is such contingent events which could have direct impact on infant responses, both immediate and long term.

In this context, the response patterns of institutional infants will be compared not only with those of nuclear family and *kibbutz* babies but also in terms of differences in the *patterns of stimulation* afforded within the group. As we are not interested focally (only incidentally) in demographic variables as indices of environmental conditions, there would have been no need to select such apparently diverse groups for study, except that infant behavior patterns were expected to differ among environmental groups. However, instead of explaining differences in outcome only through assumptions about the differential learning histories of the environmental groups [from such variables as 'age', as was done by Gewirtz (1965)], we expect to demonstrate how the different patterns of the provision of stimuli and patterns of the occurrence of what appear to be learning contingencies actually vary within and between the conventional variety of demographic groupings that we have been investigating.

Second, the occurrences of events are described in stripped-down objective observation units. These minimize the burden of subjective interpretation on the part of the observer. At the same time, there is flexibility for summarizing or grouping such basic data at any level and in any desired way at later stages of analysis.

Third, our recording of ongoing environmental events and infant responses is continuous throughout the period of an entire day that the infant is observed. The sequence of events in time is preserved, and the record may be ordered (in half-minute multiples) into time units of any desired length. At the same time, details of the flow of observed events are caught in their entirety.

Fourth, the decision to use pre-established observation categories, and the nature of the ones selected for use, is due in part to the requirements of our theoretical approach, in part to leads stemming from theories and empirical findings in the literature, and in part to those possibilities and limitations inherent in our observation and recording techniques which became evident after extensive pilot work. In this context, our purpose was to benefit from the conceptual and methodological efficiency implied in the use of pre-determined behavior categories and their codes. Nevertheless, because this investigation was directed toward a wide range of events with little methodological precedent on the patterns with which we dealt, it was thought important to keep the observers alert to occurrences which would not readily fall under the categories as defined, to insure the overall precision of the method.

An Observation Excerpt

A detailed description of our basic procedure has already been presented (J. L. & Hava B. Gewirtz, 1965). The observations collected can be described at a number of different levels. These range from a description in terms of the category definitions and coding system in the original observation manual through the final form of the data as transcribed in terms of the perfected computer code that was entered on the 80-column punch cards. In this sequel to the earlier paper, an 8-minute observation excerpt can serve to illustrate the nature of our raw data as well as the way they were transformed for computer processing.

Table 24 describes the observation sample in a prose narrative form which basically consists of the condensed definitions of the behavior categories as they appeared in the observation manual. Table 25 presents the same observation sample in the form of the two-character alpha-numeric computer codes into which all observation records were finally transcribed. This sample is taken from the observation record of a 24-week-old *kibbutz* boy, and begins at 5:52 a.m. towards the end of the first feeding session of the day. The excerpt begins with the infant in his mother's lap as she breast feeds him (the mode of feeding typical of *kibbutz* rearing for much of the first year of life). The four classes of coded information in Table 25 (Time, Background, Setting, and Discrete Behaviors and Interaction) are entered within fixed column areas on the punch cards. Each card represents a successive 30-second observation block. To

TABLE 24

Sample Observation in Narrative Form: 8 Minutes Excerpted from the Day of a 24-week-old Kibbutz Boy

Time (a.m.)	Background	Setting	Discrete Behaviors and Interaction
5 : 52	mother present	Feeding	mother removes her breast from S's mouth; mother changes S's position; mother burps S;
5 : 52½	mother present	Feeding	mother burps S; mother kisses S; mother kisses S; S touches mother; S looks around;
5 : 53	mother present	Feeding	mother kisses S; [mother burps S – S burps – mother talks to S]; mother lifts-up S; mother carries S;
5 : 53½	mother present; main-caretaker enters		mother carries S; mother places S on his back on surface of dressing table; S vocalizes repeatedly;
5 : 54	mother present; main-caretaker present		[S vocalizes and smiles at mother – mother talks and smiles at S]; [S vocalizes– mother talks and smiles at S – S looks at mother];
5 : 54½	mother moves around the room; main-caretaker present		mother leaves S's side; S vocalizes repeatedly; S vocalizes;
5 : 55	mother moves around the room; main-caretaker present		S follows mother (visually);
5 : 55½	mother moves around the room; main-caretaker present		[S looks at main-caretaker – main-caretaker approaches S and touches S and talks to S and smiles at him – S smiles at main-caretaker]; main-caretaker leaves S's side; S looks around; S fusses;

Table 23 continued overleaf

TABLE 24—continued

Time (a.m.)	Background	Setting	Discrete Behaviors and Interaction
5 : 56	mother present; main-caretaker present	Diapering	[S fusses – mother approaches and talks to him]; mother starts changing S's diapers; mother talks to S;
5 : 56½	mother present; main-caretaker present	Diapering	[S vocalizes repeatedly – mother talks to him]; S touches mother; [mother talks to S and tickles him – S smiles – mother smiles back at S];
5 : 57	mother converses with main-caretaker	Diapering	S vocalizes;
5 : 57½	mother converses with main-caretaker	Diapering	[S increases his motility and smiles at mother – mother smiles back at him]; mother leaves S's side;
5 : 58	mother moves around the room; main-caretaker exits room		S changes his position; S vocalizes repeatedly; [main-caretaker talks to S – S follows her (visually)];
5 : 58½	mother present		[mother approaches S – S looks at her – mother picks up S and talks to him – S smiles at her]; S increases his motility;
5 : 59	mother present		mother carries S; [S vocalizes – mother talks to him]; mother places S in his crib;
5 : 59½	mother exits room		mother talks to S; mother arranges S's clothes; S smiles at mother; [mother leaves S's side – S follows her (visually)]; S manipulates an object;

Note: Activities in brackets in Behavior column represent interaction corresponding to codes listed within double parentheses in Table 25.

simplify this presentation, column spacing has been modified. Also, three classes of information normally included on each card have been omitted. These are subject Identification details, Continuation Card Number, and Continuous Behaviors.

TABLE 25

Sample Observation (Coded) for Computer Summaries:
8 Minutes Excerpted from the Day of a 24-week-old Kibbutz Boy

Time	Background	Setting	Discrete Behaviors and Interaction
(5 : 52 a.m.)			
104	MMHR	FD	MMDUSJ MMPSSJ MMBPSJ
105	MMHR	FD	MMBPSJ MMKSSJ MMKSSJ SJTCMM
			SJLR——
106	MMHR	FD	MMKSSJ ((MM43BPBHTO)) MMUPSJ
			MMCRSJ
107	MMHR CMIN		MMCRSJ MMSFSJ SJVP——
108	MMHR CMHR		((MM72VOSSTOSM)) ((MM23VOTOSMLK))
109	MMMV CMHR		MMLVSJ SJVP—— SJVO——
110	MMMV CMHR		SJFLMM
111	MMMV CMHR		((CM23LKAPTSTOSMSS)) CMLVSJ
			SJLR—— SJFO——
112	MMHR CMHR	CH	((MM72FOAPTO)) MMCHSJ MMTOSJ
113	MMHR CMHR	CH	((MM72VPTO)) SJTCMM
			((MM43TOTISSSM))
114	MMTOCM	CH	SJVO——
115	MMTOCM	CH	((MM72MTSSSM)) MMLVSJ
116	MMMV CMOT		SJPO—— SJVP—— ((CM52TOFL))
117	MMHR		((MM54APLKPKTOSS)) SJMT——
118	MMHR		MMCRSJ ((MM72VOTO)) MMCBSJ
119	MMOT		MMTOSJ MMRRSJ SJSSMM ((MM52LVFL))
			SJMNOJ
(5 : 59½ a.m.)			

In general, the Behavior acts represent the onset of discrete isolated responses, without account being taken of the duration of the response, i.e., a mother's 'talk' to S represents a discrete natural unit of talk, whether it involves a single word or a sentence. Similarly, significant changes in S's position are coded as units regardless of their 2- or 20-second duration. However, a selected number of behaviors which tend to appear repeatedly in short time spans, in addition to single occurrences, are coded accordingly. Thus, there are three codes for vowel vocalizations: a single vocal response, a

237

rapidly repeated response, and an ongoing vocalization. The observers were trained to discriminate among response categories of such sets.

While the observation units appearing in the Background and Setting also have the form of discrete events, their interpretation differs. Thus, 'talks' in the Background means that some talking went on during the time unit indicated. Further, 'feeding' under Setting means that the particular time unit is characterized by, or occurs during, a situation characterized by a feeding *theme*, without reference to the component behaviors that occur in the Setting or their frequencies.

Preliminary Data Analyses

In our earlier 1965 report, hand-tallied count data were presented for two Ss from the middle-class town-family environments. These were for one 'only' and one 'youngest' infant. The summary counts presented there were not final, and served as illustrations of the variables which seemed to us to show promising results for our preliminary report. Since then we have completed computer processing (i.e., sorting) of our data through the *first level* of summarization. This summary consists of frequency counts and rate measures for each unique event (i.e., code combination) within every one of the five classes of observations, and while not final, more closely approximates the descriptive statistics that will be presented in the final report. For example, we have the total frequency of Feed time units (Setting), the total frequency of time units in which mother was present (Background), and the total frequency of occurrence of S's smiles or caretaker talk to S (Behavior). The more definitive findings under our theoretical approach are, of course, to be expected when we delve into the examination of infant and adult behaviors, and the sequential contingencies characterizing them.

These basic counts, which consumed a great deal of computer sorting time, were first summarized separately for each S. They are now being refined to provide separate counts for selected conditions within each observation record, e.g., for behavior rate under different Background or Setting conditions. These differentiated summaries will generate the scores for subsequent inferential-statistical tests of the differences among the various environment and age groups.

In this paper, we shall present some descriptive statistical data from the first-level summaries for a group of 24-week-old boys from each of the four environments sampled in this study. The four groups each contained five Ss. No attempt is made here to test differences among the four groups by inferential statistics. Nevertheless, the descriptive statistics presented can be useful here to suggest group trends as well as to indicate the direction of our subsequent work.

1. *The Structural Frame of the Environment*

In our 1965 report, we illustrated the utility of an analysis in terms of the structural frame of the environment with the observation that, while the 'only' and the 'youngest' child each spent approximately the same amount of time awake and alone, they appeared to differ consistently and predictably in the pattern of their contact with other persons. With the availability of more extensive computer counts, we are now able to examine the structural trends that separate the four environmental groups at 24 weeks of age. [Analyses of age and sex trends on caretaking and background themes for *kibbutz* infants are being presented in a separate report (Hava B. & J. L. Gewirtz, 1968).]

Table 26 illustrates some of these structural or gross 'ecological' features of the day, both Background and Setting, which constitute the *context* for the experiences of Ss in the four environmental groups. Total minutes of observation and percentage of time awake are seen to be relatively homogeneous for all groups. For preliminary comparisons, the duration indices of Table 26 are presented as percentages of S's time awake (rather than in numbers of minutes). The summary statistics for 'visits' of the various persons entering S's environment overlap to a considerable extent. Further, this summary does not yield figures for the simultaneous presence of two or more persons. Nevertheless, the separate summaries for the various caretakers and visitors, as well as the duration of time during which Ss received instrumental caretaking, all reflect plausible differences among the different environments. In terms of percentage of the time S is awake, the institutional environment appears to provide infants the *least* variation in terms of total caretaking time, of visits by persons other than caretakers, and of exposure to locations other than the 'home room'. In contrast, both *kibbutz* and multiple-child-family infant groups seem *most* exposed to such social and physical variations, while the environment of the single-child-family infant appears to be relatively more insulated from such exposures. On the other hand, in the institution, at least one caretaker is present on the

239

TABLE 26

Setting and Background Summaries for 24-week-old Boys in the Four Child-rearing Environments

Environment	Time			Locations		Visitors											
	Total Min. of Observation	% Time S Awake	% Time in Caretaking Setting	Locations Other than S's Room		Father		Mother		Main-Caretaker		Other Caretakers*		All Other Visitors		
				% Time Present	No. of Locations	% Time Present	No. of Visits	% Time Present	No. of Visits	% Time Present	No. of Visits	% Time Present	No. of Visits	% Time Present	No. of Visits	No. of Different Visitors
Institution (N=5)																
Mean	680	74	10	12	1	—	—	—	—	3	4	70	36	5	3	2
Median	678	77	9	14	1	—	—	—	—	1	4	78	42	2	1	1
Range	672-699	54-90	8-14	0-21	0-1	—	—	—	—	0-9	0-7	52-82	7-59	1-17	1-7	1-3
Kibbutz (N=5)																
Mean	742	70	16	44	2	10	2	36	10	13	8	8	10	21	14	4+
Median	744	76	18	42	2	8	3	33	9	14	8	9	11	21	16	4+
Range	679-807	46-85	10-21	9-91	1-4	4-16	1-3	25-48	6-16	8-20	4-11	1-16	1-19	2-43	5-23	2-7+
Youngest-child (Town) (N=5)																
Mean	680	74	16	27	2	16	9	37	33	—	—	—	—	23	17	3
Median	663	77	18	30	3	9	8	30	29	—	—	—	—	20	17	3
Range	490-810	53-85	10-22	0-54	0-3	2-56	7-16	23-68	22-51	—	—	—	—	1-43	4-34	1-4
Single-child (Town) (N=5)																
Mean	712	76	14	19	1	12	9	59	43	—	—	—	—	10	6	1
Median	730	77	13	14	1	10	7	60	42	—	—	—	—	11	4	1
Range	558-798	69-83	12-18	0-56	0-2	5-31	4-17	42-80	21-63	—	—	—	—	0-21	0-16	0-4

*'Other caretakers' includes one or more caretakers, excluding the Main-Caretaker (Caretaker-in-Charge).

average 70 per cent of S's waking time, and the mother in the single-child family appears on the average to spend considerably more time in her infant's vicinity than does the average *kibbutz* or multiple-child family mother. Thus, it is interesting to note that the variety of background events as such appears to be independent of the duration of caretaker (or mother) presence.

2. *The Normative Behavioral Assessment of Subject and Environment*

As may be recalled from our earlier report, this phase of the analyses involves establishing relevant frequency and rate measures for all classes of S behaviors, whether or not they are directed towards a specific social object, and similar measures for the behaviors directed toward S by all persons in his vicinity, and especially by his caretakers. These measures are specified separately for those responses occurring *within* an interaction chain and for those occurring *outside* of such chains as 'isolated' responses. Isolated responses would include those made in the absence of other persons as well as responses which do not evoke (or even require) an immediate reply from their recipients.

Our previous analysis suggested that there are systematic tendencies for some behaviors to be generally more prominent than others, regardless of environment, while the frequency of specific behaviors such as mother's talking and subject's smiling showed up differentially among the environments.

Let us now examine the records of the same five Ss from each environmental group for which selected Setting and Background summaries have been presented in Table 26. The normative behavioral descriptions from these records are illustrated in Table 27. Presented there are frequency and rate measures for caretaker and mother 'talk' and 'smile' responses and for child 'vowel vocalization' and 'smile' responses. (Scores for S's behaviors exhibited when there was no person – other than the observer – present are not given in this table.) Even at this crude level of analysis, some general trends can be gleaned from the central tendency indices. Thus, for both infants and adults, vocal (and talk) responses seem relatively more frequent than smile responses. Further, in contrast to infant vowel vocalizations and adult talk responses, smile responses of both infants and adults seem to be relatively more under social stimulus control, since they occur predominantly in interaction sequences. Moreover, relative to smiles, it appears that in interaction vocal responses are exhibited

Adult and Infant Behavior Summaries for 24-week

Environment	Adults					
	Mother				Main Caretaker	
	Talk		Smile		Talk	
	Isolated	Inter-action	Isolated	Inter-action	Isolated	Inter-action
Institution (N=5)						
Frequencies —Mean	—	—	—	—	1	1
Median	—	—	—	—	0	0
Range	—	—	—	—	0-3	0-5
Rate/minute[1]—Mean	—	—	—	—	·03	·04
Median	—	—	—	—	0	0
Range	—	—	—	—	0-·10	0-·10
Kibbutz (N=5)						
Frequencies —Mean	23	119	1	58	6	17
Median	12	98	1	64	5	13
Range	4-49	58-196	0-2	35-74	2-11	4-39
Rate/minute —Mean	·13	·66	·006	·32	·10	·25
Median	·07	·52	·003	·31	·08	·18
Range	·02-·28	·36-1·12	0-·01	·22-·42	·02-·16	·13-·56
Youngest-child (*Town*) (N=5)						
Frequencies —Mean	27	144	1	34	—	—
Median	19	135	1	28	—	—
Range	17-59	117-192	0-1	11-84	—	—
Rate/minute —Mean	·18	·71	·003	·22	—	—
Median	·10	·68	·003	·18	—	—
Range	·06-·38	·12-1·52	0-·01	·04-·45	—	—
Single-child (*Town*) (N=5)						
Frequencies —Mean	68	348	1	71	—	—
Median	31	240	1	56	—	—
Range	10-141	117-797	0-5	2-150	—	—
Rate/minute —Mean	·20	1·17	·004	·26	—	—
Median	·12	·95	0	·22	—	—
Range	·09-·46	·34-2·60	0-·02	·01-·62	—	—

[1] Rates per minute are based on the frequency of a behavior per number of minutes o: of minutes awake for S.

Hava B. Gewirtz and Jacob L. Gewirtz

old Boys in the Four Child-rearing Environments

Adults						Infant			
Main Caretaker		Other Caretakers							
Smile		Talk		Smile		Vocalize		Smile	
Iso-lated	Inter-action	Iso-lated	Inter-action	Iso-lated	Inter-action	Iso-lated	Inter-action	Iso-lated	Inter-action
0	1	13	68	0	17	276	31	8	37
0	1	5	48	0	18	82	30	7	45
0	0-4	3-35	26-100	0	8-25	24-921	19-47	1-16	8-59
0	·09	·05	·22	0	·05	·52	·06	·02	·08
0	0	·01	·16	0	·06	·22	·06	·01	·07
0	0-·40	·01-·13	·06-·52	0	·02-·08	·04-1·69	·04-·09	0-·03	·01-·12
0	5	3	7	0	4	290	75	18	93
0	5	1	3	0	3	254	50	12	78
0-1	0-10	0-10	0-22	0-1	0-13	63-526	44-117	2-29	48-146
0	·08	·05	·10	0	·06	·55	·14	·04	·18
0	·09	·01	·03	0	·03	·45	·12	·02	·16
0-·01	·01-·16	0-·21	0-·24	0-·02	0-·14	·14-1·09	·07-·23	0-·09	·09-·28
—	—	—	—	—	—	293	84	13	75
—	—	—	—	—	—	263	71	15	74
—	—	—	—	—	—	76-504	29-166	3-19	44-107
—	—	—	—	—	—	·62	·19	·03	·15
—	—	—	—	—	—	·53	·13	·03	·17
—	—	—	—	—	—	·17-1·33	·05-·44	0-·05	·10-·18
—	—	—	—	—	—	323	180	10	101
—	—	—	—	—	—	186	115	13	81
—	—	—	—	—	—	105-652	81-371	2-19	71-159
—	—	—	—	—	—	·65	·36	·02	·20
—	—	—	—	—	—	·32	·20	0	·16
—	—	—	—	—	—	·18-1·32	·14-·84	0-·03	·12-·36

the adult's presence (for mother, main caretaker, and other caretakers), and per number proportionately less often by infants than are talk responses exhibited by adults. Some inter-environment differences also emerge. Median smile and vocal rates of institutional infants appear about half or less of what they are for infants in the other environments; in turn, institution infants themselves appear to be exposed to the lowest rate of adult talking and smiling. Mothers of single-child-family infants seem to exhibit the highest overall rate of talking towards their infants, and *kibbutz* mothers seem to smile more to their infants than do mothers of urban families.

There is no need to comment further on the contents of the two tables, for the comparisons they contain must be qualified by factors inherent in the nature of the environments and/or our observation method. For instance, it may be assumed that the parents of the town-family Ss had contact with their infants both before and after our observation hours, which was less likely to be the case for the parents of *kibbutz* Ss or the caretakers of institutional Ss. Also, it should be added that the caretaker-in-charge ('main caretaker') in the institution has a predominantly supervisory role, and the actual caretaking of the infants is carried out by those labeled 'other caretakers'. In contrast, the 'main caretaker' in the *kibbutz* environment is directly involved in routine caretaking and socialization, and much more so than her helper or relief-substitute. These sample qualifications should be considered in addition to the fact that the data presented in these tables are not complete. However, it is especially important at this juncture to emphasize that these summaries represent artificially separated aspects of analyses which should go together. In other words, the normative Behavior summaries must be fully integrated with the structural description of the environment to permit meaningful interpretations. Thus, adult behaviors would be counted separately for periods of instrumental caretaking of various kinds, for periods during which there was no caretaking, for periods of play interaction, and the like. And S's behaviors would be counted separately under diverse or no caretaking conditions, when directed toward particular persons in the background, when no adult was present, and the like. Also, time of day or time relative to S's schedule (such as periods preceding meals) would need to be taken into account when assessing such behaviors as fusses, responses to entering or departing adults, etc. Our current preparation of summaries of Behavior classes under selected context conditions will provide leverage on these questions.

3. *Interaction Sequence Analysis*

The focus of our theoretical approach remains on interaction sequences comprised of the behaviors which occur as part of social interchanges rather than as isolated behaviors. Our conviction is that research efficiency in the arena of parent-child interaction would be increased significantly by attendance to the sequential details of the interaction flow. For instance, it would be possible to separate those contingencies between an adult's acts (which provide antecedent stimuli) and an infant's acts (as consequent responses), and vice versa, that are relatively invariant from those contingencies that vary. The latter contingencies might vary with identifiable contextual conditions, or with the particular combination of antecedent stimuli provided by the sequential responses of the adult to the sequential pattern of S's behaviors. It would also be of interest to analyze the influence of timing and order factors on the interaction contingencies. Further, it would be possible to catalogue instances where a particular behavior of the first actor would lead to a particular behavior from the second actor, and vice versa. Thus, also, each actor's response might be classified further according to some more abstract scheme, for instance, as one reflecting instrumental or emotional dependence, or as one that is cooperative-complementary or antagonistic.

In our report of 1965, gross interaction patterns were compared, and it was found, for example, that the 'only' child had approximately twice as many interaction episodes as the 'youngest' child (496 vs. 227); that in both cases more of these were initiated by adults; and a greater proportion of these adult-initiated sequences was directed to the 'only' than to the 'youngest' child.

Although we do not yet have inferential statistics for our analyses of interactions, we have refined our method and now have a notion of some differences to expect. Thus, it is likely we will detect environmental differences in the overall rate of interactions (total number of interaction chains per S). For example, in terms of time units observed, institutional Ss show a low rate of interaction while single-child-family Ss show a rather high rate. However, such assessment of overall rate would be inadequate, even when all Background and Setting variables are controlled, without further classification of the interaction chains themselves into specific patterns or types. As a first step toward this end of classification, the attempt is being made to determine whether there are discriminable clusters or contingent pairs of stimuli and responses, i.e., specific adult responses and specific infant responses which tend to occur in temporal or functional contiguity. A beginning has been made by carrying out a preliminary analysis on all interaction responses occurring in the records of one 32-week-old S from each of the four caretaking environments most common in terms of the *conditional probability* (*cp*) for the proportion of times in one observation day that a response of one actor will be followed by a given response of the other actor. This was not done for the purpose of generalization, but was a by-product of our testing a computer program. Hence, the Ss, taken from that at the 'top of the pile' for each environment, were not selected to be representative. Even so, from these results there emerges a picture of the ranges of index values through which such variables might operate.

A number of reasonable contingency patterns emerge from an examination of behavior categories having substantial incidences of occurrence. These are characterized by *cp* values like those which, in a variety of analyses, could serve as individual difference measures (i.e., dependent variables). Some examples of patterns of adult responses *to* child behavior follow: the *cp*s that a child's *vocalization* will be followed by adult *talking* in four Ss (one from each of our four environments) range from ·52 to ·81; the *cp*s that a child's *vocalization* will be followed by an adult *smile* range from ·21 to ·42; the *cp*s that a child's *smile* will be followed by an adult *smile* range from ·46 to ·88; and the *cp*s that his *smile* will be followed by adult *talking* range from ·25 to ·51. Some examples of patterns of infant responses *to* adult behavior for the same four Ss are the following: the *cp*s that an infant's *smile* will follow an adult's *approach* range from ·24 to ·44; the *cp*s that an infant's *smile* will follow an adult *smile* range from ·50 to ·79; and that an infant's *smile* will follow an adult's *talking* range from ·30 to ·57; and, lastly, the *cp*s that an infant's vowel *vocalization* will follow an adult's *talking* range from ·09 to ·15.

In connection with adult-child contingency clusters, our preliminary impression is, first, that aside from visual orientation responses, the child's predominant response to various adult initiations (e.g., approaches, smiles, talks, hugs) is smiling, regardless of the 'modality' of the adult's evoking initiation. In contrast, the adult's predominant responses to the child's initiations appear more to be of the same 'modality' as the initiator's, at least with respect to the child's smiles and vocalizations. Further analyses will determine whether such contingency clusters are a function of the stimulation in the environment, of developmental level, or perhaps whether they reflect only residual variation that is not to be explained in terms of the independent variables of this study.

A number of simplifying methodological conditions were required for the preliminary adult-child contingency analysis presented above. Thus, while several behaviors of a child or of an adult might be concurrent (i.e., part of a response complex) and occur before a response of the other actor, it was necessary for that analysis to treat each behavior as orthogonal, as if it were a single act not occurring with any other behavior. It was also necessary to pool across actor positions in the interaction sequence, thereby ignoring the actual actor position at which single acts occurred. Thus, this analysis attended only to the *order* of single acts of the child and adult, i.e., which act of one followed immediately an act of the other.

We are preparing computer programs to make possible somewhat more complex interaction sequence analyses than the one just illustrated. These include contingency analyses, as follows: *First,* the complex of concurrent or sequential acts as a single act by an actor before the other actor responds will be treated by dyadic contingency analysis. *Second,* the same complexes will be analyzed three-at-a-time by a contingency analysis. *Third,* an analysis of single behaviors and of behavior complexes across pairs of actor positions in the interaction sequence will be made. This analysis will also include the occurrence of single behaviors within each actor position. These contingency analyses will evaluate the deviation from chance of the incidence of each response combination.

Further analyses of interaction sequences will involve classification of patterns in terms of the initiator and the terminator of the sequence. Underlying this principle of classification is our key assumption that the infant's behavior is not simply a function of evoking stimuli in the environment, but a function also of whether and how the environment responds to his behaviors. Accordingly, the plan is to classify as a unit each of the interaction sequences in which an S has been involved in terms of the identities of initiator and terminator, of the number of actor positions (one more than the number of shifts), of the nature of the initiating and terminating response of each sequence, of concurrent responses at each position, and the like. The frequencies and rates of occurrence of each of these patterns for an S would then be considered in the context of time and of indices for Behaviors, Background and Setting events.

247

Some Closing Points about the Approach

With its pre-established observation categories for environment and infant behaviors, our approach attempts to remain open with respect to the relevance at any time point of events that do not fall readily under the behavior categories. Various relationships among variables we might look for, and sometimes also the forms of the relationships, are suggested under the aegis of a learning-behavior theory. Our interest, however, is not in these relationships alone but also in the way in which to research the broad area of infant-adult interaction.

A final point about our approach and method of analyses is in place here. In all analyses, S is to be placed first of all in his individual context. That is, initially, his behaviors are to be related to the stimuli provided to him in his environment. This would involve not only structural or normative aspects of his environment (such as the duration and times he was observed, the number of feeding periods, or the number of persons visiting while he was observed), but also the events comprising and the patterns characterizing interaction. This approach would be in keeping with the theoretical orientation outlined at the start of this paper, the intent of which was to move beyond sociological and role definitions of environmental variables and into a functional analysis of the elements which underlie them, at the level of stimulus and response. Thus, we could conceive of an institutional S who 'deviates' from his group in terms of the pattern of stimulation to which he has been exposed, as well as in reinforcement contingencies and behaviors exhibited. For instance, he might be the institution 'pet' who is provided extensive stimulation of all types and is heavily reinforced for social approach behaviors. His pattern might thus resemble that of an 'only' family-child or a *kibbutz* child, more than that of an institution child. The identification of such 'overlapping' cases would support the utility of the functional analyses employed. After such intra- and inter-group and intra- and inter-subject analyses, rate measures will be employed to compare the age trends across the caretaking groups. If, as expected, behavior rates increase across the four age-levels, but differentially in the different caretaking environments according to the incidence of learning contingencies provided, there would be presumptive support for interpretations of the developmental changes in learning terms.

APPENDIX

Observer Training and Reliability

Because of the interest in our observation procedure, some details of observer training and results for observer reliability determinations are presented in this section.

The emphasis in observer training was (a) on the final selection of categories to be employed in recording theoretically relevant behaviors, (b) on sharpening category definitions, and (c) on determining which of the behaviors important for our theoretical approach were being omitted. In the wide range of stimulus situations to which the observers were exposed, they scored events under a greater number of categories than those finally selected for use. In this 'definitional' process, categories with low incidences of occurrence or characterized by low observer agreement were either discarded or combined with similarly defined categories. It was not known in advance how many categories could be scored reliably in a study of this type, and the observer reliability determination was one basis used for keeping the number within manageable bounds.

During training and subsequently while making formal observations, observers described (on the blank page facing each record page) atypical conditions which could qualify the behaviors scored as well as instances where behaviors which seemed theoretically important did not fit well under the defined categories. In addition, each observer was required to review her record during and immediately after her observation. Subsequently, where possible, the observer gave her coded record to another observer for review. Finally, some months after an observation was performed and submitted as complete, the observer checked her record against the transcription into which it had been coded for computer summarization.

Observers worked in pairs for the reliability training and determinations. One of the principal investigators was typically present during reliability training and determinations, thus insuring the independent recording of the observations and making it possible to improvise remedies for the types of observation errors being made. Equally important, the presence of a 'criterion observer' made it possible to detect 'errors of agreement', which might occur (a) when both observers agreed on the scoring of an event but *scored it incorrectly*, and (b) when both agreed by not scoring an event that *should have been scored*. A criterion observer could detect many such errors of agreement, which, if undetected, could inflate agreement percentages in reliability determinations.

The check for reliability consisted of having pairs of observers simultaneously and independently record the behavior of a given S, while using the same timer signals. Subsequently, a block-by-block comparison of their records was carried out. The reference point for calculating the reliability in terms of 'percentage observer agreement' was the identical time unit in which both observers scored the ongoing events. A check was made to see if the two observers in each pair recorded the identical behaviors in each time unit. Discrepancies from full agreement on each recorded event were further analyzed into errors of *omission* (e.g., one observer recorded 'S vocalizes' while the other observer recorded nothing), and errors of *commission* (e.g., one observer recorded 'mother touches S' while the second observer recorded 'mother pats S'). Subsequently, for each observation category, the number of agreements and the number of errors of commission and omission were totaled for the entire observation session. Percentage agreement was calculated as the number of agreements, divided by the number of agreements plus the number of the two types of disagreement, multiplied by 100.

For a severe test of the method, observer training and reliability determinations were carried out in the more difficult settings (e.g., feeding) and generally with infants 6 through 10 months old. These conditions were selected because they generated high rates of behaviors in interaction, and more complex sequences. The emphasis throughout was on preparing the observers to catch the sequence of responses in the interchange flow in terms of order of actors, and response content. During the period of reliability determination, agreement figures for several key behaviors and types of contingencies were calculated following training sessions. This routine made it possible to chart progress in the level of agreement during the training phase. Thus, the need for further training could be assessed and acted upon at any point (e.g., a pair of observers might require additional practice, or clarification of the definitions might be required in a unique setting). Generally, a trend of systematic improvement in the percentage agreement figures was found across sessions until a plateau was reached, where even a considerable investment of additional training would seem unlikely to result in appreciable improvement.

Although a wide sample of observer agreement figures was collected at the time of training, until now we have not audited these figures beyond the level of rapid spot-checking that was required at the time for the evaluation of the training progress. The complete set of reliability data is being audited. This procedure also provides a useful basis for an attempt to explore a number of alternative approaches to, and indices of, observer reliability, as well as for tactical decisions on combining sets of independent categories in the final analyses. Hence, the agreement figures presented here are but a small sample of those obtained during the training period itself. Further, it is of limited utility to emphasize observer agreement percentages *pooled across* different observer pairs, Ss, S ages, actors, objects and settings, and sometimes even across categories. The evaluation of these percentages as reliability figures would depend upon such considerations as: the incidence of each response category for each observer pair; whether 'errors of agreement' were taken into account; the lengths of the settings sampled and whether they were representative; whether the responses occurred in interaction sequences and whether singly or concurrently with other responses scored; and whether the percentages reflected progressive improvement across successive reliability sessions. Further, it would be useful to know if 'definitional drift' in the use of the behavior categories by observers could be detected by spot-checks at various points in the formal observation series. For such reasons as these, the complete set of reliability figures and the methods by which they were determined must await a definitive report of the results of this study. It is with these words of caution that some preliminary illustrative observer agreement values are given.

Observer agreement figures for those single behavior categories with high incidences of occurrence in general ranged upward from 65 per cent to 70 per cent. One set of 835 half-minute observation units (pooled across Ss, observer pairs, and the behaviors in and out of interaction) yielded the following figures for selected *child* behavior categories: smiles, 66 per cent; vowel vocalizations (all), 74 per cent; and laughs, 78 per cent. Agreement values for some *adult* behavior categories were found to be: talks, 76 per cent; smiles, 58 per cent; approaches, 64 per cent; and hugs, 71 per cent. Another set of reliability figures stemming from an observation series of the preceding year, pooled for several observer pairs, several infants, and the various behavior categories, averaged 80 per cent for infant behaviors and 84 per cent for adult caretaker behaviors. Again, we caution that these figures and those which follow have not been subjected to a final audit.

Thus far, the reliability determination has been presented in elementary terms, as it has dealt mainly with responses that have been pooled regardless of whether they form part of temporal sequences which define our concept of the interaction chain. As there is little precedent for observer agreement on interaction sequences, special forms for such analyses have had to be developed. In devising indices, the attempt was made to take into account these aspects of interaction sequences: the *identities* of sequence initiator and terminator; the *number* and *order* of behavior units for each actor; and behavior *content* of one response at each position. Thus, in one reliability determination analyses of all 1272 two-position interactions (which type appears to constitute about 75 per cent of all types of interactions in the reliability series examined) showed that levels of agreement, pooled across three pairs of observers, was 66 per cent for the above listed sequence aspects combined, and 83 per cent on the less strict criterion of

251

agreement only on the identities of the initiating and terminating actors.

The preceding sets of preliminary reliability figures for key single behaviors as well as for interaction patterns appear representative and reasonably satisfactory. If anything, they very likely *under*estimate considerably the degree of observer agreement for the sampling conditions of this investigation. Such periods of peak interaction intensity as those the reliability training sessions sampled constituted a rather small fraction of the typical observation day in the groups of children observed. Therefore, it seemed reasonable to assume that the observers could cope with the stimulus situation of the Ss in the final sample *at least as* reliably as they could during the training periods in settings of peak interaction. In the context of these considerations, it was judged that the levels of agreement found between independent observers about the essential features of behaviors occurring in and out of interaction were sufficiently high to warrant confidence that differences among groups and relationships among variables pertaining to our theoretical interest could be detected readily through the use of our behavior categories.

Reliability measures are not presented here for Setting and Background events and for actors. From the start of the pilot observations, Settings and actors proved easy to identify and were invariably recorded accurately by the observers. Therefore, it did not appear necessary to examine observer agreement for Settings and for Background (i.e., actor identities and behaviors) at the same level of detail used with the Behavior categories. The data presented in Table 25 of this report are based predominantly on duration scores for selected Background and Setting events, which constituted the least ambiguous events in the entire observation procedure. Thus, it is thought plausible that observer agreement on the duration of these events by time blocks was high and that the duration scores were distorted only to a small degree.

Infants' Responses to Strangers
During the First Year[1]

GEORGE A. MORGAN and HENRY N. RICCIUTI

One of the earliest observations reported by students of infant development was that during the last half of the first year of life, most human infants do not smile at unfamiliar people as readily as before, and many show a clearly fearful reaction to strangers (e.g.,Preyer, 1888). Although there have been a number of articles in recent years about infants' emotional reactions to people and faces, there is still little systematically gathered, empirical evidence specifically about the development of negative reactions towards strangers. Thus, one of the major aims of the present investigation was to trace the development of 'stranger anxiety' during the first year of life, using a relatively large number of normal, home-reared infants tested under controlled experimental conditions.[2]

Much of the empirical evidence concerning infants' responses to strangers has come indirectly from studies of the onset and developmental course of smiling behaviour in response to the human face, or to 'face-like' inanimate stimuli. Recent studies (Ambrose, 1961; Gewirtz, 1965) have generally confirmed the results of earlier investigations (e.g., Jones, 1926; Spitz & Wolf, 1946) indicating that the smile is readily elicited by any human face by approximately two months of age and appears to reach a maximum at three to four

[1] This research was supported in part by a grant to Cornell University from the National Institutes of Mental Health (MH-07226), and in part by a summer research grant from Hiram College. The paper is based upon a thesis by the senior author in partial fulfilment of the Ph.D. degree at Cornell. The senior author was supported by an NIMH traineeship and a Danforth Fellowship during the data collection period.

The authors wish to thank Lois Brockman for serving as the female experimenter.

[2] Although some writers attempt to distinguish between 'fear' and 'anxiety', these terms are used interchangeably in the present report and are operationally equivalent to the more descriptive phrase 'negative reactions to the strangers'.

months. Several investigations indicate a rather sharp decline in smiling at unfamiliar faces at approximately six months of age (Spitz & Wolf, 1946; Ambrose, 1961; Polak, Emde & Spitz, 1964). However, Gewirtz's (1965) study of Israeli children showed that, in home-reared infants particularly, smiling to strangers remained at a relatively consistent and high level through 18 months of age. As Gewirtz points out, his results may be due in part to the fact that his experimental technique incorporated a familiarization procedure before the testing period.

While the decline in smiling responses to strangers after three or four months of age may be interpreted as reflecting the beginning of fearful reactions to strange persons, studies such as those just summarized provide little direct evidence regarding the development of fear responses since the procedures of elicitation and observation have tended to focus primarily on the presence or absence of the smile. A few studies have provided direct evidence about negative reactions, but in most cases the observations were unsystematic or incidental to the main aim of the study. Furthermore, there is considerable disagreement about the precise nature of the age changes in fear reactions to strangers. Spitz (1950) has postulated that true stranger anxiety is most frequently manifested at eight months, and then subsides by the first quarter of the second year. Similar findings were reported in a longitudinal study of 18 infants by Tennes and Lampl (1964). They found peak intensities of stranger anxiety occurring between 7 and 9 months, but most pronounced separation anxiety from 13 to 18 months. Several earlier observational studies also suggested a peak and then a decline in negative reactions to strangers during the first year (e.g. ,Washburn, 1929; Bayley, 1932).

In contrast with the findings just summarized, Franus (1962) has reported that infants' fear of an unknown person did not reach a peak until 12 to 15 months of age. These results are consistent with several other reports suggesting that the sight of a stranger is more distressing in the second year than in the first (Escalona, 1953; Freedman, 1961). In a longitudinal study of 60 infants, Schaffer and Emerson (1964) found that by nine months almost all of the children had begun to show some indication of fear of strangers, but, unfortunately, no data were presented regarding peak intensity and decline. However, four infants discussed in an earlier paper (Schaffer, 1963) showed apparent peaks in fear responses between 10 and 13 months. Variations in the results of the above studies may be due in

George A. Morgan and *Henry N. Ricciuti*

large part to differences in the techniques employed to elicit and assess fear reactions. In the present investigation, infants from 4 to 13 months of age were included in order to observe the transition from predominantly positive to negative reactions, as well as to determine whether a peak and decline occurred by the end of the first year.

Some investigators have tended to regard the infants' negative reactions to strangers primarily as a special case of the presumably unlearned fear of the distorted, unexpected, or inherently dangerous frequently seen in the young of a number of species (e.g., Hebb, 1946; Meili, 1955; Freedman, 1961). On the other hand, the traditional psychoanalytic viewpoint has emphasized fear of separation from or loss of the loved object as the major determinant of stranger anxiety in the second half of the first year (Freud, 1936; Spitz, 1950). In recent years, it has seemed most reasonable to many investigators to regard fear of strangers as a function of both of the above determinants, which undoubtedly play differently weighted roles at different developmental levels (Bowlby, 1960; Benjamin, 1963; Tennes & Lampl, 1964).

The importance of the inter-relationship between fear of strangers and maternal attachment behaviour is increasingly reflected in recent empirical investigations with both animal and human infants. In general, the animal research suggests that there is at least a temporal, and perhaps a causal relationship between the onset of fear of strangers and the termination of the period for the formation of attachments (e.g., Scott, 1963; Sluckin, 1964). With regard to human infants, systematic studies have not yet provided consistent information as to the relative timing of onset and peak intensity of fear of strangers and specific maternal attachments (Schaffer & Emerson, 1964; Tennes & Lampl, 1964), although there is considerable reason to believe that fear of strangers may be more marked after specific maternal attachments have been formed. These studies, as well as the comments made by Spitz (1955) and Bowlby (1960) would lead one to expect that once specific maternal attachments have been established stranger anxiety would be greater if the infant is separated from the mother. In order to investigate this question systematically, each infant in the present experiment was tested both while sitting on his mother's lap and while seated in a feeding-table four feet away from mother.

The effect of the particular identity and behaviour of the stranger on the infant's emotional reactions has not been adequately investigated. Studies in this area have sometimes employed a non-responsive unsmiling adult face (Ambrose, 1961; Gewirtz, 1965), sometimes a nodding silent face (Spitz & Wolf, 1946; Polak, *et al.*, 1964), and sometimes a person who actively interacted with the infant (Jones, 1926; Rheingold, 1961). That variations such as these may produce marked differences in infants' emotional responses has been shown in studies of infant conditioning (e.g., Brackbill, 1958). Other observers have suggested that an infant is more likely to react negatively if a stranger approaches or touches the child than if he remains at a distance (Escalona, 1953; Freedman, 1961; Tennes & Lampl, 1964). Therefore, in the present study the experimenter's behaviour during testing was varied systematically so that the effect of changes in *E*'s physical closeness and 'social intrusiveness' could be analysed. With regard to the effect of the particular identity of the stranger, each infant was tested by two examiners, one male and one female. This was done in order to increase the generality of the results, as well as to provide some heuristic comparisons of responses to two different strangers.

In addition to the major questions outlined above, the research was also concerned with an exploratory examination of two subordinate questions. First, an examination was made of the developmental changes in infants' responses to two masks, one of a distorted face and the other of a realistic face. Second, consideration was given to possible relationships between the infant's previous experiences and behaviour and his observed reactions to strangers. For example, it seemed reasonable to expect that babies who see many people and go many places would be less anxious about strangers than those who have been relatively isolated.

Method

Subjects

The sample was composed of eighty infants from four to thirteen months of age drawn mostly from middle class families living in or near Ithaca, New York. Since the study was cross-sectional the infants were selected so that they fell into five age groups averaging approximately $4\frac{1}{2}$, $6\frac{1}{2}$, $8\frac{1}{2}$, $10\frac{1}{2}$ and $12\frac{1}{2}$ months. The sixteen infants (8 boys and 8 girls) in each age group were all within 18 days of the mean age of the group. The five groups were approximately matched for father's education, mother's age, number of siblings, and two variables related to the infant's experiences with people: frequency of exposure to baby sitters and to relatively unfamiliar people.

George A. Morgan and *Henry N. Ricciuti*

The Experimental Room and Apparatus

All experimental sessions were held in a small testing room similar to a simple living room. The mother was seated in an easy chair throughout the session. The infant spent half the time on the mother's lap and half separated from mother by about four feet in a baby tenda or feeding-table. The easy chair and tenda were each about seven feet from an observation booth which always contained one of the two experimenters. The other experimenter was in the room with the mother and infant, acting as the stranger. A timer in the booth controlled a signal board that provided time cues to guide the behaviour of the stranger and observer. The signal board was placed on the wall behind the mother and her infant but in view of the experimenters.

In addition to the strange experimenters, two masks were used as stimulus objects. One was a realistic plastic halloween mask of a smiling woman's face and the other a papier-mâché mask of a distorted face. Both masks were attached to dowel rods by which they were held in front of the infants.

Procedure

After the infant and mother were settled in the experimental room, the first stranger entered, said 'hello' to the mother, and began a 'run', the principal test used in this experiment. Each run was divided into eight ten-second stimulus intervals. During the first interval, the stranger sat smiling silently about 6 feet from *S*. In the second interval *E* spoke to the infant from his position across the room. During the runs *E*'s always used the same phrases: 'Hello (*S*'s name)! How are you today? What a cute baby! How about a smile?' Between the second and third intervals, *E* moved across the room and knelt about 2 feet in front of the infant. Then in the third interval *E* smiled and talked as before while he knelt near *S*. Finally, in the fourth interval, *E* put his right hand first near and then against *S*'s hand, while talking to him. This half of the run, called X, can be summarized as follows:

Interval 1 – far, silent, smiling
Interval 2 – far, talking, smiling
Interval 3 – near, talking, smiling
Interval 4 – touching, talking, smiling

257

After a thirty second pause for ratings and necessary adjustments, the sequence of four stimulus intervals was given in the reverse order (X'), thus completing the X + X' run of eight 10-second stimulus intervals.

These X + X' runs were given four times to each infant, i.e., the infant was first tested in both the lap and feeding table positions by one experimenter and then in both positions by the other experimenter. In order to balance for possible order effects, half of the subjects in each age group were exposed first to E_1 (the male stranger) and half first to E_2 (the female stranger). Likewise half were tested first while seated in the feeding table or tenda and half first while seated on their mother's lap.[1]

A second type of run called Y + Y', was also included in an attempt to obtain preliminary information about changes in *E*'s behaviour with distance from the infant held constant. In this type of run *E* did not attempt to touch *S*, substituting instead a peek-a-boo-like head movement. Due to time and fatigue limitations the Y and Y' runs were done only by E_1 when *S* was in the tenda.

At the conclusion of the final run, the second stranger presented the masks. Half the *S*'s were shown the realistic mask first and half were shown the distorted one first. Each mask was presented four times for ten seconds each. Between presentations it was put face downward on the floor in front of *S* for ten seconds. When the mask was being presented, it was held relatively motionless and about one foot in front of *S*.

Coding and Scoring the Infants' Behaviour

Coding of responses for a given condition was done by the experimenter-observer who stood behind the one-way screen and dictated symbols representing precoded categories of behaviour into a tape recorder. The categories of behaviour came from three separate scales — one was concerned with the infant's facial expression, one with vocalizations, and one with visual and gross motor activity (see Table 28).

These scales were used to code and record *S*'s behaviour just before, during, and after each run, as well as during the mask presentations.

[1] Since an examination of the data revealed no evidence of order effects, this variable was not included in the analyses of variance. Moreover, there was little or no evidence of any systematic adaptation or 'warm-up' to the strangers from the beginning to the end of the sessions.

Each of the ten-second stimulus intervals in a run was divided into three sub-intervals of approximately three seconds each. During each of these sub-intervals, *E* made and recorded successive judge-

TABLE 28

Summary of the Three Scales used for Coding
S's Behaviour During a Run
(*Weights for each type of behaviour are listed on the left*)

1. *Facial Expression*
   - +2 Broad, clear smile
   - +1 Brief or slight smile, brightening
   - 0 Any relatively neutral (sober) facial expression
   - −1 Slight frown, pout, or wrinkling of the face
   - −2 Marked and pronounced puckering or wrinkling

2. *Vocalization*
   - +2 Laugh or giggle
   - +1 Other clearly positive sounds, coo, babble, etc.
   - 0 Any vocalization that is not clearly positive or negative (V)
   - 0 No vocalization (N)
   - −1 Fuss, whimper, etc.
   - −2 Cry or scream

3. *Visual and Gross Motor Activity*
   - +2 *Reaches* out for E or tries to approach E (R)
   - +1 *Touches* E's hand when it is put nearby (T)
   - +1 Makes gross movements while looking at E. Waves arms and/or legs while smiling at and/or making positive vocalization (G)
   - 0 Looks at E (L)
   - 0 Looks at Mask (J)
   - 0 Explores the *surroundings* (other than E) visually and/or tactually (S)
   - 0 Inattention to E and environment, squirming, sleeping (I)
   - 0 Looks at *mother* (M)
   - −1 Turns to and tries to get to *mother* (M−)
   - −1 Waves arms and/or legs while looking at E with negative expression or vocalization (G−)
   - −1 *Avoids* E's glance, turns away or looks down (A)
   - −1 *Pulls* hand back when E approaches (P)
   - −2 Attempts to *withdraw* or escape bodily from E (W)

Note – The letters in parentheses were the symbols used to code behaviours that would not have been differentiated by using the weights as symbols.

ments of *S*'s facial expression, vocalizations, and activity using the category symbols listed in Table 28. Thus, the observer made nine coding judgements during each ten-second stimulus interval.

From the transcriptions of the recorded judgements, two main

S

types of scores were computed, the *run scores* and the *change scores*. Scoring of the reactions to the masks was very similar to that for reactions to strangers and produced two roughly equivalent types of score, the *mask score* and the *habituation to mask score*.

The *run scores* and *mask scores* were over-all measures of the infant's reaction toward the stranger, or toward the mask during each run. Each judgement made by the observer was given a weight as shown in Table 28. The algebraic sum of these weights was transformed so that a low score represented a run in which the infant's responses were primarily negative while a high score indicated mainly positive reactions.

The *change scores* were meant to measure changes in the infant's behaviour due to the stranger's approach in the first half of each $X + X'$ run. The score was derived from the difference of the summed weights of the infant's reactions in intervals 1 and 2 (the far conditions) and those of intervals 3 and 4 (the near and touching conditions). A high score indicated that the infant became more positive, less negative or changed from negative to positive after the stranger approached. A low score indicated the opposite.

Reliability

Seven pretest sessions were used to check the reliability of the coding and scoring system. During these sessions a third person acted as the stranger while E_1 and E_2 independently coded the infant's behaviour. The scored observations of E_1 and E_2 correlated ·95 for the run scores and ·91 for the change scores.

The Home Interview

Before coming to the laboratory with her infant, each mother was interviewed in her home by the male experimenter (E_1) at a time when the infant was asleep. The interview questions were standardized, presented in a set order, and phrased so that they required only a brief, easily coded answer or rating by the mother. Some questions led to measures of the infant's past and present contacts with both familiar and unfamiliar people. Other questions produced scores for the infant's usual reaction to strangers and the peak period of negative reactions, if any had occurred. Because only a preliminary analysis of the interview has been completed, reporting of the data in this paper is restricted to a few general findings.

Results and Discussion

Age Trends

In general the younger infants reacted very positively toward the strangers by smiling, cooing, and reaching out, but the older infants, especially those in the twelve months group[1], were often very negative; frowning, crying, and turning away. Table 29 and Figure 30 show that the mean run scores for all conditions decreased regularly as age increased. Notice that there were no reversals in this trend and that the means for all age groups except the oldest one were above

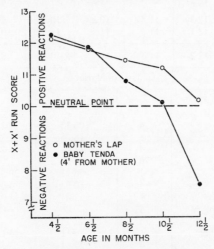

FIG. 30 Infants' response to strangers as a function of age and distance from mother. N=16 at each age level.

the neutral point, indicating that it was not until 12 months that infants exhibited more negative than positive responses. The differences among the age group means were significant ($F=11.23$, $p < .001$), and there was a highly significant linear decline ($F=39.98$, $p < .001$). This same trend is reflected in a correlation of $-.59$ between age and the infant's overall reaction. With regard to particular age comparisons, it was found that the twelve-month mean was significantly lower than all four of the other age group means (with $\alpha = .01$), and the ten-month mean was significantly lower than the four and six month means (with $\alpha = .05$).[1]

1 For simplicity the age groups were called the 4, 6, 8, 10 and 12 month groups. However, it should be remembered that the average age of infants in each group was approximately one-half month more than is indicated by these labels.

TABLE 29

Summary of the Means, Analysis of Variance and Trend
Analysis for the $X + X'$ Run Scores
($N = 16$ at each age level)

Condition	Means					
	4 mo.	6 mo.	8 mo.	10 mo.	12 mo.	Total
E_1 Tenda	11·8	11·6	10·7	8·8	7·4	10·1
E_1 Lap	11·9	11·2	11·3	10·3	10·2	11·0
E_2 Tenda	12·8	12·1	10·9	11·4	7·7	11·0
E_2 Lap	12·3	12·4	11·6	12·1	10·2	11·7
to E_1	11·8	11·4	11·0	9·5	8·8	10·5
to E_2	12·5	12·3	11·3	11·8	8·9	11·3
to Tenda	12·3	11·8	10·8	10·1	7·5	10·5
to Lap	12·1	11·8	11·4	11·2	10·2	11·3
Total	12·2	11·8	11·1	10·6	8·9	10·9

Analysis of Variance

Source of Variation	df	Mean Square	F	p
Age	4	108·13	11·23	< ·001
Sex	1	18·05	1·87	
Sex × Age	4	11·61	1·21	
Error (b)	70	9·63		
Experimenter	1	56·11	20·55	< ·001
Age × Exp.	4	10·93	4·00	< ·01
Sex × Exp.	1	2·81	1·03	
Age × Sex × Exp.	4	·80	—	
$Error_1$ (w)	70	2·73		
Dist. from Mother	1	56·11	15·14	< ·001
Age × Distance	4	20·64	5·57	< ·001
Sex × Distance	1	5·51	1·49	
Age × Sex × Dist.	4	7·59	2·05	
$Error_2$ (w)	70	3·71		
Exp. × Dist.	1	·45	—	
Age × Exp. × Dist.	4	1·43	—	
Sex × Exp. × Dist.	1	1·80	—	
Age × Sex × Exp. × Dist.	4	·46	—	
$Error_3$ (w)	70	2·77		
Total	319			

Trend Analysis

Linear Regression	1	393·76	39·98	< ·001
Deviations	3	12·92	1·31	
Within Groups	75	9·85		
Total	79			

Note – Scores ranged from 2 to 18, with a score of 10 indicating that the reaction toward the stranger was affectively neutral; a score greater than 10 indicates that the infant reacted positively; and a score less than 10 indicates that the infant reacted negatively.

These results give general support to the common observation that infants are less likely to smile and more likely to show indications of fear of strangers after six or seven months than before. However, the findings of the present study are in better agreement with the scattered reports that fear of unfamiliar people is most easily elicited in the second year (Escalona, 1953; Freedman, 1961; Franus, 1962) than with the more commonly cited suggestion that 'stranger anxiety' is most intense at about eight months. Since Spitz's (1950) observations and concept of 'eight months' anxiety' have been widely referred to, it seems important to emphasize that there was no indication of a peak around eight or even ten months in any of the measures used in the present study. The studies which indicate a peak in negative

TABLE 30

Reaction of Infants to the First Approach by a Stranger

Reaction	Number of infants				
	4 mo	6 mo	8 mo	10 mo	12 mo
Highly Positive	6	7	0	3	1
Mildly Positive	7	6	7	3	3
Neutral (sober)	3	2	5	6	4
Mildly Negative	0	1	1	2	5
Highly Negative	0	0	3	2	3

Note – Data are from intervals 3 and 4 of each infant's first run.

reactions before ten months have been primarily longitudinal (e.g., Washburn, 1929; Bayley, 1932; Spitz, 1950; Tennes & Lampl, 1964). In such instances, the infants may become familiar enough with the situation and examiner that his effect as a stranger becomes attenuated by the end of the first year. This factor may account for some of the discrepancy with the cross-sectional results of the present study.

Some writers have suggested that nonsmiling, sober staring may be an early indication of fear of the stranger (e.g., Ambrose, 1963a). It is important to note that in the present experiment sober facial expressions were always scored as neutral rather than negative responses. However, even if one includes sober staring as an indication of fear, *runs* in which *S* either became or remained sober when *E* approached were unusual before eight months. For example, it can be seen from Table 30 that only one infant in the four- and

263

six-month groups was clearly negative toward the stranger and only five of the remaining 31 were sober and unsmiling when first approached.

Several observers (e.g., Tennes & Lampl, 1964) have reported clear negative reactions to strangers as early as three to six months. Even though in the present study there were very few negative reactions to the strangers observed before eight months, it is clear that under some circumstances younger infants can be frightened rather easily. For example, the mothers of half of the infants in the present research reported that, on at least one occasion before seven months, the baby had reacted negatively toward a strange person. However, it seemed that most of these cases involved relatively isolated incidents which were more likely the result of loud talking, sudden movements, or fatigue than the result of the newness of the person. This conclusion is supported by the fact that several mothers reported negative reactions toward themselves and their husbands under similar conditions. In the present study the stranger's approach was relatively gradual and natural. Furthermore, the present study did not include conditions such as restraining the infant, putting him in a supine position, or giving him an injection which have been suggested as determinants of negative reactions before six months (Escalona, 1953; Benjamin, 1963). In addition, general fussiness was partially eliminated by testing the infants at a time of day when their mothers expected them to be rested and not hungry.

It seems that at least in the first year of life the infant's sex is not an important determinant of the reaction toward strangers. The average reaction of boy infants was slightly, but not significantly, more positive than that for girl infants ($F = 1.87$). None of the interactions involving sex was significant.

The Effect of Separation from Mother

As indicated in Table 29 and Figure 30, the four- and six-month infants reacted just as positively toward the stranger when they were separated from mother as when they were on mother's lap. But, as expected, the older infants reacted more negatively when they were in the feeding-table. The significant interaction between age and distance from mother ($F = 5.57$, p < .001) indicates that, with increasing age, proximity to mother is an increasingly important determinant of the infant's stranger reaction. Because separation produced so much more negative behaviour at eight, ten, and especially

264

twelve months, the overall effect of proximity to mother was also significant ($F = 15\cdot14$, $p < \cdot001$).

The results of the present experiment generally support Bowlby's (1960) suggestion that 'fright' reactions are increased under conditions which separate the infant from mother, the normally available 'haven of safety'. Since Bowlby's theory includes the concept of 'expectant anxiety', which is anxiety based on foresight about potential separation, it would have no difficulty accounting for the finding that nearly half of the older infants reacted negatively even while on their mother's lap. Bowlby's theory, as well as the recent studies by Schaffer & Emerson (1964) and Tennes & Lampl (1964), suggest that infants' protests at separation from mother will begin around seven months and be greatest during the second year. This is consistent with the present finding that the younger infants' reactions to the stranger were not affected by separation from mother, whereas the 10- and 12-month old infants were very much more upset by the stranger when they were separated from mother by as little as four feet.

Spitz (1950) proposed the rather extreme theory that the infant's negative reaction upon seeing a stranger is due to his anxiety that he has lost his mother, i.e. the expectation of her return is destroyed by seeing the stranger. Hence, one should not expect stranger anxiety if the infant is actually in contact with mother. Freedman (1961) criticized this theory by pointing out that Spitz (1950) himself cited examples of stranger anxiety when the mother was holding the infant. Although it may well be that the infant anticipates loss of the love object, upon sight of the stranger, it would seem improbable that in such a situation the baby actually feels that mother *has been* lost. Spitz (1955), in replying to an earlier criticism, stated that 'those few children who showed anxiety in front of the stranger while sitting on mother's arm were rare exceptions, extreme cases' (p. 164). Both the present study and the recent report by Benjamin (1963) strongly dispute Spitz's claim about the rarity of this phenomenon. The results of the present research show that 13 of the 32 infants in the 10- and 12-month groups reacted negatively to at least one of the two strangers while sitting on mother's lap.

Escalona (1953) suggested that infants around one year are better equipped cognitively and emotionally to tolerate spatial separation from mother than are infants of six to eight months. The data of the present study do not support this point of view. Not only did separation of only four feet produce highly negative reactions at 12 months, but the relative difference between lap and tenda was greatest at that age.

The Effect of E's *Particular Identity and Behaviour*

Figure 31 shows that mean reaction to the female stranger (E_2) was consistently, although slightly, more positive than the reaction to the male stranger (E_1). The overall difference was clearly significant ($F = 20.55$, $p < .001$), but since there was only one male and one female

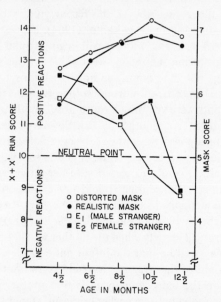

FIG. 31 Comparison of infants' responses
to two face-like masks and two human
strangers. N=16 at each age level.

stranger, it is not possible from this experiment to make a general statement comparing infants' reactions to male and female strangers. In addition to differences commonly associated with sexual classification, there were other differences in appearance such as height, glasses, etc., that may have been important determinants of the infants' significant preference for the female stranger. Also, although E_1 and E_2 followed the same prescribed procedure, there may have been subtle differences in their approaches to the baby. If so, it is possible that E_2's approach may have been more like the typical approaches of the infants' mothers, in terms of more gentle movements, a more softly intoned voice, etc. However, the present study did not permit an empirical test of this possibility. The significant age by experimenter interaction does not appear to reflect any systematic relationship between age and experimenter differences. [1]

The results of several of the analyses emphasize that the stranger's behaviour is an important determinant of the infant's reaction and that the effects of certain behaviours, like E's approach, change as the infant develops. The X *change scores* indicated that the younger infants generally became even more positive when E approached and touched them than they had been when E was across the room. On the other hand the 10- and 12-month old infants were likely to become more negative or even change from a positive to a negative reaction when E approached. The reliability of this age trend in the change scores was supported by the fact that the age group means were significantly different $(F = 7 \cdot 43, p < \cdot 001)$ and that the trend was linear $(F = 27 \cdot 78, p < \cdot 001)$.

A somewhat different analysis of the change score data makes more explicit the various types of response change that occurred when the stranger moved from the far position to the near and touching positions. Table 31 lists, by age group, the number of times that each type of change occurred during all four X runs. It can be seen that the four and six month infants became relatively more positive when the stranger approached in 68 runs and relatively more negative in only 10. At eight months the proportion of positive and negative changes was about equal, but by 10- and 12-month the infants became relatively more positive in only 23 runs, and relatively more negative in 44.

However, during the Y & Y' runs when the stranger did not touch the infant, but smiled, talked, and moved his head as if playing peek-a-boo, even the 10- and 12-month infants reacted mildly positively. This seems especially significant when one remembers that the Y & Y' runs were always done by the male stranger when the infant was separated from mother. Furthermore, the $Y + Y'$ runs always followed

[1] Several other response measures support the general results described thus far. In addition to the run scores, a subjective, overall rating of the infant's stranger reactions was made immediately after the experimental session by consensus of the two observers. The means and analysis of variance for these overall ratings, which correlated ·73 with the run scores, were very similar to those already described. The last thing that each stranger did was attempt to pick up the infant and carry him around the room. As with the run scores there was a significant inverse relationship between age and the infant's response to being held $(\bar{r} = - \cdot 52)$.

the $X + X'$ tenda runs by E_1, which generally produced very negative reactions from the 10- and 12-month old infants. Thus, even when these older infants were separated from mother, the stranger's behaviour was an important determinant of whether the infant displayed fearful or positive reactions.

Escalona (1953) has suggested that, given a child who reacts

TABLE 31

Summary of Changes in S's Behaviour When the Stranger Moved from Across the Room to Near and Touching ($N = 64$ at each age level, X runs only, 4 per subject)

	Number of Runs				
	4 mo	6 mo	8 mo	10 mo	12 mo
Positive changes					
negative to positive	3	2	0	2	1
more positive	32	30	17	10	7
less negative	1	0	0	0	3
Total	36	32	17	12	11
No change					
equally positive	20	20	18	19	10
neutral throughout	4	4	5	3	0
equally negative	1	1	6	14	15
Total	25	25	29	36	25
Negative changes					
less positive	3	3	7	7	4
more negative	0	1	3	5	14
positive to negative	0	3	8	4	10
Total	3	7	18	16	28

negatively to strangers, this effect will not be observable in infants under 8 months unless the stranger comes very close, but in babies over eleven months just the appearance of the stranger across the room may be upsetting. The present data are not directly relevant to her hypotheses, but several pertinent points can be made. There was some indication that the sight of a stranger across the room was more likely to be upsetting to older infants. For example, seven out of 32 infants over ten months, but none under seven months, showed signs of being afraid of the stranger *before* his first approach. Notice, however, that the majority of infants in every age group reacted positively during this initial period. This finding is consistent with Gewirtz's (1965) results indicating a consistent high level of smiling from 4 to 18 months.

As has been implied above, it is clear that the infant's reactions were to a considerable extent dependent on the particular unfamiliar setting, strangers, and behavioural sequence used in the present research. However, confidence in the reliability of the obtained age trends is supported by the relatively high correlations between the mothers' reports of the infants' usual reactions to strangers and their actual reactions in the experimental session ($r = \cdot47$, $p < \cdot01$). The case for generality is also strengthened by the fact that there was a high correlation between the infants' reactions to the two strangers ($r = \cdot70$).

Reactions to the Masks

Figure 31 shows that infants of all ages reacted quite positively toward both masks. Unexpectedly the infants seemed to show a slight preference for the *distorted* mask, but this difference was not significant. Actually the infant's reactions to the two masks were very similar, as noted by the high correlation between them ($r = \cdot73$).

It was also surprising to find that the older infants reacted somewhat, but again not significantly, more positively toward the masks than the younger infants. This is especially interesting because these older infants were negative toward the human strangers. Since the mask scores and run scores were based on the same scoring categories, weightings, and time intervals, it is possible to make at least a rough comparison between reactions to the masks and the strangers. It is clear from Figure 31 that the 8-, 10-, and 12-month old infants reacted much more positively to the masks than to the human strangers. Although the masks were always presented at the end of the session, adaptation does not seem to have been a major factor here. First, very little adaptation occurred during the sessions as indicated by a comparison of the reactions during the first and lasts runs. Second, 37 out of 48 of the 8-, 10-, and 12-month old infants responded more favourably to the masks than they had to *E* on the immediately preceding run. The older infants seem to have perceived the masks as toys instead of distorted faces. This may have resulted from the masks being presented on sticks rather than being worn by a person, which has been shown to produce negative reactions (e.g., Franus, 1962).

One of the most peculiar things about the results with the masks was the apparently very poor agreement with studies on the effects of novelty in infant nonhuman primates. Novel objects and distortions of familiar objects are usually avoided by young primates, at least until they have had some experience with them (e.g., Hebb, 1946; Welker, 1956). The reactions of the human infants to the masks used in the present study were almost always positive and there was no indication of a warm-up or adaptation effect with repeated presentations of the masks. Berlyne (1960) suggested that novel objects often produce vacillation between attack and escape, but there was very little indication of vacillation in the infant's reactions to the masks.

Although there was little vacillation during the mask presentations, this kind of behaviour in response to the human strangers was seen in 24 infants above 7 months, but in only 2 below this age. Some infants simply changed from smiling in the far conditions to frowning and pulling back when the stranger approached. Others alternated positive and negative reactions, and a few even displayed simultaneous positive and negative reactions like smiling and pulling back at the same time.

Role of Previous Experience

With regard to the role played by the infant's previous experience, it seems clear from studies which have compared the social-emotional reactions of institutional and home babies (e.g., Ambrose, 1961; Rheingold, 1961; Gewirtz, 1965) that the infant's environment should be an important determinant of his reaction to strangers. However, a preliminary analysis of the interview data from the present study indicated no significant correlations between *any* of the previous experience variables and the infant's reaction during the experimental sessions. This seems to indicate, for example, that babies from small families, who seldom see strangers and/or are seldom left with baby sitters are no more likely to be upset by a stranger than infants who have much more contact with people. It is possible that the relative homogeneity of the subjects with respect to several of these variables may have obscured any relationships that exist. However, Noel (1965) in a recent exploratory study of 31 infants found no relationship between household size and fear reactions to strangers. This agreement between the present study and Noel's study seems especially important in that he tested infants with widely varying family sizes.

Summary and Conclusions

The results of the present study suggest that among the major determinants of negative reactions toward strangers during the first year of life are (1) developmental level or age of the infant, (2) degree of proximity to the mother, and (3) the particular identity, behaviour, and proximity of the stranger.

On the basis of these empirical findings and the previous literature, one might speculate further about some of the major factors which contribute to the increasing prevalence of negative reactions shown by one year. One type of analysis emphasizes the role played by the infant's bond with mother and fear of separation. By nine or ten months the infant has usually formed a strong specific attachment to mother (Schaffer & Emerson, 1964). This leads to a particularly marked stranger reaction when the infant is actually separated from mother because he must cope with the stranger without the immediate presence of mother, the usual source of comfort and safety (Bowlby, 1960). In addition since the infant by the end of the first year has developed foresight and can anticipate potential separation (Bowlby, 1960), he may protest when a stranger approaches even if he is on mother's lap. On the other hand young infants lacking both specific attachments and foresight may react to new people by generalization from their experiences with both familiar and other unfamiliar people. If these experiences have generally been positive, young infants would be expected generally to react positively to strangers.

A second way of viewing the development of negative reactions to strangers is in terms of the learned expectancies infants have about what is appropriate behaviour on the part of objects and people. It would seem that if a stranger's behaviour is unexpected or inappropriate the infant will be upset, perhaps, for example, due to some kind of conflicting cerebral processes (Hebb, 1946). It seems quite easy for a stranger to act appropriately towards infants under seven months. Some common expectations seem to involve smiling, soft talking and relatively slow movement (Benjamin, 1963). However, after eight months infants may have developed more idiosyncratic expectations

271

about what is appropriate behaviour, and thus it becomes harder to meet these expectations. According to this notion, for infants around one year in the present study, the Y runs with their 'peak-a-boo' condition were closer to being familiar or 'expected' behaviour than the X runs, which included touching. There were several other features of the procedure in the present study that may have appeared strange or inappropriate to the older infants. For example, *E*'s speech during the runs was stereotyped and mixed with periods of silence. Likewise the abrupt approach, blank stare, or silence used by many other investigators (e.g., Spitz & Wolf, 1946; Ambrose, 1961; Tennes & Lampl, 1964) may have been particularly unexpected or inappropriate behaviour for even very young infants, and thus produced negative reactions.

While it seems fairly clear that the unexpected or unfamiliar behaviour of a stranger may produce fearful reactions in infants, it is considerably more difficult to evaluate the effect, if any, of the infant's perception of the stranger as a partially familiar, partially unfamiliar or 'strange' visual stimulus. The infants' generally positive reactions to the masks in the present study do not seem to support the suggestion that this is an important determinant.

Discussion on Causes of Distress
in Infants

MACKEITH *You said that infants appear to have no adverse response to strangers. Did you mean that there was no response at all, no greater alerting or anything like that?*

WOLFF *During the period when such people are still novelties, let us say for the first half hour, there seems to be just as much social response to strangers as to other people, except perhaps the mother and father, who are favoured, at least by infants up to six months. There is certainly no marked negative response although something rather less than the definitely positive response that is seen in reaction to the mother. In Japan, for instance, everybody picks up babies at will, and this starts at a relatively early age. I have never seen anything like an adverse reaction to a stranger in Japan, although I am sure it must exist. I asked people there, even psychiatrists, about anxiety to strangers, and they did not seem to know the concept, but perhaps this was a translation difficulty. Continuous exposure to many people for short periods might, however, reduce or eliminate the occurrence of stranger anxiety.*

RICCIUTI *In the study by my student, George Morgan, and myself (published in this volume—ed.) we found no relation between individual differences in negative reaction to strangers and the degree to which infants had been exposed to a wide variety of people.*

AINSWORTH *I have not done anything systematic about this with my Baltimore babies, but my impression is that very few cry or fuss in response to strangers during the first six months of life, and indeed stranger anxiety was infrequent throughout the first year. There was one child, however, who showed stranger anxiety at about eight months, which became very intense at ten months and continued for the rest of the first year. Furthermore there was a tendency in the sample as a whole for babies to stare at strangers, even though they did not seem to be anxious. In the group of*

273

African children I studied, this staring response began to be conspicuous at about five months of age, and was later succeeded by marked stranger anxiety. It might have been because I was the stranger and my face was white. Babies whom I began to visit at about eight months of age (and in one or two cases even earlier) seemed very afraid of me. Babies whom I had been visiting since they were say three months old accepted me until they were about eight months old, then they suddenly reacted to me negatively, although their reactions were less intense than those of babies to whom I was a complete stranger.

RICCIUTI *Doesn't a great deal depend upon what the experimenter does? In several studies, for instance that of Tennes and Lampl (1964), quite a lot of negative reaction to strangers occurs by three months, but that is when the stranger approaches the baby abruptly, talks to him and finally touches him. We ought to specify what the stranger does and not simply call him a stranger.*

DÉCARIE *I think there might be two stages. First the infant recognizes the stranger and this shows not so much in the lack of a smile as in a differential smile (there is a delay in the response) and then perhaps the child sees the stranger doing something which is normally done by a familiar person and negative reactions might result. In research we are doing on this particular problem, with infants between 32 and 56 weeks, we found as Morgan and Ricciuti did that there was a great deal of positive reaction at all ages but that most negative reaction appeared at 56 weeks during the sequence when the stranger touched the babies hand or tried to take him in his arms. As expected, the absence of the mother increased withdrawal and fright reactions while her silent presence facilitated curiosity and approach. For your Japanese babies, was not the mother present when the baby was being held by someone else?*

WOLFF *No, I have seen babies taken to a restaurant who were not distressed when the waitress stops being a waitress and takes the baby to a separate room and does a bit of baby-sitting.*

GEWIRTZ *We must not lose sight of the direct role the mother often plays in determining her child's response to strangers. For instance-many mothers think it normal for infants to show distress when confronted with strange-appearing or strange-behaving persons, or at least for them to behave differently to such strangers than to familiar persons, and as a result she may provide cues that deter-*

mine the quality of her child's response to strangers. A mother may be holding her child when someone approaches whom she considers to be a 'stranger' – a bearded man, or someone of a different race. As a result of her attitude, the mother with a sudden movement, draws the infant closer to her, or turns him away from the oncoming stranger. Such a movement has probably already became associated by the baby with noxious or hazardous events, so that he now comes to associate avoidance responses with 'strangers'. Also, I have often noted that mothers, particularly primiparae, seem ill at ease when their young infant is being held by a stranger, and often take him back as soon as possible.

APPELL *We have found something similar: mothers differ very much from each other in the attitude they have to a stranger holding their child. Some mothers are constantly interrupting if the child shows interest in a stranger, whereas others help. This sort of thing starts when the child is very young. I suspect that the mother's attitude matters more than the amount of experience which babies have of strangers.*

WOLFF *One point I want to add is that we should evaluate not only the attitude of the mother but also the state of the infant. If he has recently awoken he responds in a totally different way than if you take a child who is inert and inactive, or is already responding positively. I would assume that the significance of the encounter with the stranger changes with the baby's state.*

GEWIRTZ *I was trying to point out that in evaluating this kind of behaviour we should take into account the total learning environment of the child. The issue of fear of strangers fits so well with parts of the imprinting literature, and it is very tempting to think of that fear pattern as being a parallel of the flight-fear pattern sometimes seen in different species. But we must remember that not all species imprint or show the flight-fear pattern and that not all children show fear of strangers. If we analysed the situation more carefully we would probably find that very special experiential conditions were necessary for imprinting as well as for showing fear of strangers.*

FREEDMAN *In this regard, it has never really been demonstrated that imprinting and fear responses have much to do with each other, except that the flight response tends to terminate the period in which imprinting may occur. But there are animals which have more or less had the flight response bred out of them and they*

T 275

nevertheless relate to other members of their species, as for example many of the birds on the Galapagos.

HINDE *I think that the literature on imprinting, at least as studied in birds, now shows quite clearly that fear of strangers is not a thing, as Gewirtz says, that comes in at a certain age, but is a consequence of experience during the imprinting period. The limitation of this period is determined by what the animal has learned during it. Bateson (1964, 1966) has shown that birds reared in pens which are more conspicuous to the human eye avoided moving objects more when three days old than did birds reared in inconspicuous pens.*

GEWIRTZ *I think perhaps my comment was not clear. I was suggesting that an analogy between the fear of strangers pattern in human infants and the flight-avoidance pattern in birds may be very superficial and that, when the two patterns are analysed in detail, the factors leading to them may be found to be quite different. Thus, differences in experience will be most important, and in human infants the fear of strangers may be exhibited either not at all or much later than at the age which is modal for a defined experience group . . . for instance, in Ricciuti's observations, not until around twelve months.*

FREEDMAN *However, Ricciuti has suggested that the appearance of fear of strangers depends on the particular conditions. For instance, Spock finds that in his office fear of strangers is to be seen as early as three months, which is to be expected since the total situation is strange, and the baby is being closely attended to and manipulated. Also, I have demonstrated (Freedman, 1965) that genetic elements come in too, so that the particular children studied will matter.*

AINSWORTH *Some of the early literature suggested that the emergence of fear of strangers was a criterion of the baby being able to differentiate his mother from other people but I think the evidence is not that recognition of the mother frequently occurs long before fear of strangers is seen.*

BOWLBY *But it may go with lack of a positive response rather than an actual aversive response.*

KRAMER *One of the things we don't know is what significant stimuli are sent out by the so-called stranger. I know one case where, when a grandmother approached a five-week old infant for the first time, the grandmother elicited a response of intense pleasurable excita-*

tion, much more so than the mother did. This pleasurable excitation pattern to the grandmother continued for over two years.

WOLFF *In various ways I have tried to specify what stimulus configuration constitute a mother or a stranger. I have mentioned the case that when the mother wore a bathing cap, this immediately seemed frightening to the infant.*

RHEINGOLD *I am pleased to hear discussion on the non-prevalence or non-characteristic fear response to strangers and of course I myself have not seen it as often as one might expect from some reports in the literature. We are faced with the trouble that we cannot really talk about approach and avoidance responses in infants since they cannot move toward and away from people. We are forced therefore to look for other kinds of response. At one end of the continuum we have the smiling response and non-distress vocalizations and somewhere in the middle what might be called the staring response of interest and at the other end we have crying and distress. Sometimes I have seen infants cry when the mother has returned to them. Now I would think this is not fear of the mother; we have therefore to be very careful in interpreting crying when a stranger appears. My belief is that the total environment of the infant is extremely important in deciding what the reaction will be. If for instance the child is in a completely strange environment, then you may get crying responses not only to strangers but to the mother also.*

HINDE *I am not sure that it is satisfactory to have a neutral point putting smiling on one side and crying on the other. It seems to me that we're still using an analogy with approach and avoidance and I'm not sure that the analogy holds.*

BOWLBY *The thing which strikes me is the regularity with which some change in head-dress or hair-style seems to upset babies.*

HINDE *Am I right in understanding that for babies with fistulae if the food goes right into the stomach then crying stops?*

WOLFF *Yes, but after a certain time lapse which is probably about 15-30 minutes. That probably applies only to mildly fussy babies. If the baby is very fussy, then it is very difficult to get the food into the stomach at all. In that case it is sometimes necessary to give the baby a pacifier in order to calm him down so that the milk can enter the stomach. One of the interesting things is that babies will be quieted by a pacifier even though they have never* been fed by mouth. *The rhythm of sucking seems to be quite independent of the food going into the stomach.*

RICCIUTI *Do you ever find babies who cry after being fed, instead of being pacified; so-called colic babies perhaps?*

WOLFF *Yes certainly; but one of the problems here is knowing what the crying is all about. If a child has gas or constipation, the only way you can be sure or even infer that it caused crying is when a child eructs or passes stool. One of the complicating factors is that giving a child something to suck on or something to eat occasionally stops crying even if a child is not hungry. Many mothers know this.*

MACKEITH *But what about so-called twelve-week colic, when babies tend to cry after being fed?*

WOLFF *I am not very sure about that. One of the troubles is that as a child gets older occasions for crying change and these are partly a function of the new skills which mothers and infants develop in coping with each other.*

GUNTHER *I was particularly interested in the crying you get when the child is undressed. I wonder if this is at all like the birth cry because in a sense being undressed is a sort of recapitulation of birth.*

WOLFF *No, the birth cry is something with very particular morphological features and perceptual qualities. One never again hears or sees anything like it after birth.*

GUNTHER *The other possibility about nakedness is that the child is crying to make himself warm.*

WOLFF *I want to emphasize the distinction between cold and nakedness as causes of crying. Even in cases where we kept a child at a reasonable ambient temperature, he might still cry when the clothes were removed.*

BOWLBY *It does look as though nakedness has some special properties about it. For instance it seems often to occur that when a child is unclothed he will grasp very much more than when he is clothed.*

HARLOW *I think it is quite possible that what I have called contact comfort and clinging, or grasping, are two quite separate variables but that they do relate to each other.*

GUNTHER *When babies are picked up from the bath, especially when they are very young, they usually give a most desperate cry. It seems like the birth cry.*

Discussion

WOLFF *Well, it's very interesting what happens in Japan. There babies within twenty minutes after birth are put in a very hot steaming tub. They are scrubbed, soaped and have their hair combed and are then presented to the mothers. Every day subsequently the baby gets this treatment in a hot steaming bath but they always put a sort of cloth over the baby's body, wet the cloth and then put the baby into the bath; and you see almost no crying at all either going in or coming out of the bath. Perhaps the great heat alters the situation completely but I have always thought that the cloth had something to do with it.*

KRAMER *It sounds as though you believe that crying has no regulatory or homeostatic function at all but that all its functions are signal ones.*

WOLFF *I have not really studied its regulatory function, but I think that the first or birth cry, for instance, certainly has a regulatory function.*

DÉCARIE *I wonder if you have any explanation for your observation that sometimes the sound of the human voice will stop crying but not necessarily stop fussiness, whereas on other occasions it doesn't even stop crying?*

WOLFF *Well, I am sure that the result on the infant depends on the state which he is in.*

DÉCARIE *Could it be that the baby who is fussy is expecting something different from the baby who is crying:*

WOLFF *Yes, I think expectation is a good way of putting it. It reminds me of the remark made earlier by Kramer about what exactly made a stranger, and what made a mother – what was the stimulus difference between the two. My impression is that the stimulus which appears strange is one which involves a dissonance of some kind from the familiar. That was the point of the bathing cap and glasses. Anything which is radically strange does not have this effect. It reminds one of Hebb's original observations on chimpanzees which reacted fearfully to sinister rather than strange objects – sinister in the sense that something was familiar but had been varied slightly. An interesting point is that for an infant of an earlier age something which is quite unfamiliar and therefore novel will tend to stop crying rather than be alarming; for instance moving objects and so on.*

CALDWELL *You mentioned that sometimes when babies were in a fussy state, but not actually crying, they would vocalize and they would continue for three or four minutes before they started crying; there was a sort of transition stage. Have you any idea whether the mother may have reinforced or not reinforced behaviour during these stages? You mentioned that some of the mothers were attuned to their babies – isn't it possible that babies are differentially reinforced either for fussiness or crying?*

WOLFF *I have really no evidence for this. My impression is that mothers are not really consistent anyway in their response to babies' crying or fussiness.*

CALDWELL *One reason I am interested is because there is an un-answered question whether early vocalization in a child occurs primarily when he is contented or when he is wanting attention. Most mothers say that babies talk the most when they are by themselves and content, and this is said to be the case any time from say two months of age, when babbling starts up, to about seven or eight months. Some people have suggested that the function of this babbling is to bring the mother to the child or to maintain her interest, but this violates a frequent conception that speech arises entirely out of interpersonal transactions.*

WOLFF *Our impression is that when babies vocalize when they are not in a mildly fussy state, then they do it much more when they are by themselves. If another person is there, then it must be a talking person and not just a visual one.*

FOSS *My impression is that when talking birds first start to babble in a way which sounds like humans talking they do so very much more when there is nobody present.*

AINSWORTH *Especially from studying African babies, I get the impression that this talking to oneself fits very well with the concept of the circular reaction. There seems to be something self-reinforcing about this babbling.*

HARLOW *You find something very like this in chimpanzees but it lasts for only a short period of time. It is the so-called lulling language. In fact the chimpanzee can almost talk except for the fact that he is aphasic. Even when one tries to reinforce this kind of behaviour in the chimpanzee it doesn't last, it just evaporates.*

AINSWORTH *I would like to ask about crying and fussiness during feeding. I find in the work I have been doing recently that infants are extremely fussy while they are being fed. I think there may be two reasons for this. First, the baby may be too hungry, having*

had to wait too long before being fed. *Some of the mothers claimed
that they were feeding on demand, but in fact they were doing
nothing of the sort. One baby, for example, was down to three
feedings a day by six weeks of age, although the mother still said
'I feed on demand'. Such babies were frantic when the time for
feeding finally arrived. The second factor which seems to me
important is the rate at which food is given to the baby. This applies
especially to the feeding of solid foods. Some mothers feed their
babies at an arbitary rate that is not well geared to the child's
own rate of intake, being either too fast or too slow. Some such
mothers even try to control the rate of the baby's intake in bottle
feeding. If the food comes too fast or too slow, the baby tends to
fuss during feeding. Later, if such a baby is permitted to manage
his own bottle or to feed himself food with his fingers, and thus
control his own rate of intake, the fussiness disappears.*

GUNTHER *I think it's quite useful to remember what a wild baby, so
to speak, would do. In taking milk from the breast the baby would
get between one and two ounces per minute in the first minutes and
a bottle-fed baby never gets it at that rate at all; and then ordinarily
the milk ejection reflex works in spasms so that the baby has a
phase of quietness and when its ready for more it calls up the flow
of milk on its own, and has it under its own control. This has no
relation to present-day methods of feeding a baby at all. In suckling,
a tranquil mother is played on as if she were a musical instrument
or a responsive partner in a dance without any possibility of
conscious active response. Spoon feeding of pap is a mother's
driving activity which the baby's responses cope with as best they
may.*

KRAMER *My impression, based on a number of observations, is that
the speed of feeding may be important as to whether or not you
get fussiness and crying. Quite often, when food is put into a baby's
mouth, especially if it has a novel taste, the baby responds with
many kinds of facial and bodily reactions, including turning of the
head, spasms of the facial musculature, movements of the arms,
modifications of the respiratory pattern, and so on. If you try to
give more food while these reactions are going on, the infant can't
cope with it, and fussiness and crying eventually result. It seems
to be best if the mother has both the time and patience to allow
these reactions to run their natural course, and to give the infant
more food only when he is ready for it. It is interesting that fruits,*

especially sweet fruits, seem to be more pacifying than some other solids. This may be because the sugar content comes to have a pacifying effect related to the presence of lactose in the mother's own milk. I am not recommending however that sweetened foods be given to infants to pacify them. On the contrary, continuous pacification of infants and young children with sweetened foods is not only undesirable but may have detrimental effects in the long run.

References

AINSWORTH, M. D. (1962) 'The effects of maternal deprivation: a review of findings and controversy in the context of research strategy' *In deprivation of maternal care; a reassessment of its effects* Public Health Papers No. 14. Geneva: World Health Organization, pp. 97-165

AINSWORTH, M. D. (1963) 'The development of infant-mother interaction among the Ganda' In B. M. Foss (Ed.) *Determinants of infant behaviour II* London: Methuen; and New York: John Wiley, pp. 67-104

AINSWORTH, M. D. (1964) 'Patterns of attachment behavior shown by the infant in interaction with his mother' *Merrill-Palmer Quart*, **10**, 51-58

AINSWORTH, M. D. S. (1967) *Infancy in Uganda: infant care and the growth of love* Baltimore: Johns Hopkins Univ. Press.

ALDRICH, C. A., NORVAL, M., KNOP, C. & VENEGAS, F. (1949) 'The crying of newborn babies' *J. Pediat.*, **28**, 665-70

ALEXANDER, B. K. (1966) The effects of early peer deprivation on juvenile behavior of rhesus monkeys. Unpublished doctoral dissertation, Univ. of Wisconsin

AMBROSE, J. A. (1961) 'The development of the smiling response in early infancy' In B. M. Foss (Ed.) *Determinants of infant behaviour I* London: Methuen; and New York: John Wiley

AMBROSE, J. A. (1963a) 'The concept of a critical period for the development of social responsiveness in early infancy' In B. M. Foss (Ed.) *Determinants of infant behaviour II* London: Methuen; and New York: John Wiley

AMBROSE, J. A. (1963b) 'Age of onset of ambivalence in early infancy' *J. Child Psychol. Psychiat.*, **4**, 167-81

ANAND, B. K. (1963) 'Regulation of alimentary behavior' In M. A. B. Brazier (Ed.) *Brain and behavior* Washington: American Institute of Biological Sciences, pp. 43-116

ANTHONY, E. J. (1958) 'An experimental approach to the psychopathology of childhood autism' *Brit. J. Med. Psychol.*, **21**, 211-25

ARLING, G. L. (1966) 'Effects of social deprivation on maternal behavior of rhesus monkeys'. Unpublished M. A. Thesis, Univ. of Wisconsin

ARSENIAN, J. M. (1943) 'Young children in an insecure situation' *J. abn. soc. Psychol.*, **38**, 225-49

BAYLEY, N. (1932) 'A study of the crying of infants during mental and physical tests' *J. genet. Psychol.*, **40**, 306-29

BEACH, F. A. & WILSON, J. R. (1963) 'Effects of prolactin, progesterone and estrogen on reactions of non-pregnant rats to foster young' *Psychol. Rep.*, **13**, 231-9

BENIEST-NOIROT, E. (1958) 'Analyse du comportement dit maternal chez las souris' *Monog. Francaises de Psychol.*, Paris, No. 1

BENJAMIN, J. D. (1963) 'Further comments on some developmental aspects of anxiety' In H. S. Gaskill (Ed.) *Counterpoint*. New York: International Univ. Press, pp. 121-53

BERLYNE, D. E. (1960) *Conflict, arousal and curiosity* New York: McGraw-Hill

BLAKESLEE, B. (1963) *The limb deficient child* Los Angeles: Univ. of California Press

BLATZ, W. E. (1966) *Human security; some reflections* Toronto: Univ. of Toronto Press

BOELKINS, R. C. (1963) The development of social behavior in the infant rhesus monkey following a period of social isolation. Unpublished M.S. thesis, Univ. of Wisconsin

BOWLBY, J. (1951) *Maternal care and mental health* Geneva: World Health Organization

BOWLBY, J. (1952) *Maternal care and mental health* Geneva: World Health Organization (second edition)

BOWLBY, J. (1958) 'The nature of the child's tie to his mother' *Int. J. Psychoanal.*, **39**, 350-73

BOWLBY, J. (1960) 'Separation anxiety' *Int. J. Psychoanal.*, **41**, 89-113

BRACKBILL, Y. (1958) 'Extinction of the smiling response in infants as a function of reinforcement schedule' *Child Devel.*, **29**, 115-24

CHAMOVE, A. S. (1966) The effects of varying infant peer experience on social behavior in the rhesus monkey. Unpublished M.A. thesis, Univ. of Wisconsin

COLLIAS, N. & JOOS, M. (1953) 'The spectrographic analysis of the sound signal of the domestic fowl' *Behaviour*, **5**, 175-89

CROSS, H. A. & HARLOW, H. F. (1965) 'Prolonged and progressive effects of partial isolation on the behavior of macaque monkeys' *J. exp. Res. Pers.*, **1**, 39-49

References

DEVORE, I. (1965) (Ed.) *Primate behavior; field studies of monkeys and apes* New York: Holt, Rinehart & Winston

ELLIOTT, O. & SCOTT, J. P. (1961) 'The development of emotional distress reactions to separation in puppies' *J. gen. Psychol.*, **99**, 3-22

ESCALONA, S. (1953) 'Emotional development in the first year of life' In M. Senn (Ed.) *Problems of infancy and childhood* New York: Josiah Macy Foundation, pp. 11-92

ESCALONA, S. (1959) *Prediction and outcome* New York: Basic Books

FANT, C. G. M. (1960) *Acoustic theory of speech*, The Hague: Mouton

FESTINGER, L. (1957) *A theory of cognitive dissonance* Evanston: Row Peterson

FLAVELL, J. H. (1963) *The developmental psychology of Jean Piaget* New York: Van Nostrand

FRANUS, E. (1962) *Psychologia Wychowawcza*, **5**, 392-401 ('More on infants' fear reactions at the sight and sound of an unknown and masked person' *Psychol. Abstr.*, **37**, 7861)

FREEDMAN, D. G. (1961) 'The infant's fear of strangers and the flight response' *J. child psychol. Psychiat.*, **2**, 242-8

FREUD, A. & DANN, S. (1951) 'An experiment in group upbringing' In *The psychoanalytic study of the child, vol. VI* New York: International Univ. Press, pp. 127-68

FREUD, S. (1936) *The problem of anxiety* New York: W. W. Norton (First published in 1926)

GEWIRTZ, HAVA B., & GEWIRTZ, J. L. (1968) Visiting and caretaking patterns for kibbutz infants: Age and sex trends. *American Journal of Orthopsychiatry*, **38**, 427-443.

GEWIRTZ, J. L. (1961) 'A learning analysis on the effects of normal stimulation, privation and deprivation on the acquisition of social motivation and attachment' In B. M. Foss (Ed.) *Determinants of infant behaviour I* London: Methuen; and New York: John Wiley, pp. 213-99

GEWIRTZ, J. L. (1965) 'The course of infant smiling in four child-rearing environments in Israel' In B. M. Foss (Ed.) *Determinants of infant behaviour III* London: Methuen; and New York: John Wiley, pp. 205-48

GEWIRTZ, J. L. (1968a) The role of stimulation in models for child development. In Laura L. Dittmann (Ed.), *Early child care: The new perspectives.* New York: Atherton, 1968. Chapter 7. Pp. 139-168. (a)

GEWIRTZ, J. L. (1968b) On designing the functional environment of the child to facilitate behavioral development. In Laura L. Dittmann (Ed.), *Early child care: The new perspectives.* New York: Atherton, 1968. Chapter 8. Pp. 169-213. (b)

GEWIRTZ, J. L. & GEWIRTZ, H. B. (1965) 'Stimulus conditions, infant behaviors, and social learning in four Israeli child-rearing environments: a preliminary report illustrating differences in environment and behavior between the "only" and the "youngest" child' In B. M. Foss (Ed.) *Determinants of infant behaviour III* London: Methuen; and New York: John Wiley, pp. 161-84

GOLDSTEIN, K. (1939) *The organism* Boston: Beacon Press (1963)

GOUIN DÉCARIE, T. (1953) 'Quelques symptômes d'enfants atypiques en regard des théories de Jean Piaget' *Contributions à l'étude des sciences de l'homme,* **2,** 87-93

GOUIN DÉCARIE, T. (1962) *Intelligence and affectivity in early childhood* (Trans. by E. & L. Brandt) New York: International Universities Press

GRIFFIN, G. A. (1966) The effects of multiple mothering on the infant-mother and infant-infant affectional systems. Unpublished doctoral dissertation. Univ. of Wisconsin

GRIFFIN, G. A. & HARLOW, H. F. (1966) 'Effects of three months of total social deprivation on social adjustment and learning in the rhesus monkey' *Child Develpm.,* **37,** 533-47

GRIFFITHS, RUTH (1954) *The abilities of babies* London: Univ. of London Press

HAEUSSERMAN, E. (1958) *The developmental potential of pre-school children* New York: Grune & Stratton

HANSEN, E. W. (1966) 'The development of maternal and infant behavior in the rhesus monkey' *Behaviour,* **27,** 107-49

HARLOW, H. F. (1958) 'The nature of love' *Amer. Psychologist,* **13,** 673-85

HARLOW, H. F. (1961) 'The development of affectional patterns in infant monkeys' In B. M. Foss (Ed.) *Determinants of infant behaviour I* London: Methuen and New York: John Wiley, pp. 75-88

HARLOW, H. F. (1963) 'The maternal affectional system.' In B. M. Foss (Ed.) *Determinants of infant behaviour II* London: Methuen; and New York: John Wiley, pp. 3-34

HARLOW, H. F., DODSWORTH, R. O. & HARLOW, M. K. (1965) 'Total social isolation in monkeys' *Proc. Nat. Acad. Sci.,* **54,** 90-7

References

HARLOW, H. F. & HARLOW, M. K. (1962) 'Social deprivation in monkeys' *Sci. Amer.*, **207**, 136-46

HARLOW, H. F., HARLOW, M. K., DODSWORTH, R. O. & ARLING, G. L. (1966) 'Maternal behavior of rhesus monkeys deprived of mothering and peer associations in infancy' *Proc. Amer. Philos. Soc.*, **110**, 58-66

HARLOW, H. F., HARLOW, M. K. & HANSEN, E. W. (1963) 'The maternal affectional system of rhesus monkeys' In H. L. Rheingold (Ed.) *Maternal behavior in mammals* New York: John Wiley.

HARLOW, H. F. & ZIMMERMANN, R. R. (1959) 'Affectional responses in the infant monkey' *Science*, **130**, 421-32

HARTMAN, H. (1939) *Ego psychology and the problem of adaptation*, New York: International Univ. Press (1958)

HEBB, D. O. (1946) 'On the nature of fear' *Psychol. Rev.*, **53**, 259-76

HELLBRüGGE, T., LANGE, J. & RUTENFRANZ, J. (1959) 'Schlafen und Wachen in der Kindlichen Entwickelung' *Beihefte Arch. Kinderheilk.* No. 39. Stuttgart: Enke

HINDE, R. A. (1965) 'Rhesus monkey aunts' In B. M. Foss (Ed.) *Determinants of infant behaviour III* London: Methuen; and New York: John Wiley, pp. 67-71

HINDE, R. A., ROWELL, T. E. & SPENCER-BOOTH, Y. (1964) 'Behavior of socially living rhesus monkeys in their first six months' *Proc. Zool. Soc. Lond.*, **143**, 609-49

HINDE, R. A. & SPENCER-BOOTH, Y. (1967) 'The effect of social companions on mother-infant relations in rhesus monkeys.' In D. Morris (Ed.) *Primate ethology*, London: Weidenfeld and Nicolson

HINES, M. (1942) 'The development and regression of reflexes, postures and progression in the young macaque' *Contr. to Embryol.*, No. 196, Carnegie Institution of Washington, **541**, 153-209

HOCKETT, C. F. (1959) 'Animal "languages" and human language' *Hum. Biol.*, **31**, 32-40

HUNT, J. MCV. (1961) *Intelligence and experience* New York: Ronald Press

ILLINGWORTH, R. S. (1963) *The development of the infant and the young child* Edinburgh: Livingstone

IRWIN, O. C. (1932) 'The distribution of the amount of motility in young infants between two nursing periods' *J. Comp. Psychol.*, **14**, 429-445

IRWIN, O. C. (1933) 'Motility in young infants: I. Relation to body temperature' *Amer. J. Dis. Child.*, **45**, 531-3

287

JAY, P. (1962) 'Aspects of maternal behavior in Langurs' *Proc. N. Y. Acad. Sci.*, **102**, 468-76

JAY, P. (1963) 'Mother-infant relations in Langurs' In H. L. Rheingold (Ed.) *Maternal behavior in mammals* New York: John Wiley, pp. 282-304

JAY, P. (1967) *Primates; studies in adaptation and variability* New York: Holt, Rinehart & Winston

JENSEN, G. D. & BOBBITT, R. A. (1965) 'On observational methodology and preliminary studies of mother-infant interaction in monkeys' In B. M. Foss (Ed.) *Determinants of infant behaviour III* London: Methuen; and New York: John Wiley, pp. 47-63

JENSEN, G. D. & TOLMAN, C. W. (1962) 'Mother-infant relationship in the monkey *Macaca nemestrina;* the effect of brief separation and mother-infant specificity' *J. comp. physiol. Psychol.*, **55**, 131-6

JONES, MARY C. (1926) 'The development of early behavior patterns in young children' *Pedagogical seminary*, **33**, 537-85

JOOS, M. (1948) 'Acoustic phonetics' Suppl. to *Language* 24, monogr. no. 23, 1-136

JOSLYN, W. D. The effects of social isolation during pre-adolescence upon social adjustment in rhesus monkeys. Unpublished doctoral dissertation, Univ. of Wisconsin

KAUFMAN, I. C. & ROSENBLUM, L. A. (1966) 'A behavioral taxonomy for *Macaca nemestrina* and *Macaca radiata;* based on longitudinal observation of family groups in the laboratory' *Primates*, **7**, no. 2

KAUFMANN, J. H. (1966) 'Behavior of infant rhesus monkeys and their mothers in a free-ranging band' *Zoologica*, **51**, no. 1

KARELITZ, S., KARELITZ, R. F. & ROSENFELD, L. S. (1963) 'Infants' vocalizations and their significance' *Mental Retardation, Proc. 1st Internat. Med. Conf.*, Portland, Maine

KRAMER, C. Y. (1956) 'Extension of multiple range tests to group means with unequal numbers of replications' *Biometrics*, **12**, 307-10

LASHLEY, K. S. & WATSON, J. B. (1913) 'Notes on the development of a young monkey' *Anim. Behav.*, **3**, 114-39

LEBLOND, C. P. (1940) 'Nervous and hormonal factors in the maternal behavior of the mouse.' *J. genet. Psychol.*, **57**, 327-44

LEBLOND, C. P. & NELSON, W. O. (1937) 'Maternal behavior in hypophysectomised male and female mice' *Amer. J. Physiol.*, **120**, 167-72

References

LENNEBERG, E. H. (1964) 'Speech as a motor skill with special reference to non-aphasic disorders' *Child Developm. Monogr.*, **29**, 115-26

LEUBA, C. (1941) 'Tickling and laughter, two genetic studies' *J. genet. Psychol.*, **58**, 201-9

LEWIS, M. M. (1951) *Infant speech* London: Routledge & Kegan Paul

LOTT, D. F. (1962) 'The role of progesterone in the maternal behavior of rodents' *J. comp. physiol. Psychol.*, **55**, 610-3

LOTT, D. F. & FUCHS, S. S. (1962) 'Failure to induce retrieving by sensitization or injection of prolactin' *J. comp. physiol. Psychol.*, **55**, 1111-3

LYNIP, A. W. (1951) 'The use of magnetic devices in the collection and analysis of the preverbal utterances of an infant' *Genet. Psychol. Monogr.*, **44**, 221-62

MACKAY, D. M. (1955) 'The epistemological problem for automata' In C. E. Shannon & J. McCarthy (Eds.) *Automata studies* Princeton Univ. Press, pp. 235-51

MACKAY, D. M. (1956) 'Towards an information-flow model of cerebral organization' Symposium on cerebral activity. *Advancement of Sci.*, **42**, 392

MASON, W. A. (1963) 'The effects of environmental restriction on the social development of rhesus monkeys' In C. H. Southwick (Ed.) *Primate social behavior* New York: Van Nostrand, pp. 161-73

MASON, W. A. (1965) 'The social development of monkeys and apes' In I. DeVore (Ed.) *Primate behavior* New York: Holt, Rinehart & Winston

MASON, W. A. & SPONHOLZ, R. R. (1963) 'Behavior of rhesus monkeys raised in isolation' *Psychiat. Res.*, **1**, 1-8

MEILI, R. (1955) 'Angstentstehung bei Kleinkindern' *Schweiz. Z. Psychol. Anwend.*, **14**, 195-212

La Methode genetique en psychologie (1965) *Psychol. Franc.*, **10**, 1-109

MILLER, G. A., GALANTER, E. & PRIBRAM, K. (1960) *Plans and the structure of behavior* New York: Henry Holt

Ministry of Health (1964) 'Deformities caused by thalidomide' *Report on Public Health and medical subjects*, no. 112

MITCHELL, G. D., RAYMOND, E. J., RUPPENTHAL, G. & HARLOW, H. F. (1966) 'Long-term effects of total social isolation upon the behavior of rhesus monkeys' *Psychol. Rep.*, **18,** 567-80

NISSEN, H. (1958) 'Axes of behavioral comparison' In A. Roe & G. G. Simpson (Eds.) *Behavior and evolution* New Haven: Yale Univ. Press

NOEL, J. R. (1965) Functional household size as a contributing cause of the variance of infants' fear of strangers. Unpublished paper, Univ. of Chicago

NOIROT, E. (1964a) 'Changes in responsiveness to young in the adult mouse: the effect of external stimuli' *J. comp. physiol. Psychol.*, **57,** 97-9

NOIROT, E. (1964b) 'Changes in responsiveness to young in the adult mouse: IV. The effect of an initial contact with a strong stimulus' *Anim. Behav.*, **12,** 442-5

NOIROT, E. (1964c) 'Changes in responsiveness to young in the adult mouse: I. The problematical effect of hormones' *Anim. Behav.*, **12,** 52-8

NOIROT, E. (1965) 'Changes in responsiveness to young in the adult mouse: III. The effect of immediately preceding performances' *Behaviour*, **14,** 318-25

NOIROT, E. & RICHARDS, M. P. M. (1966) 'Maternal behavior in virgin female golden hamsters: changes consequent upon initial contact with pups' *Anim. Behav.*, **14,** 7-10

O'NEILL, M. (1965) Preliminary evaluation of the intellectual development of children with congenital limb malformations associated with thalidomide. Thèse de licence inédite, Université de Montréal

PALMER, M. N. (1940) 'The speech development of normal children' *J. Speech Disord.*, **5,** 185-8

PAVENSTEDT, E. (1964) 'Description of a research project on: the influence of the maternal character structure on the development of child's personality' *Japan J. Child Psychiat.*, **5,** no. 1, 19-28

PAVENSTEDT, E. (1965) 'A comparison of the child rearing environment of upper-lower and very low-lower class families' *Amer. J. Orthopsychiat.*, **35,** no. 1, 89-98

PEIPER, A. (1963) *Cerebral function in infancy and childhood* New York: Consultants Bureau

PIAGET, J. (1936) *La Naissance de l'intelligence* Neuchâtel: Delachaux et Niestlé. (*The origins of intelligence in children*, New York: International Univ. Press, 1952)

References

PIAGET, J. (1937) *La construction du réel chez l'enfant* Neuchâtel: Delachaux et Niestlé

PIAGET, J. (1945) *La formation du symbole chez l'enfant* Neuchâtel: Delachaux et Niestlé

PIAGET, J. (1954) *Les relations entre l'affectivité et l'intelligence dans le développement mental de l'enfant* Paris: Centre de documentation universitaire

PIDDINGTON, R. (1963) *The psychology of laughter* New York: Gamut Press

POLAK, P. R., EMDE, R. N. & SPITZ, R. A. (1964) 'The smiling response to the human face. I. Methodology, quantification and natural history' *J. Nerv. Ment. Dis.*, **139**, 103-9

POTTER, R. K., KOPP, G. A. & GREEN, H. C. (1947) *Visible speech* New York: Dover Publications

PREYER, W. T. (1888) *The mind of the child* vol. 1 New York: D. Appleton (Originally published 1882)

PRIBRAM, K. (1963) 'Reinforcement revisited: a structural view' In M. R. Jones (Ed.) *Nebraska Symposium on Motivation* Univ. of Nebraska Press

PROVENCE, S. & LIPTON, R. (1962) *Infants in institutions* New York: International Univ. Press

RHEINGOLD, H. L. (1960) 'The measurement of maternal care' *Child Developm.*, **31**, 565-75

RHEINGOLD, H. L. (1961) 'The effect of environmental stimulation upon social and exploratory behaviour in the human infant' In B. M. Foss (Ed.) *Determinants of infant behaviour I* London: Methuen; and New York: John Wiley, pp. 143-77

RICHARDS, M. P. M. (1965) Aspects of maternal behaviour in the golden hamster. Unpublished Ph.D. thesis, Cambridge Univ.

RICHARDS, M. P. M. (1966a) 'Maternal behaviour in virgin female golden hamsters: the role of the age of the test pup' *Anim. Behav.*, **14**, 303-9

RICHARDS, M. P. M. (1966b) 'Maternal behaviour in the golden hamster: responsiveness to young in virgin, pregnant and lactating females' *Anim. Behav.*, **14**, 310-3

RICHARDS, M. P. M. (1967) 'Maternal behaviour in rodents and lagomorphs' In A. McLaren (Ed.) *Advances in reproductive physiology, vol. II* New York: Academic Press

RICHARDS, T. W. (1936) 'The importance of hunger in the bodily activity of the neonate' *Psychol. Bull.*, **33**, 817-35

U

RIDDLE, O., LAHR, E. L. & BATES, R. W. (1942) 'The role of hormones in the initiation of maternal behavior in rats' *Amer. J. Physiol.*, **137**, 299-317

ROSENBLATT, J. S. (1967) 'Nonhormonal basis of maternal behavior in the rat' *Science*, **156**, 1512-4

ROSENBLATT, J. S. & LEHRMAN, D. S. (1963) 'Maternal behavior of the laboratory rat' In H. L. Rheingold (Ed.) *Maternal behavior in mammals* New York: John Wiley

ROSENBLATT, J. S., TURKEWITZ, G. & SCHNEIRLA, T. C. (1961) 'Early socialization in the domestic cat as based on feeding and other relationships between female and young.' In B. M. Foss (Ed.) *Determinants of infant behaviour I* London: Methuen; and New York: John Wiley

ROSENBLUM, L. A. (1961) The development of social behavior in the rhesus monkey. Unpublished doctoral dissertation, Univ. of Wisconsin

ROSENBLUM, L. A. & HARLOW, H. F. (1963)'Approach-avoidance conflict in the mother-surrogate situation' *Psychol. Rep.*, **12**, 83-5

ROSENBLUM, L. A. & KAUFMAN, I. C. (1966) 'Laboratory observation of early mother-infant relations in pigtail and bonnet macaques' In S. A. Altman (Ed.) *Social interaction among primates* Chicago: Univ. of Chicago Press

ROSENBLUM, L. A., KAUFMAN, I. C. & STYNES, A. J. (1964) 'Individual distance in two species of macaque' *Anim. Behav.*, **12**, 2-3

ROSENBLUM, L. A., WITKIN, H. A., KAUFMAN, I. C. & BROSGOLE, L. (1965) 'Perceptual disembedding in monkeys: note on method and preliminary findings' *Perceptual & Motor Skills*, **20**, 729-36

ROWELL, T. E. (1959) Maternal behaviour in the golden hamster. Unpublished Ph.D. thesis, Cambridge Univ.

ROWELL, T. E. (1960) 'On the retrieving of young and other behaviour in lactating golden hamsters' *Proc. zool. Soc. Lond.*, **135**, 265-82

ROWELL, T. E. (1961) 'Maternal behaviour in non-maternal golden hamsters' *Anim. Behav.*, **9**, 11-15

ROWELL, T. E. (1965) 'Some observations on a hand-reared baboon' In B. M. Foss (Ed.) *Determinants of infant behaviour III* London: Methuen; and New York: John Wiley

ROWLAND, G. L. (1964) The effects of total social isolation upon learning and social behavior in rhesus monkeys. Unpublished doctoral dissertation, Univ. of Wisconsin

References

SACKETT, G. P., GRIFFIN, G. A., PRATT, C. L., JOSLYN, W. D. & RUPPENTHAL, G. C. (1966) 'Mother-infant choice behavior in rhesus monkeys after various rearing experiences' Paper presented at meetings of Midwestern Psychological Association, May 1966, Chicago, Ill.

SACKETT, G. P., PORTER, M. & HOLMES, H. (1965) 'Choice behavior in rhesus monkeys: an effect of stimulation during the first month of life.' *Science*, **147**, 304-6

SANDER, L. W. (1962) 'Issues in early mother-child interaction' *J. Amer. Acad. Child Psychiat.*, **1**, no. 1, 141-66

SANDER, L. W. (1964) 'Adaptive relationships in early mother-child interaction' *J. Amer. Acad. Child Psychiat.*, **3**, no. 2, 231-65

SCHAFFER, H. R. (1963) 'Some issues for research in the study of attachment behaviour.' In B. M. Foss (Ed.) *Determinants of infant behaviour II* London: Methuen; and New York: John Wiley, pp. 179-99

SCHAFFER, H. R. & CALLENDER, W. M. (1959) 'Psychological effects of hospitalization in infancy' *Pediatrics*, **24**, 528-39

SCHAFFER, H. R. & EMERSON, P. E. (1964) 'The development of social attachments in infancy' *Monogr. Soc. Res. Child Developm.*, **29**, no. 3 (serial no. 94)

SCHRIER, A., HARLOW, H. F. & STOLLNITZ, F. (1965) *Behavior of nonhuman primates vol. II* New York: Academic Press.

SCOTT, J. P. (1963) 'The process of primary socialization in canine and human infants' *Monogr. Soc. Res. Child Developm.*, **28**, no. 1 (serial no. 85)

SEAY, B, ALEXANDER, B. K. & HARLOW, H. F. (1964) 'Maternal behavior of socially deprived rhesus monkeys' *J. abnorm. soc. Psychol.*, **69**, 345-54

SEAY, B, HANSEN, E. & HARLOW, H. F. (1962) 'Mother-infant separation in monkeys' *J. Child Psychol. Psychiat.*, **3**, 123-32

SEAY, B. & HARLOW, H. F. (1965) 'Maternal separation in the rhesus monkey.' *J. nerv. ment. Dis.*, **140**, 434-41

SIMONDS, P. E. (1965) 'The bonnet macaque in South India' In I. DeVore (Ed.) *Primate behavior* New York: Holt, Rinehart & Winston, pp. 175-96

SLUCKIN, W. (1966) *Imprinting and early learning* London: Methuen

SPENCER-BOOTH, Y. & HINDE, R. A. (1966) 'The effects of separating rhesus monkey infants from their mothers for 6 days' *J. Child Psychol. Psychiatry*, **7**, 179-197

SPIRO, M. E. (1958) *Children of the kibbutz*, Cambridge, Mass.: Harvard Univ. Press

SPITZ, R. A. (1950) 'Anxiety in infancy: a study of its manifestations in the first year of life' *Int. J. Pschoanal.*, **31**, 138-43

SPITZ, R. A. (1955) 'A note on the extrapolation of ethological findings' *Int. J. Psychoanal.*, **36**, 162-5

SPITZ, R. A. (1957) *No and yes; on the beginnings of human communication*, New York: International Univ. Press

SPITZ, R. A. (1959) *A genetic field theory of ego formation. Its implications for pathology*, New York: International Univ. Press

SPITZ, R. A. (1965) *The first year of life*, New York: International Univ. Press

SPITZ, R. A. & WOLF, K. A. (1946) 'The smiling response: a contribution to the ontogenesis of social relations' *Genet. Psychol. Monogr.*, **34**, 57-125

SPOCK, B. & LERRIGO, M. (1965) *Caring for your disabled child* New York: MacMillan

STECHLER, G. (1964) 'A longitudinal follow-up of neonatal apnea' *Child Develpm.*, **35**, 333-48

STRASSER, H. & SIEVERT, G. (1964) 'On psycho-social aspects of ectromelia' Research report of the Mental Health Group, Munich

STRASSER, H. & SIEVERT, G. (1965) 'Ehrebungen über die Entwicklung einer Gruppe gliedmassenfehlgebildeter Kinder und ihre Lebensbedingungen' Research report of the Mental Health Group, Munich

TENNES, K. H. & LAMPL, E. E. (1964) 'Stranger and separation anxiety' *J. Nerv. Ment. Dis.*, **139**, 247-54

THORPE, W. H. (1961) *Bird song*, Cambridge monogrs. in exp. biol. no. 12. Cambridge: Univ. Press

TINKLEPAUGH, O. L. & HARTMAN, C. G. (1932) 'Behavior and maternal care of the newborn monkey (*Macaca mulatta* . . . '*m. rhesus*')' *Ped.Sem. & J. Genet. Psychol.*, **40**, 257-85

TRUBY, H. M. (1962) 'A technique for visual-acoustic analysis of the sounds of infant cry' *J. Acous. Soc. Amer.*,

VON BERTALANFFY, L. (1952) *Problems of life* New York: Harper 1960

WASHBURN, R. W. (1929) 'A study of smiling and laughing of infants in the first year of life' *Genet. Psychol. Monogr.*, **6**, 397-537

References

WASZ-HOCKERT, V., VUORENKOSKI, V., VOLANNE, E., & MICHELSON, K. (1962) 'Tonspectrographische Untersuchungen des Sauglingschreis' *Experientia*, **18**, 1-4

WEBB, JEAN (1963) 'Canadian thalidomide experience' *J. Canad. Med. Assoc.*, **89**, 987-92

WEISS, P. (1949) 'The biological basis of adaptation' In J. Romano (Ed.) *Adaptation* Ithaca, N.Y.: Cornell Univ. Press

WELKER, W. I. (1956) 'Effects of age and experience on play and exploration of young chimpanzees' *J. comp. physiol. Psychol.*, **49**, 223-6

WELKER, W. I. (1961) 'An analysis of exploratory and play behavior in animals.' In D. W. Fiske & S. R. Maddi (Eds.) *Functions of varied experience*, Homewood, Ill: Dorsey Press

WERNER, H. (1947) *Comparative psychology of mental development* New York: International Univ. Press (2nd ed. 1957)

WHITE, R. W. (1963) *Ego and reality in psychoanalytic theory* New York: International Universities Press

WIESNER, B. P. & SHEARD, N. M. (1933) *Maternal behaviour in the rat* Edinburgh: Oliver & Boyd

WOLFF, P. H. (1963) 'The early development of smiling' In B. M. Foss (Ed.) *Determinants of infant behaviour II* London: Methuen; and New York: John Wiley, pp. 113-34

WOLFF, P. H. (1965) 'The development of attention in young infants' *Ann. N.Y. Acad. Sci.*, **118**, 815-30

WOLFF, P. W. (1966a) 'The causes, controls and organization of behavior in the young infant' *Psychol. Issues Monogr. Series* New York: International Univ. Press

WOLFF, P. H. (1966b) 'The serial organization of sucking in the young infant.'

WOLFF, P. H. & WHITE, B. L. (1965) 'Visual pursuit and attention in young infants' *J. Amer. Acad. Child Psychiat.*, **4**, 413-84

YAMAMOTO, W. S. & BROBECK, J. R. (1965) *Physiological controls and regulations* Philadelphia: W. B. Saunders

YERKES, R. M. & TOMILIN, M. I. (1935) 'Mother-infant relations in chimpanzee' *J. comp. Psychol.*, **20**, 321-59

Index

Index

activity, locomotor, 141-166
adaptation, 220-221
  and fear, 13, 14
  to ground living, 7
  to loss, 14
adaptive value, 57
adoption in chimpanzees, 14
affectional systems, 35-36, 204
aggression, 182, 219
  in primates, 10, 16, 17, 19, 20, 21, 25, 27, 28, 29, 32 see tantrum
Ainsworth, M. D. Salter, 39, 112, 135, 136, 182, 283
Aldrich, C. A., 86, 283
Alexander, B. K., 20, 23, 31, 283, 293
Allyn, G. D., 111
ambivalence, 196, 203, 207
Ambrose, J. A., 100, 253, 254, 256, 263, 270, 272, 283
Anand, B. K., 87, 283
angry cry
  see cry
Anthony, E. J., 171, 283
anxiety
  see separation; stranger anxiety
Arling, G. L., 31, 32, 283, 286
Arsenian, J. M., 112, 137, 138, 165, 166, 284
attachment, infant to mother, 111-136, 181-182
  see mother-infant bond
attention and crying, 96
aunts, monkey, 10, 37

babbling
  see vocalizing
baboon, 4, 6, 9, 10, 13, 184
Bates, R. W., 61, 77, 291
Bateson, P., 276
Bayley, N., 137, 165, 254, 263, 284
Beach, F. A., 61, 77, 284
behaviour categories, 44-46, 192, 224-225, 234-238, 245-246, 258-260
Beniest-Noirot, E., 74, 284
  see Noirot, E.

Benjamin, J. D., 136, 255, 264, 265, 271, 284
Berlyne, D. E., 137, 270, 284
birth cry, 279
birth of second infant, 56, 215
birth order, 231, 233
Blakeslee, B., 169, 284
Blatz, W. E., 112, 284
Bobbitt, R. A., 41, 42, 284
Boelkins, R. C., 17, 284
bonnet monkey, 43-59
Bowlby, J., 38, 112, 135, 171, 187, 190, 255, 265, 271, 284
Brackbill, Y., 256, 284
brain damage cry, 94-95
Brobeck, J. R., 221, 295
Brockman, L., 253
Brosgole, I., 292
Burns, P., 216

Callender, W. M., 135, 165, 293
caretaking, 16, 194, 222, 229-252
  see mothering
cat, 204
catatonic contracture, 16
categories of behaviour, 44-46, 192, 224-225, 234-238, 245-246, 258-260
cathexis, 182
Chamove, A. S., 24, 284
chimpanzee, 4, 8-14, 279, 280
circular reaction, 99, 187, 280
clinging, 13, 23, 26, 39, 57, 112, 123, 171, 184-7
clutching
  self, 16, 26
  social, 26
cognitive development, 57
  see concept; intelligence
colic, 90, 278
Collias, N., 93, 284
computer, uses of, 43, 246-247
concept
  causality, 171
  object, 171, 179, 180, 183
  space, time, 171

conditional probability, 246
conservation of object, 57-58
contact comfort, 57, 278
contact, physical, 10, 19, 35, 36, 38,
    45-47, 53, 55, 57, 126, 128, 129,
    134, 136
    see clinging; nakedness
coordination, 106, 180-181
Cross, H. A., 16, 284
crying, 81-110, 112, 117-118, 121-122,
    140-166, 171, 206, 259, 273-282
    angry, 84, 94
    birth, 279
    brain damage, 94
    chimp infant, 13
    fake, 98
    frustrated, 85, 106
    function, 86, 99, 279
    hunger, 82, 86-88, 277-278, 282
    infectious, 105
    latency, 140-166
    morphology, 82-86, 95, 98-99, 101
    pain, 84-85, 89, 94
    stopping, 90-92, 277-278, 282
    see vocalization
curiosity, 18
    see exploration

Dann, S., 28, 285
death of infant rhesus, 14
deprivation, 15-28
    long term, 19
    peer, 20-23
    see maternal; separation
DeVore, I., 5, 10, 14, 41, 42, 284
diapers, wet, and crying, 88-89
discrimination of mother, 276-277
distress, 273-282
    see crying; stranger anxiety
Dodsworth, R. O., 18, 31, 286
dog, 166
dominance, 6, 8
dummy, 90-92, 106, 277-278

eating
    pups, rats, 70-77
    see feeding; sucking
Eikenberg, E. A., 111
elimination, 194
Elliott, O., 166, 285
Ellis, E. E., 111
Emde, R. N., 254, 291

Emerson, P. E., 112, 135, 136, 165, 24,5
    255, 265, 271, 293
emotion
    development, 181-182
    see anger; anxiety; fear
endocrine
    see hormone
environments, strange, 137-166, 275,
    277
Escalona, S., 220, 254, 256, 263, 264,
    265, 268, 285
estrogen, 61
evolution, 5
exploration, 7, 11, 18, 111-136, 137, 223
eye-to-eye contact, 102-103, 171

facial expressions, 183
family size, 270-271
Fant, C. G. M., 82, 285
fear, 13, 19, 253
    of strangers
    see stranger anxiety
feeding, 95, 99, 100, 194, 199-200,
    206-207, 211, 277-278, 280-282
    see crying, hunger; sucking
Festinger, L., 168, 285
field studies, 3-14
Fineman, A., 189
Flavell, J. H., 171, 285
following, 112, 171, 187
food preferences, 99, 281-282
Franus, E., 254, 263, 285
Freedman, D. G., 254, 255, 256, 263,
    265, 276, 285
Freud, Anna, 28, 285
Freud, S., 255, 285
frustration, 106, 200, 202
    see crying, frustrated
Fuchs, S. S., 61, 77, 289

Galanter, E., 289
Galapagos Islands, 276
Ganda, 112, 135
genetic factors, 276
Gewirtz, Hava B., 229, 232, 234, 239,
    285
Gewirtz, J. L., 186, 187, 229, 232, 233,
    234, 239, 253, 254, 256, 269, 270,
    285
glasses, effect on face, 108, 279
golden hamster, 69-77
Goldstein, K., 220, 286
Goodall, Jane, 4, 8, 11, 13, 14

Index

gorilla, 4, 10, 13
Gouin Décarie, T., 171, 179, 286
Green, H. C., 291
gregariousness, 56
grief, 14
Griffin, G. A., 17, 32, 33, 286, 292
Griffiths, Ruth, 178, 286
grooming, monkey, 38
groups
and evolution, 5
primate, 6
unmothered monkey, 24-28

Haeusserman, E., 174, 286
Hall, K. R. L., 13
Hamilton, W. C., 111
hamster, 69-77
hand-eye coordination, 106
hand-mouth coordination, 180-181
Hansen, E. W., 30, 39, 42, 61, 286, 287, 293
Harlow, H. F., 5, 10, 11, 15, 16, 17, 18, 20, 22, 31, 35, 39, 42, 57, 58, 77, 112, 136, 204, 284, 286, 287, 289, 292, 293
Harlow, M. K., 15, 18, 20, 22, 31, 35, 42, 286, 287
Hartman, C. G., 41, 294
Hartman, H., 194, 287
hearing, 177
Hebb, D. O., 255, 270, 271, 279, 287
Hellbrügge, 86, 287
Helwig, R. A., 137
Hill, Gertrude, 169, 185
Hinde, R. A., 10, 37, 38, 40, 41, 69, 287, 293
Hines, M., 41, 287
Hockett, C. F., 187, 287
Holmes, H., 33, 293
hormones, control of maternal behaviour, 61-77
hospitalisation, 173, 176, 178
hunger
see crying, hunger
Hunt, J. McV., 221, 287
hypophysectomy, 74

identification, 13
Illingworth, R. S., 170, 287
imitation, 11, 12, 13, 105
immaturity, prolongation in primates, 8-9
imprinting, 275-276

infant
attachment to mother, 111-136
see mother-infant bond
attention from other monkeys, 7, 10
birth of second, 56, 215
state of, 97, 109, 279
see interaction; mother-infant
independence, infant, 10, 11, 41-59
initiative, infant, 192-223, 226
institutionalization, 173, 176, 178, 229-232
intelligence, 218
and hospitalization, 176, 178
sensori-motor, 179, 220
spatial, 178
thalidomide babies, 174-178
interaction
chains or sequences, 230, 241, 245, 247-248
infant-infant, 21, 22, 24, 31
see play
mother-infant, 189-223, 229-248
primates, 3-14, 31-35, 38-40, 46
effect of 'aunts', 37
primate groups, 5
Irwin, O. C., 86, 89, 287
isolation
see separation; social isolation; deprivation

Japan Monkey Center, 8
Japanese babies, 81, 273, 274, 279
Jay, P., 5, 42, 287, 288
jealousy, 183
Jensen, G. D., 39, 41, 42, 288
Jones, Mary C., 253, 256, 288
Joos, M., 82, 93, 284, 288
Joslyn, W. D., 22, 33, 288, 292

Karelitz, R. F., 288
Karelitz, S., 82, 288
Kaufman, I. C., 41, 288, 292
Kaufmann, J. H., 42, 288
kibbutz, 229-248
Knop, C., 283
Kopp, G. A., 291
Kramer, C. Y., 65, 288

laboratory v. field studies, 5
Lahr, E. L., 61, 77, 291
Lampl, E. E., 136, 254, 255, 256, 263, 264, 265, 272, 274, 294
Lange, J., 287

language, in thalidomide babies, 177-178
see circular reaction; speech; vocalization
langur, 7, 10, 13
Lashley, K. S., 41, 288
laughter, 82, 100, 101
Leblond, C. P., 74, 288
Lehrman, D. S., 61, 74, 292
Lenneberg, E. H., 104, 288
Lerrigo, M., 178, 294
Leuba, C., 100, 288
Lewis, M. M., 109, 289
libido, 182
Lipton, R., 178, 231, 291
locomotor development, 178, 195
see activity
loss
of infant chimp, 14
of object, 101, 183
Lott, D. F., 61, 77, 289
Lynip, A. W., 82, 289

macaque
Japanese, 8
nemestrina, 43-59
radiata, 43-59
rhesus, *see* rhesus
McCulloch, E. S., 111
McGinnis, M., 189
MacKay, D. M., 221, 289
male
dominant baboon, 6
relation to infant ape, 7, 10
masks, 106-107, 256, 266, 272, 279
Mason, W. A., 20, 184, 289
maternal behaviour, hormones and experience, 61-77
maternal care, 10
see mothering
maternal deprivation, 6, 15-28, 38-40
maternal discrimination, 33
maternal oversolicitousness, 20
maternal punishment, 20-22, 42, 44, 53, 56
maternal responsiveness, 61-77
maternal restrictiveness, 38
Mattick, I., 189
Meili, R., 255, 289
Michelson, K., 294
Miller, G. A., 221, 289
Mitchell, G. D., 19, 289
mother, attitude to strangers, 274-275

mother-infant
adjustment, 191-223
bond, 8
waning, 39-59
interaction, *see* interaction
mother's reaction to crying, 93-94
mothering
indifferent and brutal, 31-32
multiple, 32-34
see caretaking
motherless mothers, 31-34
mouse, 71, 73, 74

nakedness and crying, 89, 96, 278-279
Nelson, W. O., 74, 288
nest-building
chimpanzees, 13
hamsters, 70-77
rats, 62, 66
nipple withdrawal, 51-53, 56
see weaning
Nissen, H., 3, 289
Noel, J. R., 270, 271, 290
Noirot, E., 69, 70, 71, 73, 74, 290
see Beniest-Noirot, E.
Norval, M., 283
novelty, 270

object concept, 171, 179, 180, 183
object relationship, 57-58, 182
observation techniques, 43, 81, 113-114, 118-119, 193, 226, 233-238, 249-252, 258-260
observational learning
see imitation
Old World monkeys, 8, 11
O'Neill, Monica, 168, 178, 290
only child, 231, 245, 248
orang-utan, 4
ovariectomy, 63
oxytocin, 61

pacifier, 90-92, 106, 277-278
pain
see crying, pain
Palmer, M. N., 290
pat-a-cake, 97
patas monkey, 13
Pavenstedt, E., 190, 198, 290
peek-a-boo, 207
peer deprivation, 20-23
Peiper, A., 99, 290

physical contact
see contact
Piaget, J., 57, 99, 105, 170, 171, 178, 179, 182, 187, 220, 221, 290, 291
Piddington, R., 100, 291
pigtail monkey, 43-59
pituitary, 74, 76
play
 aggressive, 29
 exercise, 54, 55
 rhesus, 17-19, 21, 22, 24-27, 29-32, 35, 36, 45, 54, 55
 social, 54, 55
Polak, P. R., 254, 256, 291
Porter, M., 33, 293
Potter, R. K., 82, 291
Pratt, C. L., 33, 292
predators, 6
pregnancy, maternal responsiveness during, 61-77
Preyer, W. T., 253, 291
Pribram, K., 221, 289, 291
primate
 field studies, 3-14
 groups, 5, 6
 see baboon, chimpanzee, macaque, rhesus, etc.
progesterone, 61
prolactin, 61, 77
Provence, S., 178, 231, 291
psychoanalysis, 182, 255
punishment
 see maternal punishment; mothering, indifferent and brutal

Rancourt, R., 168, 183
rat, 61-67, 77
Raymond, E. J., 19, 289
rejection by mother, 53-55, 57, 58
 see maternal punishment
retrieval of infant, 45, 48, 50, 52, 62, 64-66
Rheingold, H. L., 41, 231, 256, 270, 291
rhesus monkey, 4, 6, 15-40, 42, 57, 77, 166, 204
Richards, M. P. M., 70, 74, 76, 77, 290, 291
Richards, T. W., 86, 291
Riddle, O., 61, 77, 291
Robinson, M. E., 170
Rosenblatt, J. S., 61, 74, 204, 292
Rosenblum, L. A., 29, 41, 43, 56, 57, 58, 59, 288, 292

Rosenfeld, L. S., 288
Roskies, E., 168
Ross, A., 189
Rowell, T. E., 37, 71, 74, 184, 287, 292
Rowland, G. L., 18, 292
rubella, 168
Ruppenthal, G. C., 19, 33, 289, 292
Rutenfranz, J., 287

Sackett, G. P., 18, 33, 292, 293
Samuels, H. R., 137
Sander, L. W., 191, 205, 219, 293
Santiago, 42
Schaffer, H. R., 112, 135, 136, 165, 254, 255, 265, 271, 293
schema, 170, 179, 180, 181, 221, 222
Schneirla, T. C., 292
Schrier, A., 5, 293
Scott, J. P., 166, 255, 285, 293
Seay, B., 39, 293
sensori-motor development, 59, 179
separation, temporary, 105, 111-166, 201, 206, 255, 265
 in rhesus, 37-40
 see maternal deprivation; social isolation
sex differences, 10, 160-161, 264, 266
sexual behaviour, 13, 18, 19, 20, 21, 23, 31, 32, 35
sexual dimorphism, 7
Sheard, N. M., 62, 65, 71, 74, 295
Sievert, G., 170, 294
Simner, M., 137
Simonds, P. E., 51, 293
sleep, 194
 and crying, 87, 91
Sluckin, W., 255, 293
smiling, 112, 171, 183, 241, 244, 246, 253-254, 259, 263, 277
social development, 16, 21, 23, 29-30, 32, 181, 184
social isolation, 15-28
social organization, animal, 6, 7
social status, 8
speech, 177-178
 and crying, 109, 280
 see vocalization
Spencer-Booth, Y., 37, 38, 40, 287, 293
Spiro, M. E., 231, 293
Spitz, R. A., 182, 197, 253, 254, 255, 256, 263, 265, 272, 291, 294
Spock, B., 178, 294

Sponholz, R. R., 20, 289
state of infant, 97, 109, 279
Stechler, G., 189, 210, 218, 294
stereotyped movements, 16
Stollnitz, F., 293
strange environment, 137-166
stranger anxiety, 106-108, 111-166, 253-272, 273-277
Strasser, H., 170, 294
Stynes, A. J., 41, 292
sucking, 51, 112, 171, 278
   non-nutritional, 16, 38, 51, 90-92
   see feeding; pacifier
surrogate mothers, 10, 22-23, 28-31, 57
swaddling, 92

talking, 241-244, 246
   see speech: vocalization
tantrum, 207-208
techniques, observational
   see observation
temperature and crying, 89
Tennes, K. H., 136, 254, 255, 256, 263, 264, 265, 272, 274, 294
territorial marking, 70
thalidomide, 167-188
Thompson, D'A., 220
Thorpe, W. H., 93, 294
tickling, 100
Tinklepaugh, O. L., 41, 294
Tolman, C. W., 39, 288
Tomilin, M. I., 21, 295
tools, use by chimpanzee, 12
TOTE, 221, 222
toys, 103-104, 113-132, 138, 148-150, 155-159, 163
tracheo-esophageal fistula, 87-88, 277
Trattner, Alice, 61
tree *v.* ground living, 5-8
Truby, H. M., 84, 294
Turkewitz, G., 292

Venegas, F., 283
visceral pain, 90
visual exploration, 119
   orientation, 120
   pursuit, 97
vocalization, 81-109, 112, 140-141, 186, 246, 259, 280
   monkey, 39, 51
   non-cry, 98-99, 101, 104-105, 140, 143-166
   see crying; speech; talking
Volanne, E., 294
von Bertalanffy, L., 220, 294
Vuorenkoski, V., 294

Washburn, R. W., 100, 254, 263, 294
Washburn, S., 3, 4, 7
Wasz-Hockert, V., 82, 294
Watson, J. B., 41, 288
weaning, 45, 51, 99
Webb, Jean, 173, 294
Weiss, P., 219, 220, 221, 295
Welker, W. L., 137, 270, 295
Werner, H., 204, 295
White, B. L., 91, 295
White, R. W., 135, 136, 295
Wiesner, B. P., 62, 65, 71, 74, 295
Wilson, J. R., 61, 77, 284
Wisconsin Primate Laboratory, 15, 29
Witkin, H. A., 292
Wolf, K. A., 253, 254, 256, 272, 294
Wolff, P. H., 81, 86, 87, 91, 92, 97, 103, 171, 295

Yamamoto, W. S., 221, 295
Yerkes, R. M., 21, 295

Zimmermann, R. R., 22, 287